Implements
for
Farming with Horses & Mules
A Modern All-in-One Manual

Implements
for
Farming with Horses & Mules

A Modern All-in-One Manual

Sam Moore

a **RURAL HERITAGE** book

281 Dean Ridge Lane
Gainesboro, TN 38562 USA
www.ruralheritage.com

Published by *Rural Heritage*
281 Dean Ridge Lane
Gainesboro
TN 38562-5039
931-268-0655
www.ruralheritage.com

Rural Heritage magazine has served its readers since 1976 in support of farming and logging with horses, mules and oxen.

Edited by Gail Damerow
Cover design and layout by Allan Damerow
Cover photo by Luke Yoder
Line drawings and photographs by Sam Moore except as noted
Indexed by Gail Damerow

Printed in the United States of America
First Printing, 2006
06 07 08 09 10 11 12 13 14 15   10 9 8 7 6 5 4 3 2 1

Library of Congress Cataloging-in-Publication Data

Moore, Sam, 1933-
  Implements for farming with horses & mules : a modern all-in-one manual / Sam Moore.
    p. cm.
  Includes index.
  ISBN-13: 978-1-893707-10-8
 1. Agricultural implements--Handbooks, manuals, etc. 2. Farm equipment--Handbooks, manuals, etc. 3. Agricultural machinery--Handbooks, manuals, etc. I. Title.
  S676.M66 2006
  631.3--dc22
                        2006019594

*To my grandfather Sherman Moore,
who farmed with horses all his life, and
to my father Sam Moore, who was only too
happy to switch from horses to tractors.*

Contents

Foreword

Perhaps the most remarkable thing about modern farm equipment is how little it has changed over the decades, even as the power units that propel it have grown to monstrous proportions. Plows, discs, harrows, mowing machines, grain harvesters—underneath the shiny paint and sleek sheet metal is time-tested form and function. Farm implements are tools of astonishing simplicity and honesty, tools that emerged from the forge and anvil of the local smith, born of necessity, engineered through keen observation, honed to near perfection by endless hours in the field. As if lives depended on it.

In the United States and Canada, less than two percent of the population is involved in agricultural production. They are the lucky ones for whom the turn of the seasons reaffirms their connection to the land; for whom the soil, crops, and livestock are inextricably interwoven with all they do. But modern agricultural production has taken something from them. In the four-wheel-drive world of climate controlled cabs, electro-hydraulic controls, and 1,000 rpm PTOs, what are the sounds and smells of tillage, planting, and mowing? Can they remember where the sweet spots in the field are, or places that refuse to give much back at the first sign of dry weather? Not long ago, these things were important. Now we just farm more land.

By recent estimates about two billion people in at least 30 developing countries rely on draft animals for transportation and agricultural production. In North America the number of working draft animals is small, but the numbers are increasing. For many people, the use of draft animals shapes core values shared by a community of friends and neighbors. Others, separated from the farm by one or two generations, are connecting with the realities of animal draft for the first time. Perhaps some are forging a link with a simpler way of life that somehow slipped away without a ripple when one generation became the next.

These are the folks for whom the bond with working animals is neither a whim nor something that may be ignored. It is an essential slice of the sum of life experiences that defines who they are. These are the folks who find rich rewards in the smell of freshly turned soil and curing hay; taut heel chains and ears that react to murmurs imperceptible to bystanders; the drone of steel cutting soil; a soft nuzzle in return for scratching a chin; the munching of hay in the barn's half-light. These things need no explanation or apology.

Sam Moore is to be congratulated for helping fill the knowledge gap in animal-drawn implements with an unpretentious but generously illustrated and richly detailed all-in-one manual for farming with horses and mules (and oxen, too). Are you new to the walking plow or sulky plow, or confused about the line of draft? Sam walks you through plow parts and terminology, explains how to lay out lands and what to strive for in turning ground you will wish granddad could see. Have questions about deep tillage, seedbed tillage, or cultivation equipment? Look here first.

Sam commingles his love of history and farm machinery, tempering it with the no-nonsense view of one who has worked the land. History connects the past and present. The directness is clearly the result of hours on the business end of a hoe, or a fork, or in the furrow. Have an interest in using a grain drill, corn planter, or potato planter? Not sure how to make it work with a two-, three-, or four-horse hitch? You'll find it here.

Sam commingles his love of history and farm machinery, tempering it with the no-nonsense view of one who has worked the land. History connects the past and present. The directness is clearly the result of hours on the business end of a hoe, or a fork, or in the furrow. Have an interest in using a grain drill, corn planter, or potato planter? Not sure how to make it work with a two-, three-, or four-horse hitch? You'll find it here.

Many users of draft animals pursue hay harvesting with great determination. East of the Mississippi it does not take long to find out what a difficult challenge this is. Rain, clouds, and high humidity stake a claim to a portion of the crop and the fight is on. The keys to making quality hay are sunshine, air flow, and some, but not too much, mechanical manipulation of the crop. The section on hay harvesting and handling covers everything from adjusting a sickle bar mower to conditioning, raking, and tedding for rapid drying. A powered forecart will adapt a small square, or labor saving round, baler to a team, and several nice pictures show horse-drawn round bale handling and wrapping equipment in action. You will benefit from Sam's faithful attendance at the annual horse-farmer's trade show Horse Progress Days.

Those who love farm machinery find inspiration in harvesting equipment. The early grain harvesters and threshers were not only mechanical wonders but works of art, and this section of the book is where Sam really lets himself go. You will find detailed drawings and photographs with extensive explanations of repair and adjustment procedures. Need a check list for solving common corn picker problems, or recommended cylinder speeds for small grain harvesting? You've got it.

Manure spreader, utility wagon, forecart, even the humble sled and stone boat are all included with pictures and explanations. This book is not the only volume available on animal-drawn farm equipment, but in my opinion it is the best. Sam has gotten the balance exactly right: historical perspective; technical insight; a practical, Thousands of hours of thought and effort have gone into this valuable book. Draft animal practitioners owe the author a debt of gratitude.

Timothy Harrigan, Ph.D.
Biosystems and Agricultural Engineering Department
Michigan State University

Preface

Farm equipment manufacturers stopped building horse-drawn equipment during the late 1940s and early 1950s because they believed the horse was finished as a power source on modern farms. For the next three decades, horse farmers got along by buying up old horse-drawn implements and repairing, rebuilding, and modifying the machines. Eventually the supply of old machinery dried up, while at the same time modern farming methods demanded new and better equipment. Just as the original American farm machinery revolution of the 19th century started with farmers building the new equipment they needed, or improving existing machines, so too have modern horse farmers designed and built, or have had built, equipment to suit their needs. They've also figured out ways to successfully adapt high-tech implements, designed to be used with tractors, for use with animal power. Each area of the country in which a large number of farmers use horses has developed local manufacturers who cater to local needs, while a few companies have evolved to the point of selling implements all over the United States and Canada, as well as overseas.

Gail Damerow, editor of *Rural Heritage* magazine, has long seen the need for a single book covering most of the farm implements used with horses today. Her goal was not only to describe them, but furnish detailed information on how each piece of machinery is used, adjusted for good work, and maintained. Gail hears from folks every day who want to use horse machinery, but have no idea how to make it work. During the first half of the 20th century such books existed. I have many of them in my library. These books have, however, long been out of print, and operator's manuals for horse implements are difficult to find.

The upshot is that Gail convinced me to produce such a book. I've combined information from many sources with some of my personal experiences with operating farm machinery when I was younger. I have tried to offer a general idea of how to set and adjust each given type of machine to operate properly. It is, of course, impossible to cover every variation of every implement in such a book as this. Sulky plows, for instance, come in dozens of makes and styles, each a little different from all the others. Specific instructions for adjusting every sulky plow model, if such information could be located, would fill several books. Due to the many detail differences in machines built by different manufacturers, I have selected for discussion one representative, or sometimes two, for each implement. Most machines of the same type are similar enough that close examination of a particular machine should reveal how to make the necessary adjustments.

Few experiences in life are as satisfying as sitting on a well adjusted piece of machinery that's doing the job it was designed for, and doing it well. But remember that the older machines were built in the days when operators were expected to keep themselves safe, and safety shields and such devices were nonexistent. A number of safety warnings are included throughout this book; please take heed of them.

Have fun, but above all, be safe.

I: Tillage Equipment

Tillage is the term used for the operations necessary to modify and prepare soil for planting seeds. Soil conditions and climate, as well as the intended crop, all influence to a great degree the decision as to which tillage practice is best. Conventional wisdom until a couple of decades ago held that the objects of tillage included the following:

1. Opening the soil so rainwater will easily be absorbed, preventing runoff.

2. Pulverizing the soil to a fine crumb-like consistency free of clods.

3. Thoroughly covering stubble, stalks, straw, manure, and fertilizer and mixing them with the soil.

4. Aerating the soil and stimulating the growth of bacteria.

5. Controlling the soil's moisture content.

6. Destroying weeds.

7. Killing injurious insects.

Recently, the conservation and economic advantages of no-till, mulch-till, low-till, ridge-till, and strip-till crop planting practices have greatly reduced the use of moldboard plows and conventional tillage tools. It's not our intent to advocate one tillage practice over another, but to explain how the tools should be used so you can decide which is appropriate for your situation.

1

Moldboard Plows

"If ther's any spunk in a feller, plowin' will bring it out."
Abe Martin's Town Pump, The Bobbs–Merrill Co., 1929

Plows were used before history was recorded. The first plow was probably nothing more than a forked tree limb with the end of one fork sharpened. Humans or draft animals were hitched to the other end of the fork and this crude implement was drawn through the soil to loosen it and scratch out a shallow furrow. Later the sharpened end was reinforced by the addition of a flint, bronze, or iron point.

In the 17th century, the Dutch developed a plow with a curved wooden moldboard reinforced with an iron point and cutting edge. The Dutch plow had two handles, a coulter, and a beam. During the 1700s, English inventors worked to improve the primitive plows of the day, while in the United States village blacksmiths made plows similar to the European versions. Thomas Jefferson and Daniel Webster made improved plows for use on their own farms, but these plows didn't become popular with other farmers.

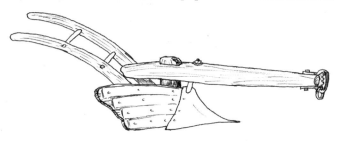

Early 19th century plow. The wooden moldboard is plated with iron strips and a wrought iron share is attached in front of the moldboard.

In 1797 Charles Newbold patented a plow with a solid cast–iron bottom, but farmers refused to use it, believing cast–iron poisoned the soil. After the turn of the 19th century, Jethro Wood and several others developed cast–iron plows with standardized replaceable parts. By this time prejudice against cast–iron was dying out and, by 1820, more than 10,000 iron plows had been sold, even though they cost twice as much as the wooden plows of the day.

The cast–iron plow grew in popularity. Both iron and wooden plows were carried with the pioneers who were drawn to the vast prairies of the Midwest. The old wooden plow proved useless in cutting the tough sod, and a cast–iron bottom wasn't much better. Although it cut the sod, the rough surface of the cast iron refused to take a polish and the sticky prairie soil adhered to the moldboard in great globs, requiring a stop every couple of feet to scrape off the buildup by hand.

About 1833, John Lane covered a wooden moldboard with strips of steel, making a plow that would scour. Steel, however, was scarce and expensive, and Lane never patented or produced his plow. In 1837, John Deere made a successful plow with a highly polished wrought–iron moldboard and a steel share. Deere's plow worked so well in the sticky prairie soil that farmers called it the singing plow. Even though steel cost about two and a half times as much as cast–iron, the steel plow was in great demand by the time of the War between the States.

After the war, plows were further improved. John Lane, son of the above–mentioned Lane, developed soft–center steel. James Oliver perfected a method of chilling cast iron. Both developments resulted in moldboards and shares that wore longer and were tougher than before. As the 19th century came to an end, walking plows had become extremely efficient and were in widespread use all over the world.

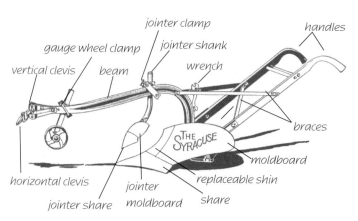

A state of the art 20th century plow with a steel beam, a jointer and gauge wheel, and a replaceable shin.
Deere & Co. Catalog # 6

Good Plowing

The moldboard plow is considered to be the most important implement in conventional tillage practices. The plow cuts, pulverizes, and inverts a strip of soil and, in the process, buries the organic material, as well as weeds and insects such as corn borers, that are on the surface. It was, and in the areas where no–till and other practices haven't become more popular, still is widely held that good plowing makes the job of preparing a seed bed much easier, helps control weeds, and makes for better crops. Some of the essentials of good plowing are:

- The coverage of weeds, stubble, and surface trash.
- Good granulation or pulverization of the plowed soil.
- Uniform depth and width of furrows.
- Straight, evenly laid furrow slices.
- Low, even, and clean back–furrows.
- Shallow, clean dead–furrows.
- Even furrow ends with no packed or unplowed soil.

Some of these essentials have nearly as much to do with cosmetics as with improving crops. Good plowing was once considered by most farmers to be a demonstration of skill or workmanship, some called it an art, and a badly plowed field was the mark of a poor or lazy farmer.

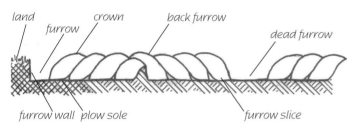

Cross section of ground plowed by a moldboard plow.

A plow bottom is designed to do its best work at a depth equal to about one–half its width at normal speed. Although an 18–inch plow may work satisfactorily at five inches of depth, and a 12–inch bottom at eight inches, poor work and inadequate trash covering usually result from any significant departure from the ideal depth–width relationship.

A properly equipped plow can usually turn under stubble up to a height equal to the width of the plow bottom. In heavy stalk conditions, smaller width bottoms, especially on gang plows, have a tendency to clog because of a lack of enough clearance between the bottoms. Stubble and stalks can be either broken over by rolling or chopped by using a stalk cutter or disc harrow.

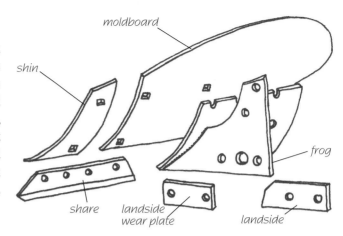

Components of a modern Raydex–style plow bottom.

Plow bottoms are designed to do their best work at a certain speed. The normal speed for horse–drawn plows is about two miles per hour, while high speed bottoms for tractor plows are meant to run much faster.

After carefully measuring the bolt–hole spacing on a vintage plow, you may find a modern Raydex bottom that will bolt right on, or will need few modifications. Using a Raydex bottom requires a new frog—the part that holds the bottom components together and connects the bottom to the beam or standard—as well as a new moldboard, shin, share, landside, and wear pad. These parts are expensive if purchased new, but used tractor plows with good bottoms are often sold for little money at farm equipment sales. Plow shares and other wearing parts are cheaper for these bottoms than for original equipment.

Plow Features

All moldboard plows have common features, although construction varies depending on the style. In general, the elements of a plow that do the work on the soil are common to any style.

The *share* is the plow's cutting edge. The *point* of the share penetrates the ground and steadies the plow while it is at work. The *heel* or *wing* is the share's outside corner. The share is the fastest wearing part of the plow and can easily be replaced.

The *moldboard* is the share's curved extension and serves to turn and pulverize the strip of soil cut by the share. The *shin,* or inner edge of the moldboard next to the unplowed ground, receives the most wear. Some plows have separate shins for easy replacement. Many older walking plows equipped with chilled bottoms used a combined shin and share.

Raydex

For a century, American farmers used plows with cast iron or steel plow shares that got broken or became dull. Dull shares could be resharpened three or four times before being discarded, but few farmers had the necessary skills or tools to resharpen shares themselves, so a trip to the local blacksmith was usually required. In 1940, Oliver introduced a new plow bottom, sold under the trade name Raydex, the share of which wore longer than one sharpening of a conventional share and cost no more than the average price a blacksmith charged for resharpening.

The Raydex bottom pulled easier than previous bottoms, because a large part of the shearing of the furrow slice was eliminated in turning the furrow. The Raydex bottom started the slice turning at the cutting edge, compared to older bottoms in which each furrow slice had a turning point both on the moldboard shin and near the wing.

Oliver must have been on the right track, because during the 1950s plow manufacturers went to the Raydex style of throw-away share for high speed tractor plows. Although Raydex-brand bottoms are no longer manufactured, all bottoms made today are of the Raydex style. Pioneer Equipment, one of the largest manufacturers of modern horse-drawn machinery, equips all their walking, sulky, and gang plows with "Oliver Raydex-type chilled steel" bottoms. Another major horse-drawn plow builder, White Horse Machine, uses "419 Radex bottoms" on their sulky and mounted plows.

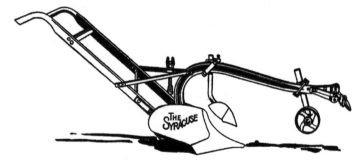

A plow with a horn-type share. When the share is replaced, the shin is also renewed.   *Deere & Co. catalog # 6*

The *landside* offsets the side pressure from the turning of the furrow slice by the moldboard. Landsides vary in length to meet different soil conditions and plow styles.

Wheeled plows usually have shorter landsides since most of the side thrust is carried by the wheels. The *heel* or rear end of the landside gets the most wear and may be replaceable, or may have a replaceable wearing plate.

The foundation on which the share, moldboard, and landside are mounted, and which holds these parts to the rest of the plow, is called the *frog*.

A *brace* is bolted between the outer edge of the moldboard and the landside to maintain the wedge position of these parts. All these parts bolted together make up the plow *bottom*, or *base*.

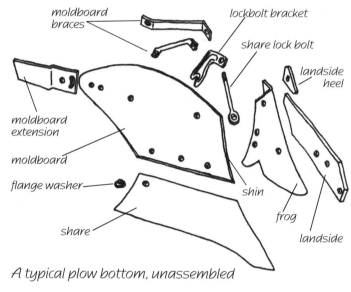

A typical plow bottom, unassembled

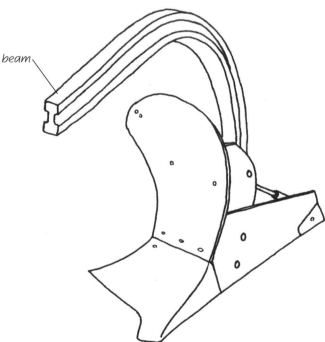

A typical plow bottom, assembled

Tillage Equipment

The *beam* has the pulling power applied to its front and the bottom attached to its rear, either directly (in the case of a curved beam) or by a standard (if the beam is straight). Multiple bottom plows have a beam for each bottom, attached at the front to a common drawbar.

The *hitch* is at the front of the beam and connects the plow to the pulling power. Hitches are adjustable to achieve correct horizontal and vertical lines of draft.

Coulters have been used on plows for centuries to help the share make the vertical cut separating the furrow slice from the land. The first coulters were thin knife–like blades, often known as cutters. Most modern plows use a rolling coulter.

A *jointer* is a miniature plow that cuts a small furrow of soil just above and a little ahead of the main bottom. This small furrow is thrown just ahead of the turning furrow slice and aids in burying stubble and trash.

Other attachments may be used to assist the plow in covering high grass or weeds, stalks, or heavy trash:

A *log chain* is often used on walking plows, and may also be used on single–bottom wheeled plows. One end of the chain is hooked to the doubletree at the furrow horse's clevis. The other end is fastened to the plow beam about 10 inches behind a point directly over the share point. The chain should be long enough to form a loop that drags on the surface of the furrow slice. This loop not only keeps the trash from pitching, but folds under high stalks and vegetation as well. You may need to experiment to obtain the proper length of loop and the best rear attachment point.

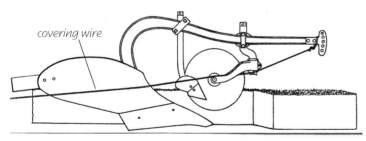

Method of attaching a covering wire to the front of the beam of a wheeled plow. The wire may also be attached directly to the coulter shank.

Ohio State University Bulletin No. 80

Covering wires are normally used on wheeled plows, but not on walkers because they tend to pull the plow out of position. A covering wire is a piece of No. 9 wire about 8 to 10 feet long, depending on where it is attached to the plow. One end is fastened to the plow ahead of the bottom so the wire drags across the surface of the furrow slice as it is being turned. The other end of the wire drags under the newly turned furrow slice, the weight of which holds the wire taut. When properly placed, the wire holds trash against the furrow slice and folds under high vegetation so it is covered.

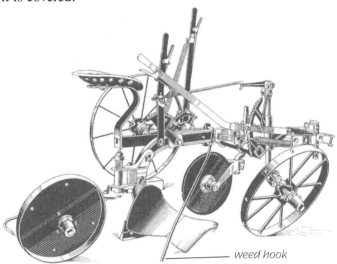

A weed hook attached to the beam of a sulky plow.

IHC catalog PO–1

A *weed hook* is a curved rod attached to the plow beam and extending to the front and side of the bottom. The rod bends over weeds, stalks, and grass so they are completely buried. *Cover boards* sometimes called *trash boards*, are used on modern Raydex–type bottoms. A cover board is a small, curved attachment bolted to the plow standard just above the regular shin. It has a much sharper curve than the plow's moldboard and throws the top layer of the furrow slice, along with any surface trash or weeds, into the bottom of the furrow before the furrow slice is completely turned. Used with a rolling coulter, but without a jointer, cover boards do a good job of covering trash. Most of today's plow manufacturers furnish cover boards as standard equipment on their riding plows, while making them optional on walking plows.

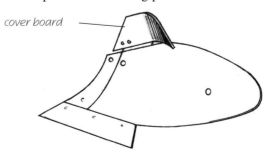

A cover board mounted above the moldboard on a modern plow bottom.

Draft of a Plow

The *draft* of any plow is determined by a number of factors, including soil type and moisture content, depth and width of furrow, speed, correct line of draft, and adjustment and sharpness of the plow itself. Early in the last century, Professor E.V. Collins of Iowa State College determined that 45 percent of the total draft is expended in cutting the furrow slice, 34 percent in turning the slice, and 21 percent in moving the plow.

Draft of plows per square inch of furrow section	
	pounds of draft
Sandy soil, lightest draft	3
Sandy loam	3 – 6
Silt loam	5 – 7
Clay loam	6 – 8
Heavy clay	7 – 10
Gumbo or adobe	15 – 20
W.M. Davies, The Journal of Agricultural Science, 1924	

The primary factor determining a plow's draft is the soil being plowed. As may be determined from the accompanying table, a 12–inch plow in clay loam turning a furrow 6–inches deep, for example, requires about 500 pounds of pull (12x6x7 = 504), if the plow is sharp and properly adjusted and the hitch is correct.

Other dynamometer tests showed that 15 to 25 percent more power is required to pull a plow through the ground when four horses are hitched abreast than when they were hitched two–and–two. This additional power is needed because excessive side draft is present with a four–abreast hitch unless an outside horse walks on the plowed ground, which is tiring for that horse. A four-abreast hitch also makes the plow harder to pull and causes all but the furrow horse to walk in a twisted position, resulting in crowding, chafing of the traces against the outside thighs, uneven pulling on the shoulders, and unnecessary overheating of the horses. When a two–and–two hitch is used, all the horses walk on solid ground and aren't crowded.

Care of the Plow Bottom

If a plow is to scour and turn the soil properly, the bottoms must be kept in good condition. Time consuming and frustrating delays are caused by plow bottoms that won't scour or penetrate the soil. The trouble may be caused by an incorrectly adjusted hitch, by dull, rusty, or improperly set shares, or by loose or misaligned bottoms. A good plowman must understand how the plow works,

how to make adjustments, and how to recognize and correct problems.

The share is the business end of the plow and its condition is vital to good plow performance. The end of a new share's point dips downward slightly, causing the plow to be drawn into the ground, creating what is called the plow's *bottom suction*. The share point is also slightly angled toward the unplowed ground, making the plow hold into the land, creating what is known as *land suction*.

A deep suction share has a point with more bottom suction than a common point. Such shares are available for use in extremely hard, dry, or stony soil.

Because the share is the part of a plow subject to the most wear, eventually the cutting edge and the point wear away. This wear causes suction to decrease until the point won't penetrate the soil. Adjusting the hitch so the plow will hold to the proper depth becomes impossible. The share must be resharpened and reset, or replaced.

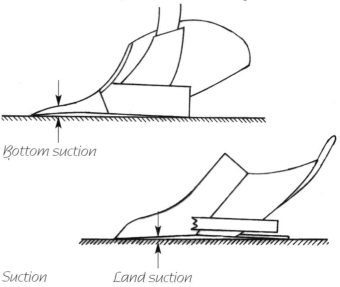

Bottom suction

Suction   *Land suction*

Coulters and Jointers

The coulter and jointer are needed for good plowing, to completely cover all stalks, stubble, grass, and weeds usually found on a field's surface. The jointer is a miniature plow that cuts a small slice off the land edge of the main furrow ahead of the bottom and throws it outward so all stubble and trash are buried. A coulter or a jointer is often used alone, particularly on walking plows. On wheeled plows they are most effective when used together in a rolling coulter–jointer combination.

The coulter makes a vertical cut to separate the furrow slice from the unplowed ground, ensuring a clean–cut furrow wall and lessening draft, as well as wear on the

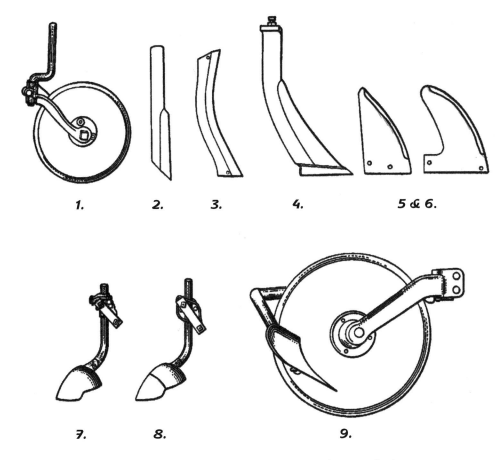

1. *rolling coulter.* 2. *knife or hanging coulter, sometimes called a cutter.*
3. *double-ended knife coulter.* 4. *heavy-duty knife coulter for brush land.*
5 & 6. *two kinds of standing or fin coulters.* 7. *one-piece jointer.*
8. *two-piece jointer.* 9. *combination rolling coulter and jointer.*

Agricultural Machinery by J. Brownlee Davidson

many roots or stones, the coulter point may be set below the plow point to prevent it from hooking under such obstacles. If you don't keep the plane of the coulter blade parallel to the plane of the landside, the coulter will tend to lead the plow into or away from the land. Knife and fin coulters should be kept sharp. Knife coulters are not satisfactory for use in heavy trash conditions where they gather trash and clog the plow.

The rolling coulter, found on most plows today, is a big help in plowing clean and covering all the trash, es-pecially when used in conjunction with a jointer or a cover board. The rolling coulter cuts the furrow slice away from the land verti-cally, reducing draft and leaving a smooth, clean furrow wall. It cuts stubble and residue to prevent them from dragging on the stationary knife or jointer and clogging the plow. The resulting shorter lengths of trash are easier for the plow to bury and cover.

moldboard shin. The coulter may be a vertical, sharpened fin attached to the share or moldboard, or a knife hanging from the beam, although these older style coulters are nearly useless in trashy conditions due to clogging. The rolling coulter common today has the advantage of rolling over and cutting through any surface trash. The combination of a sharp coulter and a properly adjusted jointer ensures thorough coverage of all but the heaviest surface trash.

Some older walking plows may be equipped with a fin or standing coulter, which is a vertical knife-like blade standing upright from the plow share point. The fin coulter requires no adjustment. Hanging knife coulters are similar, but are attached to the plow beam at their upper ends. The angle of hanging coulters may be changed by loosening the beam clamp.

In hard ground the knife coulter is inclined forward, while in mellow ground the angularity is reduced. In soil with

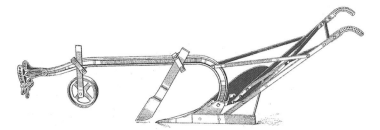

A hanging knife coulter set low for stony or rooty ground.

IHC catalog PO-1

Adjusting a Rolling Coulter

A rolling coulter must be sharp and carefully adjusted to perform properly. For general plowing set the center of the coulter directly above, or up to one inch behind, the share point by moving the coulter shank clamp along the beam.

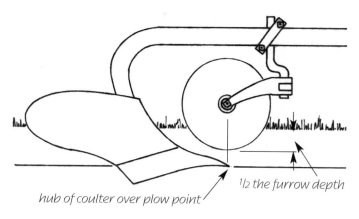

Correct setting of a rolling coulter, with the hub over the plow point and the blade cutting about one-half the depth of the furrow.

hub of coulter over plow point

$^1/_2$ the furrow depth

In stubble ground, set the coulter blade to cut $^5/_8$ inch to land of the landside, and deep enough to cut the trash, or about one-half the furrow depth under ordinary conditions. Vary the depth by moving the shank higher or lower in the clamp.

In sod, set the blade to cut $^1/_2$ to $^5/_8$ inch to land, and deep enough to cut the entire depth of the roots. To move the coulter sideways, loosen the clamp and turn the crank-shaped shank to the right or left until the coulter blade is positioned correctly.

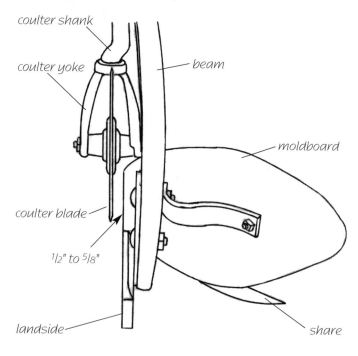

coulter shank

coulter yoke

beam

moldboard

coulter blade

$^1/_2"$ to $^5/_8"$

landside

share

Correct setting of coulter. The blade is parallel with, and $^1/_2$ to $^5/_8$ inch to the land side of the landside.

In dry trash, set the coulter a little forward of the share point and just deep enough to cut the trash. If set too deep, the coulter won't mount and cut the trash, but will push it ahead and soon clog.

In wet trash, or if the coulter is dull, set the coulter back of the share point and higher, so it will mount the trash and carry it down and cut it against the shin.

In hard ground or stony soil, set the coulter behind the share point and higher, so the coulter won't ride the plow up and out of the ground.

For two bottom plows, set the coulter on the land side as above, and space the other coulter the width of the plow bottom from the first, for example 14 inches away for a 14-inch plow.

A large diameter coulter mounts and cuts trash better than a small one. If your coulter blade has been worn until it's less than about 14 inches in diameter, get a new 16- or 18-inch blade.

Most coulter yokes are provided with a collar to hold the yoke to the shank and to keep the coulter from swinging all the way around. The collar should be adjusted so the coulter can swing the same distance to either side of the share point. Some plows have chains that keep the coulters from swinging too far.

Most coulters are equipped with adjustable bearings to take up wear. Keep the bearing adjusted tightly enough to prevent it from wobbling, and grease the bearings every eight hours of work.

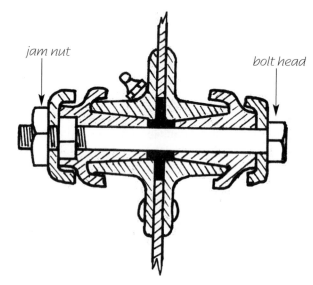

jam nut

bolt head

Cross section of a coulter bearing. To take up end play, loosen the jam nut, turn the bolt head—don't over tighten, the coulter blade must turn freely—and retighten the jam nut.

Tillage Equipment

Adjusting a Jointer

If you use only a jointer, set the jointer point over the share point by moving the jointer shank along the beam. Adjust the jointer's depth by moving the jointer shank up or down in its clamp. A jointer that is set too shallow may clog. Adjust the jointer's angle by turning the jointer shank in its clamp. Pitching the jointer at a greater angle to the ground surface often cures non–scouring of the jointer.

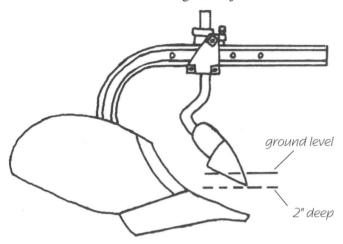

Set the jointer to cut about 2 inches deep on smooth land and a little deeper on rough, uneven ground.

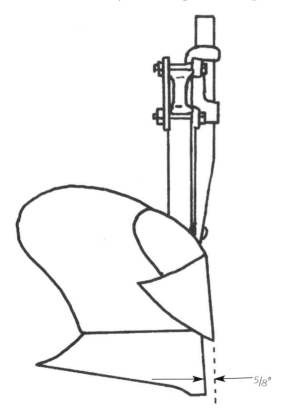

Set the jointer point to cut about 5/8 inch to land from the plow landside.

When you use the jointer with a rolling coulter, follow the same standard rules, except that you may have to set the coulter a little forward and the jointer a little behind the share point. Set the point of the jointer so it just touches the coulter blade to prevent trash from catching in the gap. The jointer edge should angle away from the coulter blade.

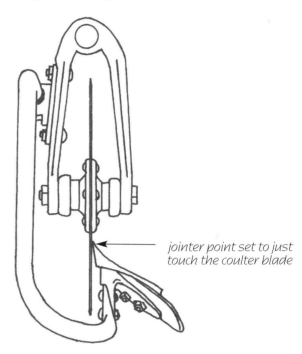

The correct setting of a jointer used with a rolling coulter.

Walking Plows

Walking plows have been made in many sizes and with a wide range of share and moldboard shapes. A plow that throws the furrow slice to the left is called a left–handed plow, while one that throws the furrow to the right is a right–handed plow. Even though much discussion has occurred (and probably a few fist fights) through the years over the advantages of one over the other, the quality of plowing is no different between a right–hand and a left–hand plow, as long as both are properly hitched and adjusted. A hillside plow has a reversible share and moldboard that allow all the furrows to be thrown one way as the plow works back and forth across the field.

Hitching a Walking Plow

If a plow hitch is incorrectly adjusted so it pulls sideways or rides on the point of the share, you will have increased draft and uneven furrows. Not only that, but you will be forced to constantly fight the plow handles in an attempt to hold the plow to its work, and the plow share will wear more rapidly.

Vertical Adjustment

If you could fasten a string to the plow's center of load, at a point 2 inches from the shin and just below the surface of the ground, then run the string through the pin that connects the evener to the plow clevis and on to the hame hook of the furrow horse, the string would demonstrate the *line of hitch*, or *line of draft*. This line of draft is one of the most important factors controlling the front end of the beam.

Because of the resistance of the plow and the power of the horses, the line of draft always tries to straighten itself. A line that is broken by an incorrect hitch throws the plow out of alignment. If you hitch so the line of draft remains straight while the plow is working, the implement will be easy to handle and do good work, and the load on your team will be reduced.

If the clevis is set too high, the line of draft is broken upward. When the team pulls, the front of the beam will be forced downward and the plow bottom will run too deep. If you try to overcome this tendency by bearing down on the handles, the plow will weave and be unsteady.

When the clevis is set too low, the straightening of the line of draft lifts the front of the beam. This lifting action breaks the sucking in of the share and the plow will ride out of the ground. If you try to counteract the problem by lifting both handles, the plow will be unsteady and you will carry part of the plow's weight as you fight the incorrect line of hitch.

The size of the team affects the correct line of draft. A small team must be hitched to the plow at a lower point than a large team. A close hitch with short traces requires a higher clevis point on the plow than when longer traces are used. A big team generally needs longer traces than a small team to attain the correct line of draft.

Another important consideration is the adjustment of the harness. If the belly bands, back straps, or hip straps are too

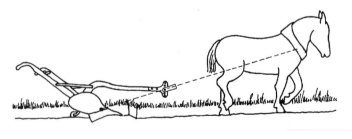

A correct line of draft. The dotted line from the plow's center of load is straight through the plow clevis to the hame hook on the furrow horse's collar.

short, the traces will be held above the straight line of draft, causing too much down pull on the horses' backs, hips, and necks, resulting in chafing and sores.

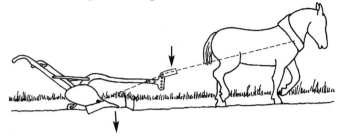

The hitch clevis is too high, breaking the line of draft upward. The pull of the team will straighten the line and force the front of the plow beam down.

The hitch clevis is too low, breaking the line of draft downward. The pull of the team will straighten the line and lift the front of the beam.

Horizontal Hitch

To correct the width of furrow, change the spacing between the horses. Allow the plow handles to go perfectly free and see if the plow is cutting too wide or too narrow a furrow. The width of furrow should be corrected, not by the horizontal clevis, but by the width of the evener and team spacing. If the plow cuts too wide, bring the horses closer together; if the furrow is too narrow, hitch the horses farther apart. The plow follows a point halfway between the two horses, and the width of the furrow depends on the position of the horse on the land.

An important part of correct hitching is to use an evener of the proper size. A too–wide evener causes the horses to walk farther apart than they should and the plow will cut too wide a furrow. To reduce the furrow width, the clevis must be moved to the left, causing the plow to tip toward the right. A too–long evener results in increased draft for the team and requires you to constantly hold the plow handles against the horses' pull. To minimize this side draft, get the horizontal hitch as nearly as possible in a direct line between the center of draft and the center of power when the plow and team are running straight ahead.

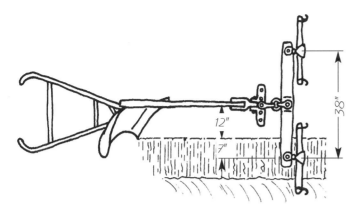

Correct evener width for a 14–inch plow.

The center of power with a two–horse team is a line from a point exactly midway between the inside hame hooks to the center clevis of the evener. The center of draft of a 14–inch two–horse walking plow is about 2 inches in from the landside and directly under the middle of the plow beam. The distance from the center of draft to the edge of the furrow wall is thus 14 minus 2, or 12 inches. The furrow horse walks in the middle of the furrow, so his singletree clevis will be 7 inches from the furrow wall. The distance then, from the center of draft, or the middle of the evener, to the singletree clevis is 19 inches, calling for a 38–inch evener.

For a 12–inch plow, the center of draft is approximately $10\frac{1}{2}$ inches from the furrow wall plus 6 inches to the middle of the furrow, or $16\frac{1}{2}$ inches. Thus, a 33–inch evener should be used on a 12–inch plow.

If you use a too–wide evener, the horses will have to walk too far apart. The hitch clevis will then have to be moved to the left to keep the plow from taking too wide a furrow. The line of draft law applies horizontally as well as vertically, and moving the clevis to the left will cause the plow to tip to the right. The draft will be increased, and you will have to constantly fight the plow handles.

Just as the center of power for a two–horse team is half way between the horses' collars, with a three–horse team it falls at the center of the middle horse's collar. If the hitch clevis is too far toward unplowed ground, the plow will tip to the right and tend to run narrow, or not take a full cut. If the hitch is too far toward the furrow, the opposite is true and the plow will run wide, or take too wide a cut.

Wood beam plows usually have an adjustment at the rear end of the beam that allows the front of the beam to be shifted to the right or left. This adjustment lets you move the front end of the beam into the line of hitch, where the same principles apply as described above.

Adjusting the Hitch

To adjust the hitch of a walking plow:

Raise the beam gauge wheel, if provided, as high as possible.

Adjust the vertical clevis for the desired depth of plowing. Start the plow into the ground and raise or lower the vertical clevis until the plow runs at the desired depth—if too deep, lower the clevis; if too shallow, raise the clevis. The same effect may be obtained by changing the length of the traces. Short traces raise the end of the plow beam and do the same as lowering the clevis. Longer traces lower the plow beam and have the same effect as raising the clevis.

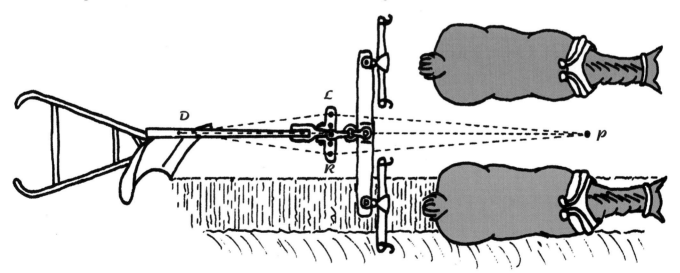

How the horizontal line of draft from the center of power **P***, to the center of draft* **D***, affects plow performance. Hitching at* **L** *causes the plow to run narrow, while hitching at* **R** *makes it run wide.*

Wing Bearing

A walking plow has no wheels to carry its weight, but has two bearing surfaces that work against the furrow bottom. Part of the weight is carried by the heel of the landside, part is carried by the flattened edge of the share's outside corner, called the wing bearing. A walking plow with too much wing bearing won't suck in properly on the wing side and is said to wing up. A plow with too little wing bearing wings down, or tends to run wide. When the soil is mellow, you need more wing bearing than when the soil is hard.

If a walking plow tends to wing up or wing down, and you try to compensate by setting the hitch over, or by fighting the plow through the handles, the bottom will not run level and poor plowing and trash covering will result. For average plowing conditions, walking plows should carry the following amounts of wing bearing:

12–inch plow — ³/₄ inch
14–inch plow — 1¹/₄ inches
16–inch plow — 1¹/₂ inches

Wing bearing on cast shares can't be changed, although it may be reduced by chipping off a little of the wing. Steel shares may be changed by forging or by bending cold.

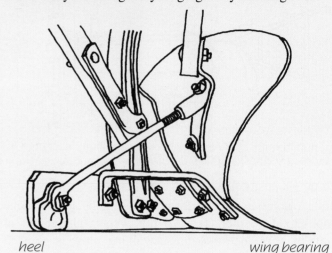

heel   wing bearing

The weight of a walking plow is carried by the landside's heel and the share's wing bearing.

Lower the beam gauge wheel until it just lightly touches the ground while plowing. The wheel is necessary only to maintain an even depth of plowing in a field containing different soil conditions or hard and soft spots, or when a rolling coulter is used. Set the depth of plowing with the hitch, rather than the gauge wheel.

Adjust the horizontal clevis to obtain the correct balance. Let go of the handles and see which way the plow tips. If the plow tips to the right move the clevis to the right, if it tips to the left move the clevis to the left, until the handles balance in the upright position. On a walking plow, the share's wing bearing affects this balance, but since changing wing bearing is difficult, adjust the horizontal clevis to balance the plow.

Two- and Three-Horse Plows

Both walking and two–way sulky plows are designed for use with two horses or three horses. Correctly adjusting a two–horse plow when using three horses is difficult, and vice versa.

On a two–horse plow the beam is parallel to the landside and in about 1¹/₂ to 2 inches from the landside. On a three–horse plow the beam isn't parallel to the landside, but is landed, or bent toward the land. The landside edge of the beam will be directly over the landside edge of the plow share. Some plows were built to be convertible, using a slotted adjustment at the rear of

the beam or, in some cases, a wedge to change the landing of the beam.

While the horizontal hitch on a two–horse plow may be adjusted to use three horses by moving the hitch clevis to the left, the resulting side draft may cause problems. If you do most of your plowing with two horses, use a two–horse plow. If you commonly work three horses, use a three–horse plow.

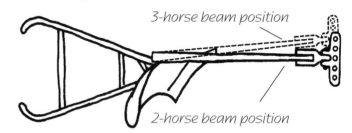

3-horse beam position

2-horse beam position

Relative positions of two–horse and three–horse plow beams.

Hillside Plows

In hilly areas throwing the furrow slice up the slope is often impractical, leading to the development of the *hillside plow*. The moldboard and share of a hillside plow are shaped like an arrowhead and swivel underneath the plow frame to allow the plow to throw the furrow to either the right or the left. When you reach the end of the land, lift up on the handles until the bottom clears the ground. With a kick of the foot, you can release a latch at the rear of the frog, allowing the bottom to swing down. If you drop the plow at exactly the right time, the bottom latches onto the opposite side, ready for the team to return down the furrow, again throwing the soil downhill.

The cutting edge of the share while on one side becomes the shin of the moldboard when on the other side. Knife coulters or jointers may be attached to the hillside plow that automatically shift position when the plow is reversed. Some hillside plows are equipped with a sliding clevis to keep the correct line of draft, while others have a clevis that may be shifted by a lever between the handles. Hillside plows are rarely used today, primarily because they don't usually do a good job of plowing.

A hillside plow equipped with a swiveling jointer and a hand shifted clevis. John Deere Plow Company catalog No. 6.

Riding Plows

When settlers moved beyond the Midwest and discovered the huge acreages of the Great Plains, the old walking plow began to look woefully inadequate. During the 1860s, several inventors patented wheeled riding plows. Improvements during the following years included a rolling coulter, foot lift, and rolling landside. Initially, many of the so-called Bonanza Farms of the Northwest used two–bottom gang plows behind which the operator walked, controlling the plow with a single handle. Eventually additional bottoms were added to sulky plows. While these implements might have as many as four bottoms, the two and three bottom versions were the most popular.

Features of a Riding Plow

Wheeled riding plows typically have one large wheel that runs on the unplowed ground and is known as the land wheel, and a front furrow wheel that runs in the previously plowed furrow. Some riding plows have a small rear furrow wheel that runs behind the bottom in the furrow that was just plowed. Most frameless sulky plows have either a long

landside or a rolling landside in place of the rear furrow wheel. A one–bottom riding plow is called a *sulky plow.*

Two–way riding plows that have only one bottom in use at a time are also known as sulky plows. The *two–way plow* is used to turn all the furrows the same direction. This ability is especially useful when plowing irregular or hilly fields, or in irrigated land where dead furrows could interfere with the proper flow of water.

The *low–lift,* or *frameless,* sulky plow is a single–bottom riding plow with its wheels and axles attached directly to the beam. The popular McCormick–Deering Little Chief and Oliver No. 11 sulky plows, as well as modern sulkies from Pioneer and White Horse Machine, are of the frameless design. The beam is raised on the land and front furrow wheel by a lever, while the rear furrow wheel, if there is one, is mounted directly on the beam and held in a straight ahead position by a spring that allows it to caster during turns. A frameless sulky plow may or may not be equipped with a pole. Many low–lift plows have a long landside or a rolling landside in place of a rear wheel.

The *high–lift,* or *framed,* sulky plow has a frame to which its three wheels are attached. The beam is raised and lowered within this frame, usually by means of a foot lift. The bottom may be raised in relation to the rear furrow wheel. This plow has a tongue, attached by a steering rod to the rear furrow wheel, that helps overcome side draft. The IHC Diamond and the New Deere plows are two examples of high–lift models.

A *gang plow* is a plow with two or more bottoms, although gang plows with more than two bottoms are rare. Most gang plows are of the framed, high–lift style.

A John Deere-Syracuse No. 4 two-way sulky plow.
John Deere Plow Company catalog No. 6.

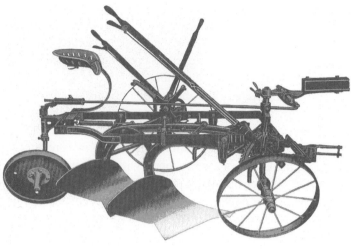

A New Deere light draft gang plow.
Soil Culture and Modern Farm Methods, 1914

An Oliver No. 11 sulky plow equipped with a combination rolling coulter and jointer. The placement of the land wheel, directly opposite the plow bottom, helps counteract side thrust.   *1923 Oliver Chilled Plow Works catalog*

and the share, landside, and moldboard polished for good scouring. Coulters and jointers, if used, must be sharp and adjusted correctly.

Wheels, rolling landsides, and rolling coulters should be well greased to prevent excessive friction and wear. Most wheel boxings and coulters have adjustable sleeves or bearings to take up wear. Keep them tight enough to prevent wobbling, but not so tight as to cause friction.

Adjust the lifting spring to have enough tension to make the plow lift easily, but not so tight as to prevent the plow from quickly entering the ground when dropped.

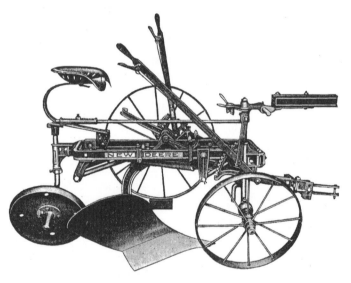

This New Deere light draft sulky plow has a steering rod from the tongue bracket to the rear wheel.
Soil Culture and Modern Farm Methods, 1914

Adjustment and Operation

To avoid heavy draft, a riding plow should be adjusted so the combined weight of the driver, the plow, and the soil being turned is carried on the plow's wheels, or the wheels and the rolling landside, if provided. Keep the share sharp,

A modern frameless sulky plow manufactured by White Horse Machine.

Tillage Equipment

Frameless Sulky Plows

Set the front furrow wheel of a frameless plow with just enough lead toward the land to hold the wheel in the corner of the furrow. This adjustment is accomplished at the pole plate on some plows, and with the landing lever on others. The landing lever is also handy for giving the plow more or less land for work on hillsides, and to straighten crooked furrows. Don't use the landing lever to change the width of cut on level ground.

Adjust the width of cut by moving the furrow wheel and axle closer to, or farther from, the beam:

- Lower the plow bottom on a level surface.
- Place a block under the land wheel to represent the furrow depth.
- Level the plow with the hand levers.
- Set the front furrow wheel to run straight.
- Place a straight-edge tight against the landside of the share point and against the landside or rear furrow wheel. Measure the distance from the inside of the front furrow wheel to the straight-edge. This distance is about $1/2$ inch less than the width of the furrow slice the plow will take. If you want the plow to take a wider slice, move the wheel away from the beam; if narrower, move it closer to the beam. A 12-inch plow should cut a 12-inch furrow slice, a 14-inch plow 14-inches, and so forth.

If a frameless sulky plow has an adjustable rear furrow wheel, use the same method to set it for $1/4$-$1/2$ inch heel clearance. Plows with no rear furrow wheel have no heel clearance—the landside takes all the downthrust and rides on the bottom of the furrow

Framed Sulky and Gang Plows

The method of measuring and adjusting the width of cut of a framed sulky plow, as well as the front bottom of a gang plow, is similar to the method for adjusting a frameless sulky. The distance between the outside edge of the share point to the inside edge of the tire on the furrow wheel should measure $1/2$ inch less than the size of the plow bottom—$11^1/2$ inches for a 12-inch plow, $13^1/2$ inches for a 14-inch plow, and so forth.

The landside of a framed plow is carried just ahead of the rear furrow wheel. To assure proper penetration, the rear furrow wheel should run straight ahead and tight against the furrow wall. The heel clearance between the heel of the landside and the bottom of the furrow should be $1/4$ to $1/2$ inch. The same distance, known as landside clearance, should be maintained between the landside and the furrow wall. These clearances need to be present, but should be kept to a minimum. Make the landside and heel clearance adjustments by moving the rear wheel in relation to the plow. Don't increase the the landside or the heel clearances just to offset a dull share; sharpen or replace the share.

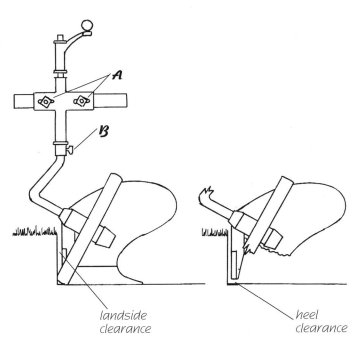

To change the width of cut, move the furrow wheel nearer to, or farther from, the beam.

Move the rear furrow wheel assembly sideways on the frame at A to set the landside clearance. Raise or lower the rear furrow wheel at B to obtain the correct heel clearance.

Hitching a Riding Plow

As with walking plows, the satisfactory performance of a riding plow depends to a large degree on a proper hitch that takes into consideration the correct line of draft. An incorrect hitch on a riding plow isn't as evident as that on a walking model, since the wheels carry the unwanted up and down or side forces that result from a wrong hitch, and the operator doesn't have to fight the plow handles. Heavy draft and a poor job of plowing, however, are the inevitable result of careless hitching without regard to the line of draft.

Vertical Adjustment

Many plowmen have a tendency to hitch too high on wheeled plows. An upward break in the correct line of draft causes the front of the plow to be pulled down and the plow to bounce along on the point of the share, while the tail wheel or landside waves in the air and the plow weaves from side to side in the furrow.

A too–low hitch, on the other hand, lifts up on the front of the plow, making penetration difficult and putting a heavy load on the team. If you are plowing deep or with tall horses, the point of hitch should be higher than when for small horses or plowing shallow. If horses are hitched

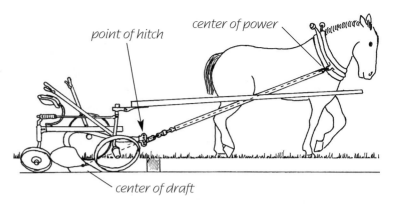

The correct vertical hitch for a high–lift riding plow is represented by the line of draft running straight from the center of draft, through the point of hitch, and on to the center of power. The same rule applies to a frameless sulky with or without a tongue.

strung out, the point of hitch must be lower than for horses hitched abreast.

The center of draft is located where the line of draft hits the plow bottom at the junction of the share and moldboard in average depth plowing. This point will be slightly higher on the moldboard for deep plowing, and somewhat lower on the share when plowing shallow.

Center of Draft

The center of draft on a wheeled plow of any size is ¹/₄ of the cutting width of one bottom to the left of center of the plow's total cutting width. To find the center of draft, first determine the total cut of the plow. Half of the total cut is the center of cut. Measure to the left (if a right–hand plow) of the center of cut one–quarter of the width of cut of one bottom to find the center of draft. On a left–hand plow, take the measurement to the right of the center of cut.

Example: Find center of draft of a two–bottom 12" plow.
  Total cut of plow = 24"
  Center of cut = ¹/₂ of 24" = 12"
  ¹/₄ of the cutting width of one bottom = ¹/₄ of 12" = 3"
  Add 3" to the center of cut = 3" + 12" = 15"

The center of draft of a two–bottom 12" plow is 15" from the furrow wall, measured at right angles to the furrow wall. For a single bottom plow, the center of draft is about 3" to the furrow side of the shin, and parallel to the open furrow.

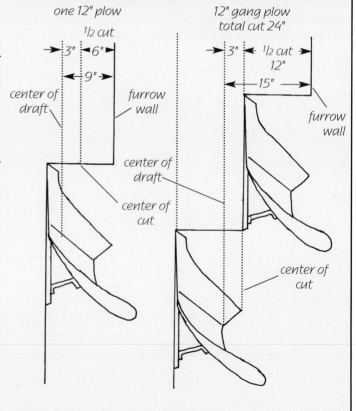

You can check for the correct height of hitch in one of two ways:

1. Stop the plow when it's operating at the desired depth. Stand in front of and between the furrow horse and the first land horse. Sight along the traces from the hame hook to a point representing the center of draft. The point of hitch at the plow clevis should be on your sight line.

2. Check to see if approximately the same amount of weight is on each of the three wheels. With the bottom in the ground, get off the plow and try to turn each wheel by hand. Each wheel should have about the same amount of weight, with slightly less on the rear furrow wheel.

Avoiding Side Draft

Wheeled plow hitches are adjustable horizontally to accommodate teams of different sizes and allow you to obtain the correct line of draft. As with walking plows, hitching to the correct line of draft is extremely important to minimize side draft, thus saving wear and tear on the horses and assuring a better job of plowing.

Side draft may be defined as an increase in the plow's resistance due to the team being hitched to one or the other side of the true line of draft. Hitching to one side causes the plow to shift to either the right or left and therefore try to run at an angle to the team's forward motion, resulting in increased draft, poor coverage of trash, and uneven furrows.

If three horses are hitched abreast on most one–bottom wheeled plows, and an outside horse walks in the open furrow, side draft is sure to result. This side draft occurs because the center of power of a three–abreast team is farther from the furrow wall than the plow's center of draft, causing the horses on the land to pull at an angle to the open furrow. The front of the plow is therefore forced toward the furrow and is said to run out. One way to offset running out is to angle the front furrow wheel toward the furrow wall just enough to keep the plow from shifting outward.

The side draft also forces the plow's landside against the furrow wall. If the furrow wheel must be angled so much that the landside crushes or tries to climb up the furrow wall, lessen the furrow wheel's angle and try to reduce the side draft by adjusting the hitch. Instead of hitching three horses abreast, using four hitched 2–2 eliminates side draft and allows for deeper plowing, especially in the fall when the ground is hard. A four–horse hitch also lets the horses walk straight and farther apart during hot weather.

On a high–lift or framed plow, when the center of pull is hitched to the plow's center of draft, the rear furrow wheel should be angled slightly to lead away from the furrow wall. If the hitch cannot be made on the true line of draft, the resulting side draft may be offset to some degree by angling the front and rear furrow wheels. Angle the front furrow wheel toward the furrow wall and angle the rear furrow wheel to lead away from the furrow wall. First, however, make every effort to hitch so as to obtain the least possible amount of side draft.

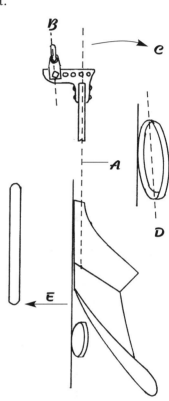

*Side draft from three hitched abreast on a low–lift sulky plow occurs because the center of power is farther from the furrow wall than the plow's point of draft **A,** causing the horses on the land to pull at an angle **B** to the open furrow and forcing the plow's front toward the furrow **C.** To offset the side draft, angle the front furrow wheel toward the furrow wall **D,** but not so much that the landside crushes or climbs up the furrow wall **E.***

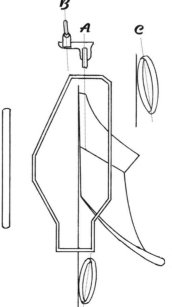

*Side draft from three hitched abreast on a high–lift sulky plow occurs because the line of hitch **B** is toward the land from the true line of draft **A.** To offset the side draft, angle the front furrow wheel toward the furrow wall **C** and angle the rear furrow wheel to lead away from the furrow wall **D.***

Two-Way Plows

The two–way or hillside plow has both a right–hand and a left–hand bottom on the same frame. Only one bottom is used at a time and they are alternated so all the furrows are thrown in the same direction. This plow is used in hilly or irregularly shaped fields, as well as where dead furrows aren't desired, such as in irrigated fields. With a two–way plow, you can begin at one side of the field and plow back and forth to the other side, without making a back furrow ridge or leaving a dead furrow. A two–way plow may also be used as a regular right– or left–hand sulky for plowing around a field.

A modern two–way plow manufactured by White Horse Machine.

Hitching a Two-Way Plow

A two–way sulky plow has a horizontal hitch that provides for automatic shifting of the evener clevis to the front of the working beam by means of a roller moving on a horizontal draft bar. When one of the beams is in its lowered or working position, the front of the beam is ahead of its raised counterpart, causing the roller on the evener clevis to move along the horizontal draft bar and automatically placing the point of hitch in line with the working beam. A two–way sulky has one of two styles of horizontal hitch:

● The rod–style hitch, also called a dial hitch, has a draft iron or rod attached to the beam about 18 inches back from the front end. The front ends of the draft irons are adjustable horizontally by rotating a support attached to the front end of each of the beams, thus the name dial hitch. The support is moved up and down on the beam to provide the correct vertical hitch adjustment.

● The second style of hitch has an offset clevis attached to the front of each beam. The clevises have several holes

for vertical adjustment, as well as three holes and an offset for horizontal adjustment.

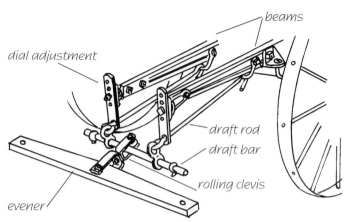

Rod–style hitch on a two–way plow.

Adjusting a Two-Way Plow

The principles of hitching and adjusting a two–way plow are much like that of a walking plow, with some significant differences.

Vertical Clevis

Keep the vertical clevis as low as possible and still maintain the desired depth of plowing. If the clevis is too high, the plow will ride on its nose and the rear end of the landside won't touch the furrow bottom. The result will be fast wearing of the share, broken and uneven furrows, and increased draft. If the clevis is too low, the plow won't go as deep as desired.

When the vertical clevis is set correctly, the landside heel will press firmly against the bottom of the furrow and the bottom will run at the desired depth. If the depth lever is moved to the deepest plowing position, the plow bottom should run only about an inch deeper than it did before. If it buries itself, the clevis is set too high.

Width of Furrow

On a two–way sulky plow, furrow width is determined by three things:

1. The position of the plow beams in the frame—The wheels of a two–way plow should run about 3 inches out from the furrow wall. The plow beams should be bolted to the frame so the distance from the landside to the wheel is 3 inches plus the width of the plow bottom. For a 12–inch plow each beam should be set 15 inches from the inside

of its wheel, and for a 14–inch plow the distance should be 17 inches.

2. The tongue shifting lever—This lever should be set so the wheels run straight and parallel to the furrow wall. The tongue shifting lever (or, on some two–way plows, the foot–operated shifting levers) allows the tongue to be shifted sideways to regulate furrow width, letting you maintain the full width of furrow when plowing around curves or on side hills.

3. The horizontal clevis—After the first two adjustments have been made, walk behind the plow and watch the plow beam to see if it's pulling in a straight line with the furrow.

If the front end of the beam is being pulled to the right, move the clevis to the right, and if to the left, move the clevis to the left until the plow pulls straight.

Setting the Tongue
On most two–way plows, the tongue may be attached to the frame at the center for two–horse operation, or, when viewed from behind the plow, at the right–hand side of the frame for use with three horses. One popular brand has a stub pole mounted in the center of the right frame half. A pole bolted to the outside of this stub tongue is set up for three horses. For two horses, the pole is bolted to the inside of the stub tongue.

Setting the Horizontal Clevis
For two horses, the horizontal hitch should be at a point approximately $1^1/_2$ inches toward the plowed land from the landside. For three horses, the hitch should be toward the unplowed land about one inch from the landside.

If the plow is an IHC No. 1 Success, an Oliver No. 23B, a John Deere No. 4, or other two–way sulky plow with a draft rod attached to each beam, make horizontal and vertical adjustments at the front of the beam by shifting the position of the draft rod.

If the plow is a John Deere–Syracuse No. 4, an Oliver No. 23A, or other two–way sulky plow with an offset clevis bolted to the front end of each beam, the clevis has three holes each for vertical and horizontal adjustment. Flip the clevis over to put the offset projection on the desired side of the beam

The clevis hitch is used on two–way plows with both straight beams (known as two–horse beams) and landed beams (three–horse beams). The offsets of the front clevises are set according to the landing of the beams. If the plow has unlanded beams, the offsets should project inward between the beams. If the beams are landed, the offsets project outward. Use these settings no matter how many horses you hitch to the plow. In both cases, if you use two horses, the hitch should be in the holes toward the plowed ground, if you use three horses, the hitch should be in the holes toward the unplowed land.

Two–way plow with the pole set up for three horse operation.

International Harvester Co.

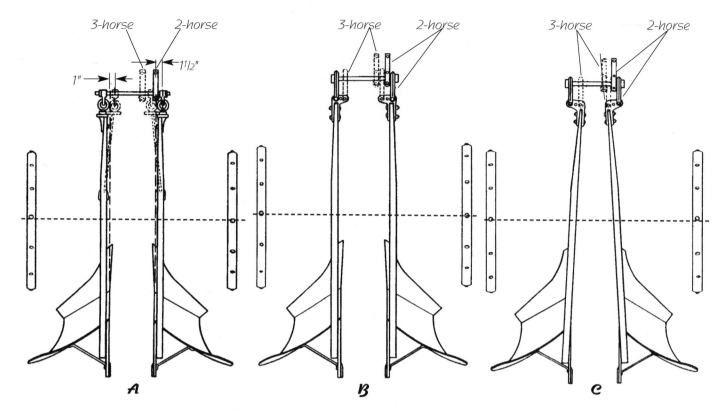

A—Setting a rod–type hitch: For two horses, the pull should be from a point 1½ inches toward the plowed land from the plow's landside. For a three horse team, adjust the hitch so the pull comes from a point 1 inch toward the unplowed land from the plow's landside.

B—Setting a clevis hitch on straight beams: For two horses, hitch in the hole toward the plowed land. For three horses, hitch in the hole toward the unplowed land.

C—Setting a clevis hitch on landed beams: For two horses, hitch in the outside hole toward the plowed land. For three horses, use the inside hole toward the unplowed land.

Cornell Extension Bulletin No. 381

Adapting a Drag Plow

Several companies once built engine gang plows for use behind mammoth steam traction engines and early gas tractors. These engine plows have a number of individual plow bottoms or pairs of plow bottoms, each controlled by a lever. The bottoms are attached to a heavy triangular frame in combinations that can turn as many as 12 furrows. A wooden platform over the frame allows the plowman to walk back and forth tending the hand lifting and lowering levers.

When gas tractors later became smaller, two–, three–, four–, and five–bottom plows were made with a rigid frame carried by two or three wheels. A mechanical power lift, operated from the tractor seat through a rope or a rod, raises the plow out of the ground and quickly returns it to plowing depth. When remote hydraulics became available, a hydraulic lifting cylinder was mounted on the plow and attached to the tractor by flexible hoses. Harry Ferguson pioneered the three–point hitch and hydraulic lifting system in the 1930s, allowing the plow to be mounted as an integral part of the tractor. Today the three–point hitch is standard, not only for plows but for other implements as well.

Many horse farmers use wheeled tractor plows behind forecarts. Like horse–drawn plows, tractor plows come in many styles and sizes, but the two–wheel and three–wheel plows of two–bottom size are best suited for horse farming. Two–wheel tractor plows carry the weight of the plow and furrow slices on a furrow wheel and land wheel, along with a landside that may be either straight or rolling. When a two–wheel plow is in the raised position, its entire weight is carried on the two wheels. Three–wheel plows have, in addition to the land and furrow wheels, a smaller rear furrow wheel. When plowing, the three wheels support the plow's weight and that of the furrow slices, while in the raised position, the plow runs on all three wheels.

Hitching a Drag Plow

When using a tractor plow, hitch your team so the center of pull of the forecart is the center hole in the drawbar. Any side draft in the forecart hitch makes hitching the plow correctly more difficult. The hitching rules apply equally to both two–wheel and three–wheel tractor plows.

Vertical Adjustment

Just as with a walking plow, if the vertical hitch is too high, the front of the plow will be pulled down and the bottoms will bounce along on the points of the shares, resulting in excessive draft and wear and a poor job of plowing. If the hitch is too low, the plow will be slow to penetrate and won't hold its depth. The plow drawbar may be raised or lowered to obtain a straight line from the center of load, through the hitch point, to the forecart's drawbar.

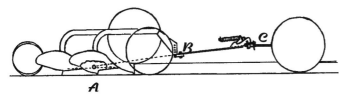

Raise or lower the tractor plow drawbar at B to obtain a straight line from the center of load A, through B to hitch point C on the forecart's drawbar.

Horizontal Hitch

The plow should pull straight behind the forecart with the plow wheels running parallel to the line of travel. The

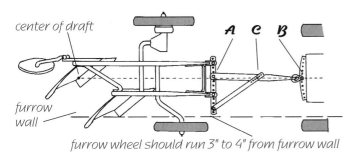

furrow wheel should run 3" to 4" from furrow wall

For a two–bottom tractor plow, the drawbar from A to B should be approximately parallel to the furrow wall. If the front bottom fails to cut the correct width, adjust the angle of the brace C to swing the drawbar a little to the right or left.

furrow wheel should be 3 to 4 inches away from the furrow wall. Using the holes in the plow's cross drawbar, position the hitch draft bar so it extends straight forward from the center of draft, through the plow drawbar, to the center of the forecart drawbar. If, after the correct hitch has been attained, the front bottom isn't taking a full cut or is taking too wide a cut, adjust the angle brace to make the front bottom cut the right size furrow slice.

Operation and Adjustment

On most tractor plows, the lever on the land side controls the depth of plowing, while the lever on the furrow side levels the bottoms. Mechanical lift plows have a lever attached to a clutch lift mechanism that's built into the land wheel hub. The lift lever is operated by a rope or rod to the forecart. The plow bottoms are dropped by pulling on the rope or rod. The plow need not be moving when the bottoms are dropped.

To raise the bottoms, however, the plow must be moving forward when the rope or rod is pulled. Don't hold the rope after the clutch has begun its operation or it may repeat and the plow will drop and then lift again. Some tractor plows are fitted with a remote hydraulic cylinder in place of the mechanical lift. Hoses run from the cylinder forward to the forecart, which must be equipped with a hydraulic pump and remote outlets. You can then raise, lower, and adjust the depth of the plow by moving a small hydraulic lever. Hydraulic plows have only one lever or a crank to control the depth of the front bottom in relation to the rear.

Make landside heel clearance adjustments by moving the rear furrow wheel the same as for a high–lift sulky plow. Jointer and coulter adjustments are identical to horse–drawn plows. Too much tension on the lifting spring, or springs, will keep the plow from penetrating quickly when the plow is dropped. Too little tension will cause the land wheel to slide when the clutch tries to lift the plow, and will make the hand levers hard to adjust while plowing.

Slipping of the lifting wheel may also be caused by poor traction of the land wheel due to wet or muddy conditions. This problem may be corrected by adding cross lugs to a steel land wheel, or a tire chain if the plow is on rubber tires.

Keep the working parts of the plow well lubricated and all bolts tight. Keep shares and coulters sharp. Scouring troubles for tractor plows are the same as for plows intended for use with horses.

Common Plow Troubles

Many plows have been condemned as being no good, when all they needed was proper adjustment and a correct hitch. If a plow of any kind doesn't work properly, a systematic review all the factors discussed here should correct the problem.

Walking Plows

Plow runs too deep.
>   hitch is too high
>   traces too long

You have to bear down on both handles.
>   same as above

Plow runs too shallow or won't hold its depth.
>   hitch too low
>   traces too long
>   share is dull
>   rolling coulter is dull

You have to raise up on both handles.
>   same as above

Plow runs wide.
>   hitch too far toward plowed ground
>   too little wing bearing
>   knife coulter set to lead toward unplowed ground

You have to raise up on furrow handle and bear down on land handle.
>   same as above

Plow runs out, or too narrow.
>   hitch too far toward unplowed ground
>   dull share with too little land suck
>   knife coulter angled toward the furrow
>   chain or covering wire too long, pulling plow sideways

You have to raise up on land handle and bear down on furrow handle.
>   same as above

Plow doesn't run steady.
>   wrong down suck
>   wrong land suck
>   wrong wing bearing
>   loose share
>   incorrectly set coulter
>   dull share
>   incorrect hitch

Uneven and broken furrow wall.
>   dull share
>   badly worn shin
>   incorrectly set jointer or coulter

Share and moldboard not scouring.
>   See "Problems Common to All Plows"

Riding Plows

Plow won't penetrate.
>   insufficient heel clearance
>   insufficient down suck
>   lifting spring too tight
>   rolling coulter dull
>   rolling coulter set too far forward
>   dull share
>   hitch too low

Plow won't hold width.
>   hitch wrong
>   furrow wheel angled wrong

Uneven furrows.
>   plow not run level

Plow runs at an angle to furrow, or twisted.
>   incorrect horizontal hitch
>   furrow wheels incorrectly angled

Trash not being covered.
>   plow bottom not scouring
>   jointer or coulter set wrong
>   plow not run level
>   incorrect horizontal hitch
>   furrow wheels incorrectly angled
>   trailing chain or wire needed

Furrow slice not being turned and pulverized properly.
>   same as above

Uneven and broken furrow wall.
>   badly worn shin
>   dull share
>   coulter or jointer set wrong
>   hitch is incorrect
>   furrow wheel angled too much

Plow bobs, jumps, gouges, and won't hold to its depth.
>   dull share
>   dull coulter
>   coulter set too deep or too far forward
>   hitch is too high

Share and moldboard not scouring.
>   See "Problems Common to All Plows"

Two-Way Plows

In addition to the problems common to other wheeled plows, two–way plows may leave furrows that are uneven in depth. Furrow unevenness occurs when one bottom either runs deeper or takes a wider furrow than the other. The probable causes are:

● The plow beams are not set alike in the frame. Set each beam 3 inches plus the width of a bottom away from the inside edge of its wheel.

● One jointer or coulter is set too wide or too deep. A

coulter set too wide will cause that bottom to take a larger slice of earth than the other. A jointer set too deep will make the furrows appear uneven.

● The tongue shifting lever doesn't move the tongue the same distance each way, because of loose, bent, or worn parts or a warped tongue. As a result, one side cuts a wider furrow than the other.

● Depth lever parts are worn, bent, or sprung, causing one bottom to run deeper than the other, even though the levers may be in the same notch on each side.

● One plow share is sharper than the other, so it penetrates and runs deeper.

Adapted Drag Plows

Failure to penetrate.
>   dull shares
>   hitch too low
>   heel clearance set incorrectly
>   coulter dull
>   coulter set too far forward in hard ground
>   lifting springs too tight in hard ground

Plow won't hold depth.
>   hitch too high
>   heel clearance set incorrectly

Plow won't hold width.
>   excessive side draft due to improper horizontal hitch

Plow runs at angle to furrow.
>   improper horizontal hitch
>   rear furrow wheel incorrectly set

Plow won't cover trash.
>   absence of jointers and coulters
>   incorrect adjustment of jointers or coulters
>   nonscouring
>   bottoms not level
>   speed too slow

Furrow crowns not the same height.
>   front bottom cutting wider or narrower than rear
>   coulters not set alike
>   plow not level
>   nonscouring

Furrow wall rough and broken.
>   coulter or jointer set wrong
>   excessive side draft
>   rear furrow wheel set wrong
>   badly worn shin
>   dull share on rear bottom

Lifting wheel slips.
>   lifting springs too loose
>   clutch trouble
>   poor traction of the land wheel

Plow enters ground slowly or not at all when dropped.
>   dull shares
>   lifting springs too tight
>   hitch too low
>   clutch trouble

All Plows

The most common plowing problem is a failure of the moldboard to scour. Another problem, although not as common on horse plows as on tractor plows, is a bent beam.

Failure to Scour

The failure of a moldboard to scour is probably the most frustrating cause of poor plowing. Temporarily setting the coulter wide or plowing deeper may help get the moldboard polished. Once you have a bright land polish, preserve it by liberally coating the polished parts with grease after each use. Reasons for failure to scour include:

● Rusty moldboard—Remove rust by rubbing the moldboard with a soft stone or brick, wire brush, or sandpaper. Running the plow fast in light, sandy soil will also do the job.

● Paint or varnish on moldboards—Primarily a problem with new or freshly painted plows. Clean off the coating with paint remover.

● Speed—Plow bottoms are designed to run at a certain speed. Too slow operation, especially in sticky soil, will cause nonscouring.

● Plow not level—Check adjustments.

● Loose or poor fitting shares—Tighten or replace shares.

● Excessive side draft—Poor scouring may result when a plow is running crooked.

Bent Beams

A bent beam can cause many troubles, such as the plow running in or out, or on a two–way or two–bottom plow, uneven furrows. Beams may be bent vertically, horizontally, or both. When a beam is bent vertically, the plow bottom points up or down too much. When a beam is bent horizontally, the plow points too much into or away from the land. Loose or bent frogs or shares also cause problems.

These serious problems are difficult to identify. A bent beam is often blamed when the trouble is actually caused by an incorrect hitch or wrong adjustment of some other part of the plow. Don't assume a bent beam until you have eliminated every other possible cause of the trouble.

Before taking any measurements, make sure the frog is tight on the beam, and fit it with a new share. Put the plow on a flat, level surface.

For a standard walking plow, the bottom of the beam at the front end should be approximately 15 inches above the plane of the plow sole. For this test, the plow must be on an even floor and have a new plow share. If the beam measures more than one inch either way from 15 inches it's probably bent.

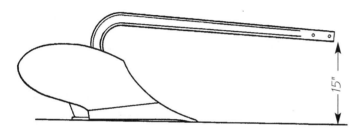

The distance from the under side of the beam to the floor should be between 14 and 16 inches.

Cornell Extension Bulletin No. 381

To find out if the beam is sprung sideways, use a string or straightedge and a carpenter's square. Stretch the string or place the straightedge along the upper part of the landside, extending forward past the front of the beam. Place the carpenter's square with the edge of the short leg on the floor and the edge of the upright long leg lined up with the exact center of the plow beam. For a two–horse plow the distance between the string and the square should be 1 1/2 inches. For a three–horse plow, the string should just touch the square. These measurements also apply to a two–way plow, although a single sprung beam often may be detected by comparing the two beams.

On wheeled plows, a straightedge held vertically against the beam on the landside should touch the point of a new share about 1 1/2 inches toward the furrow side of the share's landside. On gang plows, one bent beam may often be detected by comparing the two bottoms. Lower the bottoms onto a flat surface and level the plow; a beam that is badly bent up or down should be obvious.

A blacksmith or machine shop may be able to straighten a badly bent beam. If it is bent only a little, you may be able to overcome the problem by changing the hitch.

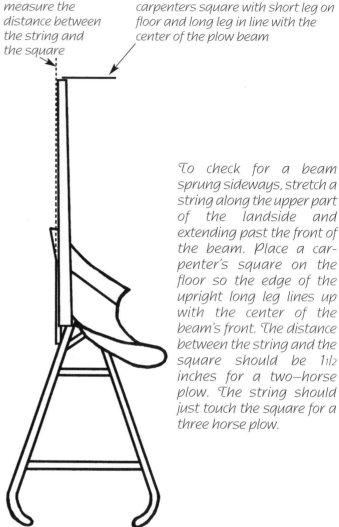

measure the distance between the string and the square

carpenters square with short leg on floor and long leg in line with the center of the plow beam

To check for a beam sprung sideways, stretch a string along the upper part of the landside and extending past the front of the beam. Place a carpenter's square on the floor so the edge of the upright long leg lines up with the center of the beam's front. The distance between the string and the square should be 1 1/2 inches for a two–horse plow. The string should just touch the square for a three horse plow.

Sharpening Plow Shares

The sharpening of shares went out when replaceable Raydex–style shares came in. Some plowmen, however, still prefer to use old–style shares. Before sharpening an old share, the first order of business is to determine whether it is made of chilled cast iron or steel. An easy way to tell the difference is to observe the way the share is marked. If the number has been stamped into the share, it is steel. If the number is raised, indicating that the figures were molded with the part, the share is cast iron.

Cast-Iron Shares

A cast–iron share cannot be forged, but must be sharpened by grinding. Grind the entire cutting edge to an abrupt beveled edge. Grind the upper side and make the edge sharp with an abrupt steep angle. A thin edge won't have

Tillage Equipment

the strength to withstand the soil's wearing action or any rocks that might be encountered. Don't waste time trying to sharpen a cast–iron share that has been worn to the point of losing its land and vertical suction; such a share must be replaced.

Steel Shares

An old–style steel plow share is generally sharpened by welding on new sections to bring the share back to its proper shape. Both soft–center and solid steel shares may also be sharpened by heating and drawing out with a hammer. This job is difficult and requires a knowledge of the proper shape of a plow share, as well as some skill as a blacksmith. To obtain best results you need a forge, anvil, heavy hammer, and blacksmith's tongs.

1. Build a good, clean coke fire in the forge. Bank the fire, allowing only a small opening in the side for the blaze and heat to escape.

2. Draw the outline of a new share on the floor with chalk to serve as a guide in reshaping the worn share.

3. Put the share in the forge and heat to a dull cherry red, but no hotter, only as much of the edge as you can hammer (approximately 2 to 3 inches). Working the share at too high a heat destroys the quality of the steel. To prevent warping, do not heat the share's body.

4. Hammer the heated portion of the edge, with the bottom of the share flat on the anvil. Hammer the share on the upper side, and draw it down to a sharp edge. Continue hammering after the steel has changed from a red heat to black, to toughen and harden the edge. Continue heating and hammering the cutting edge until it coincides as nearly as possible with your chalk outline of a new share.

5. Place the share point in the fire and heat it to a low cherry red. Forge it out until it assumes the shape of the chalk outline.

6. Heat the point again and bend it down about ¹/₈ to ³/₁₆ of an inch. Hold the share on the anvil and strike it lightly with the hammer, giving the point a gradual downward slant. Don't hit the point at its end, where it extends beyond the anvil.

7. To harden a soft–center steel share after sharpening, heat the entire share to a uniform cherry red. Take the share from the fire and dip it into a tub of cold, clean water with the cutting edge down, taking care to keep the share perpendicular during the process.

8. Solid steel shares should not be hardened.

Farm Machinery, John Wiley & Sons, 1934

Plowing a Field

The simplest way to plow a field of most any shape is to plow around the field from the outside in to the center, throwing all the furrows toward the outside. With a sulky plow, square turns may be made at the corners without lifting the plow from the ground, provided you turn left with a right–hand plow and right with a left–hand plow— otherwise you'd be in danger of tipping the plow. The advantage to plowing this way is that no time–consuming stepping off and staking are required. The big disadvantage is that the dead furrow always ends up in the center of the field, causing a low spot to develop over the years.

Lands

A popular method of plowing a wide rectangular or a square field is to divide the area into *lands* of 100 to 120 feet in width and plow each individually. A narrow field of less than about 200 feet is usually treated as a single land. An irregularly shaped field may be worked by dividing it into several straight lands and one or two irregular sections.

Marking the Headlands

Back in the days, when a beautiful job of plowing was more important than it is today, a headland of the same width was left on all four sides of the field. After the land (or lands) were finished, the headlands were plowed out by going around the field. With headlands of exactly the same width, everything came out even, but required a lot of time to measure and lay out.

Most plowmen today measure off a headland at each end of a field. Then, to throw the furrows in, start with a back furrow down the center of the field and plow right up to the edges of the field. If the furrows are to be thrown out, start at the outside long edges and end up with a dead furrow in the center. The headlands give you room to turn and start back the other way without running on already plowed ground.

To mark the headlands, step off and mark with stakes a line parallel with, and about 25 feet from, each end of the field. The space left at each end of the field is called a *headland*. Headlands for sulky and walking plows may be narrower than 25 feet, but be sure to allow enough room to conveniently turn. The headland should be twice the length of your plow rig.

Set your plow to make a shallow furrow about 2 inches deep, called a *scratch furrow*. Plow a scratch furrow at each end of the field to correspond with the stakes. If the end of the field isn't straight, neither will be your line of stakes, and your scratch furrow will follow this crooked line.

After the field is finished, plow the headlands by running back and forth along the field ends. The headlands may be plowed by throwing all the furrows the same way, which requires running one way with the plow out of the ground, unless you have a two–way plow. The headland may be also treated as just another, smaller land, and plowed out with either a back furrow down the center, or inward from each edge.

Marking Lands

Divide a wide field into lands to eliminate long runs across the headlands. Starting at the edge of the field, pace in along the scratch furrow 50 or 60 feet and drive a stake. Set up another stake opposite the first at the other end of the field the same distance in. If your field is hilly, you may need intermediate stakes to maintain a line of sight from one stake to the next. This method will result in a land of 100 to 120 feet in width. The wider your lands, the fewer dead furrows and back furrows you will have, but the more idle time you will spend running across the ends of the lands.

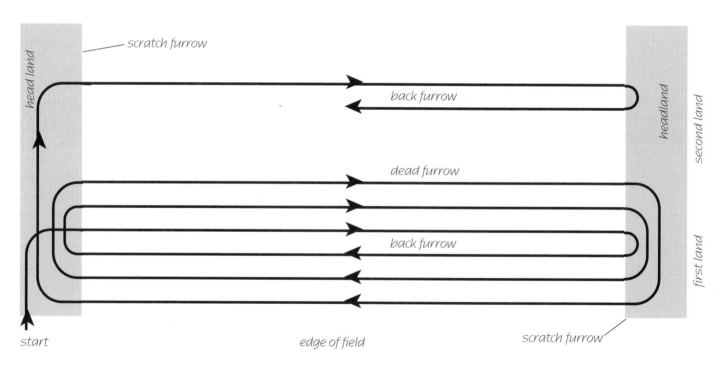

One way to lay out and plow a rectangular field.

Set the plow for about half the normal depth, and raise the furrow wheel higher than in normal plowing. Drop the plow directly on one of the stakes. Plow straight across the field to the second stake at the other side, using intermediate stakes to keep in alignment. Lift the plow from the ground exactly at the scratch furrow at the second stake.

Assuming you are using a right–hand plow, turn around to the right, so on the next trip the plow is in a position to throw the furrow back over the one just plowed. Set the plow for its normal working depth. Drop the plow exactly at the scratch furrow and plow back across the field, throwing this furrow on top of the first to form the *back furrow*. Plowing shallow on the first pass keeps the crown of the back furrow from being too high, while minimizing the strip of unplowed ground beneath the back furrow.

Set the furrow wheel lower, since it will now be running in the bottom of the open furrow. Continue to plow around the back furrow, dropping and raising the plow exactly on the scratch furrow at each end.

When you reach the edge of the field, you have finished the first land. Stake out a second land 50 or 60 feet in from the inside edge of your newly completed land and open it up with a back furrow. When you have completed this land, you will have a *dead furrow,* or open furrow, between the two lands.

Finishing

Mark and plow subsequent lands until the field is plowed out except for the headlands. Then finish up the field by plowing out each headland. Most farmers try to throw the headland furrows in alternate directions every other year, throwing the soil toward the center of the headland (leaving a dead furrow at the end of the field) one year and away from it (leaving two dead furrows, one on each side of the headland) the next. To minimize these dead furrows, make the last dead furrow across the headland shallower than the other furrows.

Plowing a Hillside

To plow a field with a hillside or two–way plow, lay out a headland of sufficient width for turning at each end of the field and mark each headland with a scratch furrow as before. Start plowing at one side of the field, throwing the furrow toward the field edge. When the plow reaches the scratch furrow at the far end, raise the plow and turn 180 degrees. Drop the opposite plow bottom, or reverse the hillside plow bottom, and plow back along the same furrow.

The back and forth motion causes all the furrows to be thrown in one direction with no dead furrows in the field. This method of plowing is an advantage not only on hillsides, but when you plan to irrigate and therefore want the land level with no dead furrows. Two–way plows are handy, too, for plowing odd shaped fields.

A modern two–bottom plow manufactured by Pioneer Equipment.

Photo by Bill Carner

2

Disc and Chisel Plows, Subsoilers, Rotary Tillers

"It dug like Parke's steel fork, and left the ground in a perfect state of tilth. It threw the earth up into the air, the earth falling first, being the heaviest and weeds being left on the surface."

Description of John Bethell's steam rotary cultivator at the British Society of Arts in 1856

Moldboard plows aren't the only tools used for primary tillage. A disc plow substitutes a large revolving concave disc for a conventional plow's coulter, share, and moldboard. A chisel plow opens and stirs the soil without inverting it. A subsoiler is used to improve soil condition by opening up the hardpan below the normal depth of plowing. A rotary tiller performs the functions of plowing, discing, and harrowing in one pass, leaving a finished seedbed ready for planting without any need for secondary tillage.

Disc Plows

Disc plows are used in dry areas where the ground is too hard for a moldboard plow to penetrate. They work well in sticky soils, such as waxy muck or gumbo, where moldboard plows don't scour well. Disc plows are useful also for loose, stony ground and land that has many roots.

Farmers once thought a rolling bottom would have less draft than a moldboard bottom, but the additional weight necessary to make the disc penetrate offsets any such advantage. While a moldboard plow is pulled into the ground solely by the plow's suction, the disc is forced into the ground by both the plow's weight and the disc's suction due to the angle at which it is set. The disc penetrates the soil and cuts loose a furrow slice, which it pulverizes and turned to one side. The soil, however, isn't inverted as with a moldboard plow, and the furrow bottom is dished, rather than flat.

In place of a coulter, share, and moldboard the disc plow has a large revolving concave disc, typically 24 or 26 inches in diameter. The disc runs at an angle to the direction of travel, as well as at an angle to the surface of the ground. The disc's width of cut is controlled by the amount of angle to the direction of travel; more angle gives a wider furrow and less angle a narrower furrow. The angle of the disc to the ground surface controls penetration; the more vertical the disc, the better the penetration, but at the expense of the disc's lifting and turning action.

As a disc plow moves forward, friction with the soil causes the disc to turn toward the operator's left. The left edge of the disc cuts the soil, carries it up, pulverizes it somewhat, and then throws it to the right. Hand levers allow you to set depth and level the plow, as well as raise and lower it. A scraper keeps the disc free of sticky soil and helps turn and pulverize the furrow slice and to cover trash.

Horse–drawn disc plows are usually of the one or two disc size. A disc plow is heavy, weighing from 300 to 500 pounds per disc. Although the width of the furrow may be adjusted, 10 to 12 inches is about right for a 24–inch disc.

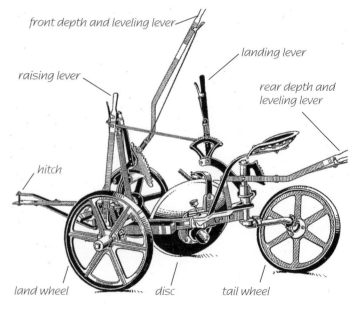

front depth and leveling lever

landing lever

raising lever

rear depth and leveling lever

hitch

land wheel　　*disc*　　*tail wheel*

A single–disc sulky plow.　　　International Harvester Co.

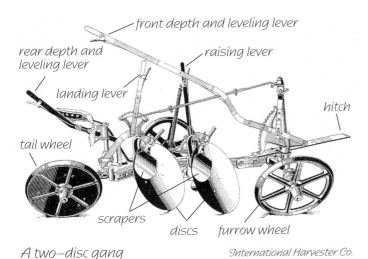

front depth and leveling lever

rear depth and leveling lever

raising lever

landing lever

hitch

tail wheel

scrapers

discs

furrow wheel

A two–disc gang

International Harvester Co.

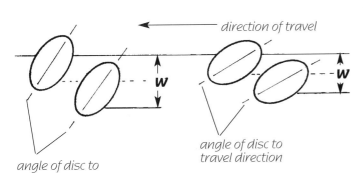

direction of travel

W

W

angle of disc to travel direction

angle of disc to travel direction

W = width of furrow

The greater horizontal angle of the discs at the left will result in wider furrow slices than the narrower angle of the discs on the right.

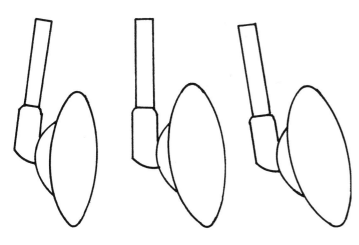

Soil penetration is affected by the disc's vertical angle; the more vertical position of the disc at the left will result in better penetration, but less lifting and turning action, than the setting at the right.

Draft of a Disc Plow

A disc plow has slightly less draft than a moldboard plow when both are plowing the same type and volume of soil. In hard ground, weight often must be added to aid penetration, which will increase the draft. Older disc plows have cast–iron cone bearings, making them harder to pull than modern plows with roller bearings. Scraper adjustment, width and depth of plowing, and soil conditions all affect the plow's draft.

Operation and Adjustment

A disc plow will not work satisfactorily if set to plow too shallow. The front furrow wheel angle is controlled by the landing lever, and used to guide the plow into or away from the land. The wider the width of cut, the deeper the disc must run to do good work. Poor work results when the discs are set too wide, because ridges of uncut and unpulverized soil are left under a shallow covering of pulverized soil.

Adjust the disc so it enters the ground at a wide enough angle to ensure clean cutting at the bottom of the furrow slice, as well as lifting and pulverizing of the soil. The more vertical the disc's position, the more easily it will penetrate, although the lifting and turning action will be diminished.

The disc's horizontal angle sets the width of furrow. A disc set more perpendicular to the direction of travel will cut wider, but will not turn as freely as a disc set more parallel to the furrow. When plowing hard ground, use less width to reduce draft.

On a multiple disc plow, the discs must be kept level with each other and with the ground to do an even job of plowing. Raise or lower the rear furrow wheel to keep the discs level.

Set the scraper so it barely touches near the center of the disc, with the scraper wing about 1/4 inch from the disc. A scraper set too close produces excessive friction. A scraper set too low increases the plow's draft by removing and turning the furrow slice too low on the disc. Always set the scrapers as high as possible, while allowing them to clean the disc blade and turn the furrow slice. In dry, hard ground, the scrapers often may be left off entirely.

If the plow labors and tries to dodge out of the furrow, run it deeper and/or reduce the width of cut. In sod ground plow deeper than in clean stubble for better coverage of trash. When plowing in hard soil, add more weight on the wheels and frame to help force the disc into the ground and hold the plow to its work.

Hitching a Disc Plow

The same rules of power and load that govern the hitching of a moldboard plow apply to a disc plow. The vertical hitch should hold the plow to the depth set and not raise or lower the front end of the plow. The horizontal hitch should be in a direct line with the plow's center of draft.

A single disc plow's center of draft is slightly below and to the left of the disc's center; the exact point varies with blade angle and depth. A two–disc plow's center of draft is halfway between that of each disc, or about half the plow's total width of cut.

The best way to get the hitch right is to make a trial hitch and closely observe the results. The land wheel should run straight and true without skidding, and the rear furrow wheel should not carry most of the side stress. If the rear furrow wheel is adjustable, give it a little lead away from the land to help hold the plow straight. Never set the rear wheel to lead into the land. The front furrow wheel should run straight or with a little lead into the land, and should never have any lead away from the land.

The hitch is the primary means for getting the plow to run straight. Move it to a different position, if necessary, to obtain good results. If you can't get the horizontal hitch on the line of draft, you may need to adjust the front furrow wheel so the front disc cuts the proper width.

Disc Plow Care

Keep the disc sharp and polished so it penetrates the ground and turns the furrow slice with the least amount of draft. Keep the disc bearing well greased. A bearing that is allowed to run dry will wear, and the disc will wobble and fail to penetrate. To preserve the polish, keep the disc surface well greased when it is not in use.

Chisel Plows

In 1933, at the height of the dustbowl, a young Oklahoma farmer named Fred Hoeme took inspiration from a road grader with a scarifier attachment. He noticed that the heavy scarifier teeth dug deeply into the earth and brought up large clods, leaving deep, uneven ridges of soil. Hoeme reasoned that roughening the surface of the land in such a way would block the wind erosion that was rapidly blowing away Oklahoma's precious topsoil. The field cultivators then being sold were too lightly constructed to dig deep enough to to do the job, so Hoeme built a heavy–duty cultivator using a truck frame with shanks made from truck springs.

Hoeme built about 2,000 of the heavy machines before selling the idea to a Texas manufacturer named W.T. Graham. Since that beginning, Hoeme's chisel plow has largely replaced the moldboard plow among farmers who practice various forms of conservation tillage. A chisel plow is similar to a field cultivator, only much heavier built. It may be anywhere from 7– to 53–feet wide, and is intended for use with a tractor. It speeds up the job of primary tillage because of the wider width of cut it takes in a single pass. A standard chisel plow is designed for higher speeds than could be sustained with draft animals, and would be a difficult for a team to pull. However, one– and two–shank implements are available that can perform some of the functions of a chisel plow if equipped with the right shovels or points and run at the correct depth. More than one pass, maybe at right angles to the first, would be required.

This two–shank J&J soil slitter may be used as a chisel plow by adding chisel points and removing the wide shovels installed halfway up the shanks.

Although using a one– or two–shank plow behind a team does not have the same advantage of a tractor–drawn plow in speeding up the job of primary tillage, it does have some of the same benefits to the soil, which is broken and deeply stirred, but not inverted as in regular plowing. A layer of crop residue, or mulch, remains on the surface to trap moisture and resist wind and water erosion. When equipped with sweeps, the chisel plow is a good tool for incorporating chemicals or clearing fallow land of weeds.

Functioning as a chisel plow, J&J's two–shank soil slitter shatters and loosens soil to a depth of 8 or 10 inches, while leaving a surface mulch of vegetation.

Draft of a Chisel Plow

The draft of a chisel plow running 6 inches deep is approximately 240 to 440 pounds per shank. The draft of a chisel plow shank is about one-half to two-thirds the draft for a moldboard at the same depth.

Operation, Adjustment and Care

The chisel plow consists of a heavy frame with several rigid or spring shanks arranged in two or more staggered rows so the furrows are spaced 12 to 16 inches apart. The shanks may be equipped with straight or twisted chisel points, sweeps, or shovels, depending on the job being done. Some chisel plows are designed to be used with a 3–point hitch, others are trailed implements carried on wheels and raised or lowered hydraulically. Many modern chisel plows have a gang of disc coulters ahead of the shanks to cut through trash and help work the soil.

A 3–point chisel plow is attached to a 3–point hitch forecart the same as any other 3–point implement. The plow frame should be leveled so the points all run at the same depth. A trailed chisel plow is hitched to the center hole of the forecart drawbar and the hydraulic hoses are connected to the cart's remote outlets.

The depth of plowing may be as shallow as desired or as deep as 12 inches, depending on the power available. On a 3–point hitch chisel plow, the depth is regulated by the hydraulic valve that controls the lift arms. A trailed plow's depth is set by the hydraulic valve that controls the remote cylinder.

Lubricate any grease fittings twice daily. Keep points sharp and replace any that are broken or worn out. At the end of the season, coat the points with grease to prevent rust.

Subsoilers

A subsoiler, sometimes also called a subsoiler plow, slitter, or deep till slitter, is a heavy duty tool designed to operate below the normal tillage depth to open up hardpan or plow sole. This action loosens the compacted soil that characteristically develops below plowing depth, and admits water and air while leaving the topsoil relatively undisturbed. Although the practice is controversial in a no–till environment, deep tilling is used by some no–till practitioners to loosen soil that has become compacted.

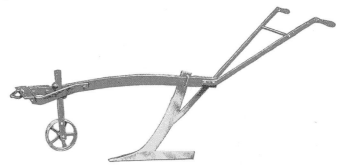

A walking subsoil plow.   *Deere & Co.*

The subsoiler has one or more strong beams and shanks that each support a narrow knife–like blade ending in a 2– to 4–inch wedge–shaped point. When drawn through the soil to a depth of 10 to 18 inches, the point cuts a gash that doesn't break up the hard–pan to any great extent, but does loosen it enough to allow air and water to penetrate. A subsoiler is usually of no benefit in sandy or gravel soil.

A walking subsoil plow has a single point, while a heavy duty model may have one or two shanks and points. The heavier models are mounted on wheels or are designed to be 3–point hitch mounted. Some modern subsoilers have automatic reset shanks that, when an underground obstacle is struck, break back against leaf springs or hydraulic pressure. After the obstacle is passed, the shank resets itself.

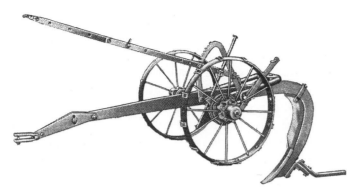

A single–shank subsoil plow requiring a forecart.

Deere & Co.

A two–tine subsoiler from White Horse Machine. If an obstruction is hit, hydraulic cylinders above each shank protect the tines from breaking by tripping the shanks back and up, then automatically resetting.

White Horse's two–shank subsoiler working approximately 18 inches deep in stubble.

Draft of a Subsoiler

The draft of a subsoiler varies greatly depending on the type and condition of the soil and the depth at which the plow is run. A single shank subsoiler cutting 10 inches deep in coarse soil has a draft of about 600 pounds, while in fine soil it will run about 1,350 pounds. At 18 inches of depth, the draft would be 1,100 pounds in coarse soil, increasing to as much as 2,400 pounds in fine soil. Pulling a subsoiler therefore takes a lot of horse power.

Operation, Adjustment and Care

If you use a walking subsoil plow, adjust the vertical hitch to hold the plow to the desired depth. The plow may have a gauge wheel or shoe to keep the plow from going too deep. The horizontal hitch requires a straight line from the beam to the center of power.

If you use a wheeled subsoil plow, hitch it to the center hole of a forecart drawbar. On some wheeled subsoil plows, including the 3–point hitch version, the depth is set hydraulically. On other models the depth is set by a lever or by moving pins in a series of holes above each wheel. Keep the points sharp and the wheels lubricated.

Rotary Tillers

Rotary tillers are power–driven implements that perform the functions of plowing, discing, and harrowing in one pass, leaving behind a nicely prepared seedbed. A tiller consists of a horizontal power–driven shaft, upon which is mounted a staggered series of curved blades or tines. As this shaft rotates at approximately 200 to 300 RPM and the tiller moves forward, the tines penetrate and pulverize the soil while chopping and incorporating any surface trash. Tillers come in two styles:

- standard rotary tiller, on which the horizontal drive shaft turns in the direction the tiller is traveling, pushing the tiller forward; and
- reverse–tine tiller, on which the horizontal drive shaft turns in the opposite direction of travel, producing draft instead of push.

A reverse–tine tiller forces the tines into the soil, preventing the problem of walking on the surface that occurs when a standard tiller is used on hard ground. The reverse–tine tiller offers the additional advantage of reducing clods and putting debris beneath finer soil particles..

Both styles are available as either pull behind or 3–point hitch. A pull tiller may be powered by an engine forecart or have its own mounted engine. A 3–point hitch tiller requires a forecart with an engine powerful enough

Tillage Equipment

to run the tiller, as well as a hydraulically operated 3–point hitch to lift the tiller, which is too heavy to be raised by hand.

The cutting tines on most machines are protected from breaking when they come into contact with a rock or any solid obstacle. Some tillers have a slip clutch on the drive shaft, others have the tines mounted to the shaft by heavy springs that give when an obstruction is encountered. Most tillers can cultivate to a depth of 6 inches.

A Maschio 7-foot rotary tiller mounted on a 3–point hitch and operated by a heavy duty 100 horse-power forecart.

Draft of a Rotary Tiller

Rotary tillers are available in widths of 3 to 7 feet and require 10 to 15 engine horsepower for each foot of width to drive the mechanism. A rotary tiller in this size range is not much of a load for a team. Larger tillers, as much as 15 feet wide, have been constructed, but since such machines require huge amounts of horsepower they are not likely to be used by the average horse farmer.

Because of the forward motion imparted by the tines of a standard tiller, the biggest concern in operating one is holding it back to a slow enough speed for good tillage. Either the forecart or the tiller may be equipped with field cultivator tines to penetrate the soil and help retard the forward motion.

Holding back is not a problem with a reverse–tine tiller, which creates its own draft. Under normal conditions, two horses should be able to pull a 6–foot reverse–tine tiller.

Operation, Adjustment and Care

As with any PTO driven machine, make sure guards and shields are in place and keep hands, feet, and loose garments clear of rotating parts. On a pull type tiller, depth is set by a lever, or by adjustable gauge wheels or shoes. A mounted tiller usually has gauge wheels or shoes.

To allow for complete soil pulverization, operate the tiller at a speed of from 1 to 2 miles per hour. Keep the tines sharp and replace any that get badly bent. Grease the PTO shaft fittings regularly and make sure the gearbox is full of oil. The rotating shaft and tines will catch and wind up roots and wire. Frequently remove any accumulations of such debris to avoid jamming the shaft.

Three-point hitch two-shank subsoiler made by Graber Equipment.

Photo by Bill Carner

Plows and Tillers

33

3 · Disc Harrows

"When tillage begins, other arts follow."

Daniel Webster, 1840

Secondary tillage is the process of stirring and working the soil to a depth that is much shallower than primary tillage, or plowing. The objects of secondary tillage are to:

• prepare the seedbed by leveling, smoothing, and pulverizing the soil after plowing;

• destroy weeds on fallow ground;

• form a surface mulch that conserves moisture and helps prevent wind erosion;

• chop crop residue or cover crops and mix this plant matter with the topsoil;

• destroy emerging weeds on tilled ground;

• cover broadcast seeds;

• incorporate manure, fertilizer, and herbicides.

Some secondary tillage tools are widely used in low–till operations to stir the soil without greatly disturbing the surface trash.

Tools for secondary tillage include harrows of several kinds, rollers and pulverizers, and field cultivators. If the moldboard plow is the main primary tillage tool, the disc harrow must be considered the most important of the secondary tillage implements.

Purpose of Discing

A disc harrow works in heavy vegetation or trash without clogging, and thus may be used to advantage before plowing to break the surface and cut up stalks and weeds left from the previous crop. Deere & Co. advocated always discing before plowing to eliminate large air spaces at the bottoms of the furrows that would interfere with water movement by capillary action.

After land has been plowed, discing pulverizes the soil and puts it in good tilth for planting. Where fall plowing is practiced, discing in the spring will destroy weeds and prepare the seedbed for planting. On fallow ground the disc harrow kills weeds and gives the soil a surface mulch to preserve moisture. A disc helps break up the soil to expose more surface area, speeding up drying and warming up the ground. If the ground is too wet, however, discing can result in a hard, lumpy seedbed and increased soil compaction.

Discing stirs and mixes the soil as deep as 6 inches, allowing the incorporation of manure, fertilizers, and herbicides. The disc harrow is also effective for covering broadcast seed, especially those sown on ground covered with vegetation.

This soil was not disced before plowing, resulting in air pockets under each furrow slice that will remain even after discing. The poor contact with the subsoil will hinder plants from drawing moisture from the subsoil by capillary action.

This soil was disced before plowing. After discing again, the seedbed will make good contact with the plow sole, allowing plants to draw water from the subsoil by capillary action. A similar effect may be obtained by using a field cultivator before plowing.

Disc Harrow Features

The disc harrow consists of a number of dished steel disc blades with sharpened outer edges, arranged into two opposing gangs. Disc blades are available in several sizes and types.

Discs

Solid disc blades have a smooth, sharpened edge and are cheaper, wear longer, weigh more, and penetrate better than cutout blades. The latter, also called cut–away or notched blades, have a series of notches or cutouts around the edge that are better at trapping and cutting trash than solid blades, but are not as durable and are more difficult to sharpen.

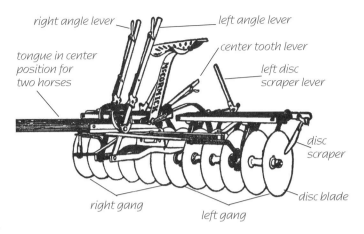

A horse–drawn disc harrow equipped with a stiff tongue arranged for two horses, and a center spring tooth to cultivate the strip between the gangs. Each angling lever sets the angle of its gang of discs; each scraper lever brings the scrapers on that gang into contact with the discs.   *International Harvester*

The discs on each gang are separated by spools and are attached to a single square axle, called a gang bolt or arbor bolt. A large nut at one end of the gang bolt is tightened, locking the discs and spools together, and causing all the discs on the gang to turn as one unit.

The discs on one gang are all dished the same way and throw the dirt in the same direction, and two gangs are paired to throw the dirt in opposite directions. These two gangs are run at an angle to each other, as well as to the forward direction of travel, causing each disc to act as a miniature plow, first slicing through the soil and then lifting and throwing it to one side. Disc harrows are available in many sizes. For use with horses the 4– to 8–foot widths are the most useful.

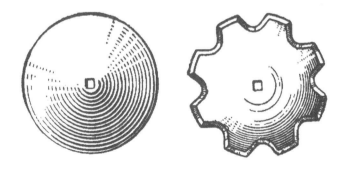

Two types of disc blade: solid (left) and cutout or notched. The square hole keys the disc blade to the square arbor bolt and keeps all the blades in a gang turning as a unit.   *International Harvester*

The bearings of a disc harrow must work in conditions of extreme dust and dirt. Each bearing, usually two or three per gang, is located in one of the spools separating the disc blades. A housing is bolted around the spool and bearing, and is attached to the harrow frame by the vertical standards. Early disc bearings were made of oil–soaked hard maple wood. Later bearings were cast iron or bronze. Modern machines use ball or roller bearings that are sealed to protect them from dirt.

Each disc has a scraper to keep it from clogging up with sticky soil. These scrapers are thin spring–like blades that usually may be moved across the inside surface of the discs by a lever, foot pedal, or rope. On some machines the scrapers are stationary and are set to run close to the disc.

Many disc harrows have a weight box or holder over each gang where weights may be added to aid penetration. These boxes are also handy for moving large rocks from the field to the fence row.

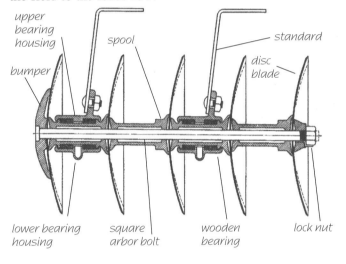

The square arbor bolt and lock nut lock the bumper, disc blades, and spools into one unit that turns on bearings within bearing housings bolted to the standards, which attach the gang to its frame. The wooden bearings shown here were later replaced by chilled cast–iron or bronze, and more recently by roller and ball bearings.   *B.F. Avery & Sons Co.*

Harrow Styles

A *single action* disc harrow consists of two gangs of discs placed end to end, with each gang throwing the soil outward.

Double, sometimes called *double–action* or *tandem*, discs have a second set of gangs behind the first that are run opposite to the front gangs. The soil that is thrown outward by the front discs is thrown back in by the rear. A single disc can achieve the same results as a double disc by overlapping half the width of the machine each round.

An *offset* disc harrow was designed to be pulled by a tractor and is so–named because it may be operated to one

Schematic top view of a single–action disc harrow; the arrow indicates the direction of travel.

Schematic top view of a double–action disc harrow.

A modern 5–foot single–action disc harrow with a one–wheel tongue truck. Made by Kota, this model has one lever to angle both gangs.

side of the pulling power. This feature allows discing under the limbs of trees in an orchard or vineyard while the tractor is out in the open. The offset disc has a single gang in front, angled one way from the direction of travel, and a second gang running behind the first, angled in the opposite direction. The disc blades on the two gangs are arranged to throw the soil in opposite directions. The hitch is adjustable so the disc may be operated directly behind the tractor or offset to either side. When used in normal field discing, the offset harrow gives you a double discing and leaves the ground smoother than a regular 4–gang double disc harrow. Heavy duty off–set discs built today for orchard and field use are generally not suitable for use with horses, but the older, smaller versions may be used behind a forecart.

Manufacturers use different means to adjust the angularity of the gangs. Most horse–drawn discs use hand

International single–action disc harrow in action.

Photo by Ruth Freeman

Schematic top view of an offset disc harrow.

Tillage Equipment

levers for the purpose, usually one lever for each gang, although some use a single lever. Early tractor discs use levers, cranks, or a rope–controlled draft lock on a sliding hitch. Later tractor discs use a hydraulic cylinder to angle the gangs.

Adapting a Tractor Disc Harrow

Modern tractor disc harrows are of two types:

● A *transport disc* has two or more wheels, usually with rubber tires. A hydraulic cylinder raises the gangs out of contact with the soil and puts the weight of the machine on the wheels. The degree of angle of the gangs on a transport disc are either fixed or adjusted manually.

● An *integral* 3–point hitch disc harrow is raised and lowered on the 3–point hitch arms and has no wheels. The harrows are usually double–action, and the angle of the gangs is fixed or manually adjusted. These disc harrows are too heavy for use on a standard 3–point hitch forecart, unless the disc is equipped with a dolly wheel.

A John Deere 7–foot double–action tractor disc harrow that may be pulled behind a forecart.

A John Deere 8–foot transport double–action disc harrow in action behind a hydraulic forecart. The gangs are raised by hydraulic power, allowing the machine to run on its rubber–tired wheels.

Draft of a Disc Harrow

The draft of a disc harrow varies so much with weight, angle adjustment, and soil condition that it's difficult to predict. Under normal conditions the expected draft of a single–action disc harrow is 40 to 130 pounds per foot of width, and a double–action tandem disc is 80 to 160 pounds per foot. Draft will be heavier the closer the disc spacing, the greater the angle of the gangs, and the deeper the cut.

Hitching a Disc Harrow

With the exception of the offset version, the center of load of a disc harrow is at, or slightly below, ground level between the front two gangs. Both horse–drawn and tractor machines have a short steel tongue. With a tractor disc, this tongue is hitched directly to the center hole of a forecart's drawbar, which should give you the correct line of draft. Tractor discs may also be hitched directly behind a team, provided either the teamster walks or some provision is made for riding.

A 5–foot tractor double–action disc harrow that has been modified by the addition of a platform, guard rail, and seat for the operator.

With horse–drawn disc harrows, a stiff pole or a tongue truck may be used. The pole is attached at the center of the harrow draw frame for two horses, or at the side for three. The stiff pole puts the main frame's weight on the horses' necks and has a tendency to whip on rough ground. For these reasons, a tongue truck, with or without a long pole, is usually used. The tongue truck supports the weight of the harrow frame and makes turning easier. The vertical clevis may be adjusted up or down to obtain the correct line of draft, and steers the tongue truck in turns. Using a long pole with a tongue truck adds leverage when making turns and keeps the tongue truck wheels running more steadily.

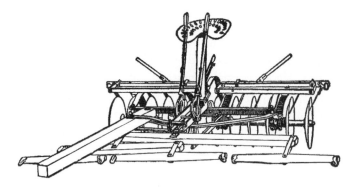

A disc harrow with the tongue offset for three horses.

International Harvester

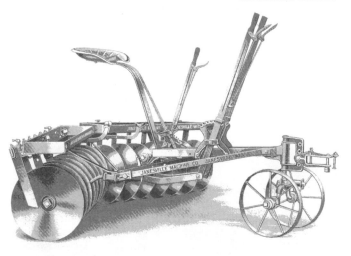

A disc harrow equipped with a tongue truck. Notice how the vertical clevis steers the truck and may be moved up or down to get the correct line of draft.

The Janesville Machine Co.

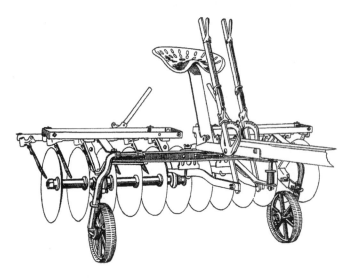

A horse–drawn disc equipped with transport trucks.

International Harvester

Transporting a Disc Harrow

To move a disc harrow from field to field, the disc gang angles must be straightened so the disc blades run straight. This position results in the least amount of damage to the blades and to the surface over which the machine is moving. A horse–drawn disc harrow may be equipped with a removable steel wheeled transport truck that holds the disc blades up high enough to prevent contact with the ground. Modern transport discs have hydraulically operated rubber–tired transport wheels.

A John Deere transport disc raised to the transport position.

Operation and Adjustment

To work effectively, a disc harrow must penetrate evenly over its entire width. The depth to which a disc harrow will penetrate is affected by factors both within and outside the harrow itself. Factors having to do with the harrow include:

- the angle of the disc gangs;
- the front–to–rear and, in some cases, side–to–side levelness of the harrow, especially if it's a transport, offset, or integral harrow;
- the weight of the disc harrow;
- the sharpness of the disc;
- the spacing of the discs;
- the size of the discs;
- the angle of the hitch.

The factor outside the disc harrow that most affects penetration is the condition of the soil, such as moisture content, whether plowed or unplowed, and the amount of surface trash.

Adjust the rear section of a double disc so the rear discs always split the ridges formed by the leading discs. The rear gangs have a tendency to ride out of the ground, especially if set at the maximum angle. You can usually correct this problem by reducing the angle somewhat or by adding weight to the weight boxes on top of the gangs.

Tillage Equipment

Extra weight on the gangs, particularly those without ball or roller bearings, causes the bearings to wear rapidly. A better plan, rather than adding weight to achieve penetration, is to change the angle of the gangs. The recommended angle for the best work is 18 to 20 degrees. Too much angle results in poor penetration just as much as too little.

Another factor that affects penetration is the sharpness of the disc cutting edges. Use a hand–held grinder to sharpen the discs.

Level a transport or an offset disc front to rear to get even penetration. The leveling device may be a crank, a turnbuckle, or a notched hold–down bar.

Level a 3–point disc harrow front to rear by adjusting the top link. Level it side to side by shortening or lengthening the 3–point hitch lift arms.

Set fixed scrapers so the scraping edge just clears the disc, with the same clearance over its entire width. Don't set the scrapers tightly against the disc, or you'll get rapid wear and increased draft. Set movable scrapers so they lightly contact the disc blades when you operate the lever or pedal, or pull the rope.

Disc Harrow Care

On most machines, the bearings are lubricated by forcing grease into them through pressure fittings, which you should do at least every 8 hours of operation. Early discs may have hard oil cups, which should be kept filled with grease and turned down at regular intervals. Keep all moving control points oiled to prevent binding and difficult operation; in extremely dusty conditions this oiling should be done sparingly.

Keep all bolts tight and replace worn parts. After each use, coat the disc blades with grease to prevent rust, and lubricate the entire machine. Keep the disc blades sharp and replace any that are worn to more than 2 or 3 inches less in diameter than a new blade.

Store your disc harrow under cover. If you must store it outside, run it up onto boards to keep the discs from sinking into the earth, where they would rust away quite rapidly.

A mounted King Kutter double disc harrow in action behind a forecart.

4

Harrows, Rollers and Drags

"The toad beneath the harrow knows exactly where each toothpoint goes. The butterfly upon the road preaches contentment to that toad."   *Rudyard Kipling*

That a deep, thoroughly pulverized and compact seedbed was necessary for good crops has long been the conventional wisdom. Except in mellow soil and ideal conditions, plowing leaves a rough field surface, as well as clods, lumps, and air spaces that detract from the formation of a good seedbed. Several implements, in addition to the disc harrow, have therefore been developed to break down clods, and pulverize and compact the soil.

Although modern no–till and low–till practices would seem to negate the importance of a good seedbed, even some no–till planters are designed to form a narrow ribbon of well tilled soil in front of each row of seed. The spaces between the rows are left untilled to hold the soil and moisture.

Harrows

Harrows are mentioned in the Bible and are as ancient as the plow. The first such implements were nothing more than a carefully selected tree trunk or limb with protruding branches that scratched the soil when pulled along by hand or behind an animal. England's Parliament felt it necessary, in 1664 to abolish "as being cruel and injurious to the animals" the practice of tying, with a rawhide cord, the brushy limb of a tree to a horse's tail for use as a harrow.

The early American farmer made an A–harrow consisting of timbers (or a forked log) through which wooden or iron pegs were driven. The A–harrow was especially useful on just–cleared fields that often were full of stumps and rocks. It was strong and slid around obstructions, rather than getting caught on them.

By the 1850s, square harrows made of wood with wrought or cast iron teeth had become popular. The iron teeth, however, often snapped off when they struck a rock or other obstruction. After the War Between the States, manufacturers began to use steel teeth and iron frames, and

added levers to change the angle of the teeth. This style of harrow was similar to today's spike tooth harrow.

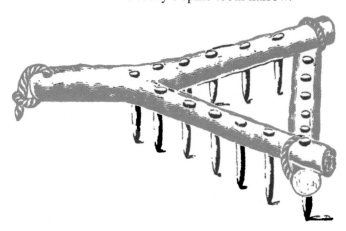

An early American A–harrow made from a forked log and wrought iron spikes.

Agricultural Machinery by J. Brownlee Davidson

Spike Tooth Harrows

The *spike tooth* harrow, also known as a peg tooth harrow, a drag harrow, or a smoothing harrow, is used primarily to level and smooth the soil prior to seeding. Its rows of staggered points tear down the high spots and fill in the hollows, while breaking up clods and lumps and pulverizing the soil to a depth of about 2 inches.

A hard rain followed by hot sun just after seeds are planted usually results in a hard baked and cracked surface that inhibits the young shoots from breaking through, and allows moisture to escape through the cracks. A spike tooth harrow is an excellent tool to break up this surface crust, leaving a loose dirt mulch to conserve moisture, and allowing the plants to readily push through. Young weeds are easily dug out when they are just breaking through the surface of the soil and the spike tooth harrow does a good job of destroying them at this time.

The spike tooth harrow isn't effective on wet ground, or in soil with large hard clods, for either smoothing or killing weeds. It isn't successful, either, in destroying deeply rooted weeds. A spike tooth harrow isn't of much use on fields that have trash or vines on the surface, as the teeth become clogged with the trash and can't penetrate the soil, nor does it penetrate well in sod, or on hard, stony ground. Where seed has been broadcast on loose soil, the spike tooth harrow may be used to cover the seed.

Features of a Spike Tooth Harrow

Spike tooth harrows are typically built in sections that range in width from 4 to 6 feet. Although the sections may be hooked side by side to a drawbar to obtain most any width, two–, three–, or four–section harrows are the most common. These combinations allow you to harrow a large area in a short time.

Each section consists of five tooth bars made of steel pipe or U–bar, to each of which 5, 6, or 7 steel teeth are bolted. The ends of some harrow sections are open and are called *open–end* harrows, while others—predictably called *closed–end* harrows—have the ends of the tooth bars enclosed by guard rails. The guard rails strengthen the section and prevent the ends of the tooth bars from catching on obstructions.

The teeth are hardened for long wear, and are typically about 8 inches long. They are diamond shaped in cross–section to present a fairly sharp edge to the soil and, when worn, may be reversed to present a new cutting edge. Some teeth are attached to the tooth bar by a clamp or a U–bolt, and have an enlarged head to prevent them from slipping through a loose clamp and becoming lost. Other teeth have a forged shoulder and threaded upper end that is placed through a hole in the tooth bar and secured with a nut and lockwasher.

The tooth bars are staggered so the teeth are distributed evenly across the harrow's width, rather than following directly behind each other. On a 5–foot harrow section with five tooth bars and six teeth, every 2 inches of ground is cut by a tooth. A hand lever on each section pivots the tooth bars, changing the angle of the teeth from a vertical position where they penetrate deeply, to a position where they slant backward with a less aggressive cutting action and less penetration. Some harrows have a relief spring built into the tilting lever linkage as a safety feature to prevent bent or broken teeth. If you encounter an obstruction, the teeth swing back and then reset after clearing the obstruction.

To keep the fields, roads, and barnyard from being torn up, and to prevent excessive wear on the harrow frame while transporting the harrow between fields, some harrow sections are equipped with a runner tooth at each corner.

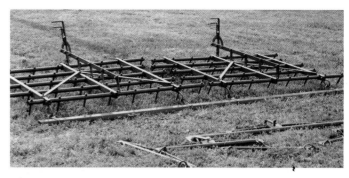

A modern two–section spike tooth harrow of the open–end style with a steel evener, made by Pioneer.

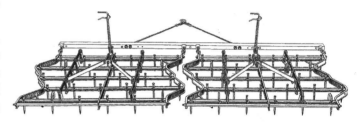

A two–section closed–end harrow. This model has a relief spring on each tilting lever that allows the teeth to swing back if an obstruction is hit, and then reset after the obstruction is passed. One of the curved runner teeth may be seen at the lower right corner.   *Deere & Co.*

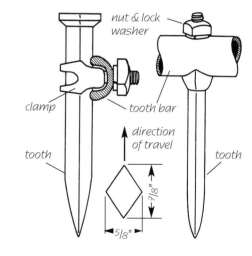

The head on a clamp style harrow tooth (left) keeps the tooth from getting lost if the clamp works loose. A through–bolt style tooth (middle) is secured with a nut and lock washer. In the center is a cross–sectional view of a diamond–shaped harrow tooth that presents a narrow cutting width for good penetration, and a wide resistance width in the direction of travel for strength. When one side of the tooth becomes rounded from wear, the tooth may be reversed to present a new cutting edge.

The top part of the runner tooth is curved forward in a half circle. When the lever is placed in its most forward position, all the teeth are laid back parallel with the frame; the curved portion of the runner teeth contact the ground and carry the secton's weight.

Harrow Carts

Walking on soft, loose soil behind a harrow is tiring and dusty, so *harrow carts,* or sulkies, were once built, although they're rarely seen today. A seat mounted on two wheels is connected to the wooden harrow evener by two arched arms that reach forward over the harrow, allowing the operator to ride, but he still eats a lot of dust. The cart usually pivots at the rear of the arms so it tracks the harrow in turns.

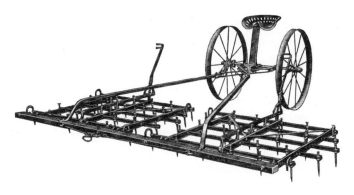

A harrow cart attached to the evener of a two–section, open–end harrow. The ad for this cart reads: "Because of large wheels and long seat spring, the operator sits high, away from the dust."　　　　　　　　Deere & Co.

Draft of a Spike Tooth Harrow

Harrows vary in weight, but average 21 pounds per foot of width. The draft of a spike tooth harrow varies greatly as well, depending on soil conditions and the angle of the teeth. Average draft ranges from 30 pounds per foot of width with the teeth inclined rearward, to 40 pounds with the teeth set to the vertical position. In normal use, the draft ranges from 20 to 60 pounds for each foot of width.

Hitching a Spike Tooth Harrow

A single section of spike tooth harrow may be hitched with two 4–foot lengths of chain and a clevis. One end of each chain is attached to the draft hook at each front corner of the section, and the other ends are attached to the clevis. The singletee or doubletree is hitched to the clevis.

If you use more than one section, you need a way to keep the sections square with each other and running the correct distance apart. For this purpose harrow manufacturers once

furnished wooden eveners, or drawbars. Modern harrows are equipped with steel box–section eveners.

The length of the evener depends on how wide each section is and how many sections you use. Each section is attached to the evener independently of the others, and the sections aren't attached to each other. Draw rods or chains lead from the evener to a hitch ring that must be directly ahead of the center of the harrow. A clevis through the hitch ring attaches to the team's evener.

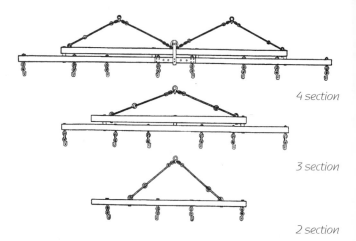

4 section

3 section

2 section

Examples of wooden eveners once furnished by International Harvester. The four–section model uses two two–section eveners joined in the center by steel plates, and a three–section evener as the front drawbar. The three–section evener uses a two–section evener as the front drawbar. The doubled eveners were used to increase strength.

Operation, Adjustment and Care

Operating a spike tooth harrow is simple—just hook it up and go. No field adjustment is needed, except using the hand levers to set the angle of the teeth, depending on soil or crop conditions. A field is usually harrowed first in the direction in which it was plowed, and then cross harrowed.

For deep aggressive work, set the teeth in the vertical position. When you need less penetration, such as when covering broadcast seeds, or to destroy young weeds after the crop has sprouted, angle the teeth with the points toward the rear. For smoothing only, or to clean out accumulated trash, as well as to transport the harrow between fields, set the teeth horizontal to the ground.

Keep all bolts tight, particularly the bolts or clamps that hold the teeth. The front edges of the teeth should be sharp. If the cutting edge becomes worn round, either turn the

Tillage Equipment

tooth to present a new cutting edge or replace it. Any tooth that is worn down until it is too short to properly penetrate the soil should be replaced.

Straighten bent teeth or tooth bars. The eye bolts through wooden eveners that connect the drag links to the evener must be kept tight. If the eye bolts have been allowed to loosen and enlarge the hole in the evener, use a larger eye bolt to completely fill the hole. Otherwise the movement of the bolt will wear the hole larger and weaken your evener.

No lubrication is necessary during use, although the moving joints should be well lubricated before the harrow is put up for the season. The harrow sections may be unhooked from the drawbar and stored by leaning them vertically, where they take up little space.

Spring Tooth Harrow

A spring tooth harrow has long, curved spring steel teeth instead of spikes, allowing it to penetrate to a much greater depth. It may be used in firm soil to dig down deep, break up clods, and stir and mix the soil. Spring tooth harrows are

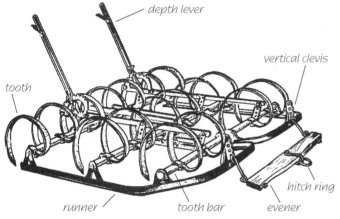

A two–section spring tooth harrow.

Farm Machinery by Archie A. Stone

A three–section spring tooth harrow with the sections hinged together, requiring only one drag link per section.

Deere & Co.

ideal for the cultivation of stony ground, since the springy teeth can pass over large rocks without damage. The harrow is effective in eradicating quack grass and similar weeds, because it digs deep, tears out the weed's roots, and brings them to the surface.

Features of a Spring Tooth Harrow

The spring tooth harrow is similar to the smoothing harrow, except the sections are narrower, being 3– or 4–feet wide, and have three rows of teeth. Each section usually has eight to twelve teeth, spaced about 4 inches apart. Depth is adjusted by a hand lever.

Each tooth consists of a heat treated and tempered curved flat bar of spring steel, one end of which is bolted rigidly to the tooth bar. The other end of the tooth is pointed to penetrate the soil. Several types of tooth points are available for different uses.

● The general purpose tooth has a broad, flat point to dig deep, break up clods, and stir and mix the soil, while destroying weeds.

● The weed point, sometimes called a quack grass point, is a little narrower and sharper, and is designed to tear up weed roots and bring them to the surface where the sun can kill them.

● The alfafa point has a narrow shank above a flat point and is used for cultivating alfalfa sod.

● The replaceable general purpose point is designed for use in abrasive soils. A modern harrow tooth has an

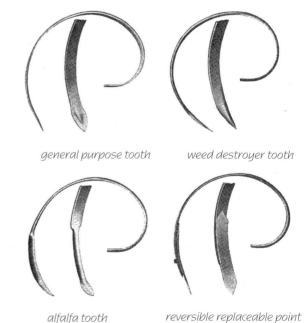

general purpose tooth   *weed destroyer tooth*

alfalfa tooth   *reversible replaceable point*

Common teeth available for a spring tooth harrow.

Deere & Co.

integral general purpose point that is punched with bolt holes to take a reversible point shovel after the original point wears out.

Most spring tooth harrows have either shoes at the front or runners along the bottom edges of the frame side rails. The shoes or runners ensure good flotation and easy turning, and are readily replaceable when worn. Some harrows were once furnished with small steel wheels instead of shoes.

Spring tooth harrow sections may be hitched beside each other to nearly any width your team can handle. On some spring tooth harrows the sections are joined to each other at the front and back by hinged joints. On other models the sections remain independent of each other. A combination harrow is a regular spring tooth machine with a raker bar, or row of straight steel tines, at the rear to help break up clods and eliminate ridging, making for a smoother seed bed.

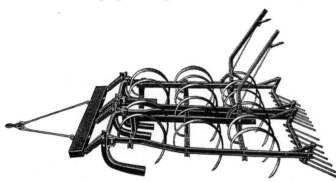

A two—section combination spring tooth harrow showing the shoes at the front of each section and the raker bars at the rear.   *Deere & Co.*

Draft of a Spring Tooth Harrow
A spring tooth harrow weighs from 40 to 50 pounds per foot of width. The draft depends on the soil condition and working depth. The average is 45 to 60 pounds per foot of width, with 125 pounds being maximum.

Hitching a Spring Tooth Harrow
The method of hitching a spring tooth harrow is similar to that used with a spike tooth harrow. You need wooden or steel eveners of the correct length, draft links and hooks for attaching the harrow sections, and a rod or chain and hitch ring for hitching to the team.

On harrows with the sections joined to each other by flexible links, you need only one drag link per section. If your harrow has sections that are independent of each other, you need two drag links per section to keep the sections running square with the evener.

Spring tooth harrow sections have a vertical clevis at the front for attaching each evener drag link. Several holes are provided in the clevis so the point of hitch may be raised or lowered to keep the front teeth penetrating to the same depth as the rear. The horizontal point of hitch must be such that the harrow pulls straight and doesn't run skewed to the direction of travel.

Drawbar Length

The drawbar for a spike tooth or spring tooth harrow has to be wide enough to span the width of however many harrow sections you attach to it. A new harrow comes with a drawbar of the correct length. A used harrow is also usually accompanied by a drawbar. If the drawbar is missing, you can easily make one from a length of steel pipe or box section, or a hardwood 2–by–4. Add together the width of each harrow section, plus 3 or 4 inches between sections, to determine how long the drawbar must be.

Operation, Adjustment and Care
Depth adjustment of a spring tooth harrow depends on field conditions and is accomplished by means of hand levers. The teeth are raised for transport and to dump accumulated trash.

Check the teeth by placing the harrow on level ground, or on a garage or shop floor, and lower the teeth until the points touch the surface. All the tooth points should touch the surface at the same time. If any do not, adjust the tooth clamps until all teeth operate at the same depth.

Keep the teeth sharp and the clamp bolts tight. Check for bent parts and straighten them as necessary. Lubricate moving parts after each use or if they bind. Check the eye bolts in a wooden evener, as you would for a spike tooth harrow. The harrow sections may easily be disconnected from the evener to facilitate storage.

A Pioneer three—section spring tooth harrow with rear mounted raker bars.

Knife Harrows

A knife harrow has fixed knife blades instead of teeth or rolling disc blades. Early versions had a row of curved knife blades 8 or 10 inches apart, which were especially useful for breaking up clods, while pulverizing the soil and killing small weeds.

A knife harrow called the soil surgeon, developed in the 1950s, is still available. Each section resembles a steel stone boat and is about 4–feet by 4–feet with a solid steel bottom. The 4–inch steel sides and back, and an angled front, provide a place to add weight or haul uprooted rocks from the field. Skid shoes on top allow you to turn the sled upside down for transport.

The business end of a soil surgeon consists of a number of heat–treated steel U–shaped blades attached to the underside of the pan. The attachment point is engineered so the straight blades are held in a position perpendicular to the direction of travel, but can swivel in turns.. The blades slice through the soil, cultivating it to a depth of about 4 inches, while the drag–like sled crushes any clods. When weighted, the drag effect helps level the ground. The 4–foot sections may be bolted together to make most any width. A knife harrow may do a better job than a disc harrow on dry, hard ground, and is also useful for training and exercising a horse or team.

Operation of a knife harrow is the same as for a spike tooth harrow. Older knife harrows had a hand lever to adjust the angle of the knives for more or less aggressive action. the soil surgeon has no adjustments. For transport, turn the sections over so they ride on the skid shoes.

The older style of knife harrow has a short tongue to which the team's evener is hitched. The soil surgeon is hitched in exactly the same way as a spike tooth harrow.

Chain Link Harrows

Chain link harrows of various sizes and shapes are made of steel rods joined together by chain links to form a square flexible mat of nearly any size. Some chain link harrows have angled teeth projecting from one side and are reversible to obtain a more or a less aggressive action.

Chain harrows are used for pasture maintenance to break up and spread lumps of manure and pull out dead, matted grass. They are effective for smoothing, leveling, and covering broadcast seed, but have little cultivating action and aren't effective for killing weeds.

No field adjustment or lubrication is required. The sections may be unhooked from the drawbar and rolled into a compact bundle for easy transport or storage.

Land Rollers

A land roller is a weighted cylinder that is rolled over the ground to crush clods and firm the soil. Rollers were originally made of stone with an axle through the center, or a heavy log with pins driven into the ends from which shafts or ropes led forward to a yoke of oxen. Some early wooden rollers had a series of iron spikes driven into the wood to help break up clods in heavy clay.

Early in the nineteenth century, smooth cast–iron rollers became common, but all smooth one piece rollers share the same disadvantages—moist, sticky soil sticks to the roller and has to be periodically scraped away, and the smooth surface tends to push hard clods into the earth, rather than crush them. During turns, unless the turn is wide, a one–piece roller tends to stop turning and skid around, causing the stationary end to dig a hole in the ground while the other end throws up a ridge of soil.

Some smooth rollers are made up of two or three cast–iron or steel cylinders mounted on an axle. These rollers turn more easily than a single drum, and may be advantageous for packing and smoothing grassland, but still have the problems of sticky soil adhering to the drums and the roller tending to push clods into loose soil.

Later land rollers were built as a series of individual ribbed rollers turning freely on a common axle. This setup makes turning much easier, and the separate ribbed rollers

A two–section soil surgeon built by D.A. Hochstetler, with double swivel–mounted blades and transport skids on top of each tray.

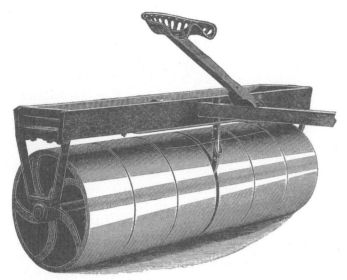

A smooth surfaced roller consisting of a drum divided into six sections for easier turning. Belcher & Taylor Co.

shed soil, do a better job of crushing clods, and leave the soil ridged to minimize moisture loss and wind erosion.

Features of a Roller

The land roller used extensively today is popularly known as a pulverizer or cultipacker. This design has a series of discs, or crushing wheels, each of which is 5– or 6–inches thick at the center and slopes toward a cutting edge. Each wheel is from 10– to 18–inches in diameter and turns freely on a common axle.

The wheels are usually arranged in two gangs, one behind the other, so the point of a wheel on the rear gang splits the ridge made by a front wheel. Some models have the front and rear gangs spaced several feet apart, with either cultivator shanks and sweeps or spring harrow teeth

A double–gang pulverizer. Deere & Co.

mounted between the gangs. The middle teeth bring clods to the surface, where they are crushed by the rear roller.

Besides packing the soil and crushing clods, the wheels leave the soil in shallow ridges, which helps prevent water and wind erosion. These rollers have a cultivating action as well, moving the soil away from each disc's edge and destroying small weeds. The pulverizer may be effectively used in the spring on winter wheat, as it resets frost–heaved plants and packs soil around the roots without harming the plants. It is also helpful for improving seed-to-soil contact after seeding grass or legume pasture and hay crops.

Action on the soil of a double–gang pulverizer, with the rear gang omitted for clarity. Deere & Co.

Draft and Operation

The draft of a roller depends on its diameter and weight. A smooth roller has a draft of between 25 and 30 pounds per 100 pounds of weight. A double roller pulverizer averages about 60 pounds per foot.

Land rollers normally have no adjustments. Bearings—which may be cast–iron or wood sleeves, or ball bearings—should be lubricated frequently.

A combination roller–harrow built by Horst Road Repair.

Tillage Equipment

Field Cultivators

The field cultivator is similar to a chisel plow, but is intended for lighter duty operations. It is a versatile implement that may be used for preparing a seedbed in previously plowed ground. It is effective in incorporating manure and other fertilizers, as well as chemicals applied for weed and insect control. The field cultivator kills weeds and mulches fallow ground, loosens soil before moldboard plowing, cultivates orchards, and renovates pastures. In some types of soil it may be used as a primary tillage tool, leaving the surface ridged and covered with trash to reduce wind and water erosion, and minimize loss of moisture.

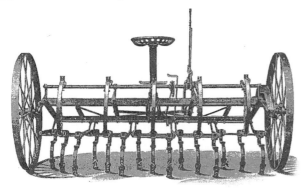

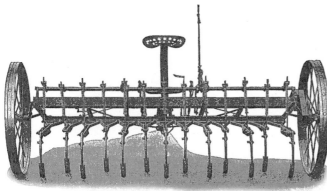

A field cultivator with spring teeth (top) and the same machine with stiff shanks (bottom) to which the shovels or sweeps are attached.

International Harvester

Features of a Cultivator

The field cultivator consists of a heavy frame mounted on two or more wheels. On the frame are mounted a series of either spring teeth or stiff shanks to hold shovels or sweeps. Shovels, chisels, and sweeps come in a wide range of sizes and styles to fit any application.

● Narrow double pointed teeth are for pasture rejuvenation and tearing out shallow weeds.

● Spear point and sweep teeth are for summer fallowing and roughing land to prevent erosion. They are also used to destroy deep–rooted weeds by cutting them below the surface.

● Large sweeps, with wings as wide as 24 inches, are used for wider spaced crops and may be set for ridging. Like the smaller sweeps, they may be used for summer fallowing and for cutting off deep–rooted weeds. The wide wings on these sweeps provide more overlap between leading and trailing teeth.

Field cultivators are available in sizes from 4–feet wide to a gigantic model that covers 53 feet of ground and

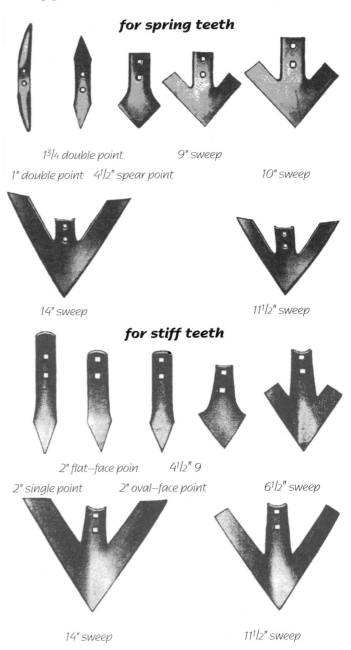

Some of the many available field cultivator shovels.

Deere & Co.

requires more than 400 horsepower. Older horse–drawn field cultivators have a hand lever to lift the gangs. Later models use a mechanical or a hydraulic lift. Also available are 3–point hitch models without wheels. The shanks or teeth on most field cultivators may be removed or set so the machine may be used for cultivating row crops.

Draft of a Cultivator

The draft of a field cultivator varies widely, depending on the kind of shovel or sweep you use, as well as on the soil condition and the depth of operation. At horse speed the draft is about 50 to 110 pounds per shank.

Operation, Adjustment and Care

A field cultivator has a few adjustments. Run the frame level, both from side to side and front to rear. In normal conditions, run the shovels or sweeps only as deep as necessary to shatter the soil, kill weeds, or properly incorporate fertilizers or chemicals. Depending on the cultivator model, the depth may be set by a crank, lever, or hydraulic control.

Periodically check all nuts and bolts for tightness, and lubricate the wheel bearings. Keep the shovels, sweeps, or points sharp and replace them when they are worn. After each use, coat the shovels with grease to preserve the earth polish, and store the machine under cover.

Massey Harris field cultivator preparing a nice seedbed.

Photo by Ruth Freeman

Drags

A wooden drag, or planker, may be used to crush clods and level soil, but has virtually no cultivating action. Usually built on the farm, this implement consists of two or three overlapped planks held together by cross members. A drag may be used alone, or pulled behind a plow or disc harrow.

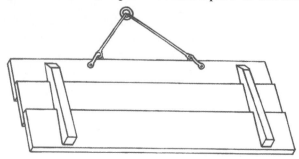

A typical drag, made of overlapping planks, used mainly for leveling.

Rod Weeders

Rod weeders are specialized tools used primarily for controlling weeds on fallow land. A rod weeder consists of a series of C–shaped beams mounted side by side on a frame supported by a wheel at each end. The lower end of each beam has a sharpened point to penetrate the soil.

This rod weeder, which requires a forecart, clearly shows the sprocket and chain, and reversing gear and shaft drive, at the right, as well as the lugs on the left wheel that drive the rod.

International Harvester

A horse–drawn rod weeder with a fore truck.

International Harvester

48   Tillage Equipment

A round or square steel rod runs parallel to the ground through a bearing just behind each point. The rod is driven from one wheel, or both, by chains and gears, and turns as the machine moves through the field.

When the rod weeder is in operation, the beams are lowered, causing the points to penetrate the soil and drag the rod along an inch or two below the surface. The action of the revolving rod, turning in the opposite direction to the wheels, loosens the soil and uproots any young plants, leaving them on the surface to die and leaving a loose dirt mulch on the soil's surface to conserve moisture. This implement cannot be used in growing crops, as the young plants would be destroyed along with the weeds, and is not useful in stony ground.

Tillage tools include many different configurations of disc harrow, field cultivator, and cultipacker combined into a single implement. This implement combines an I&J field cultivator and a custom–built cultipacker to turn plowed ground into a finished seedbed in one pass by first breaking up the clods and then smoothing and firming the seedbed.

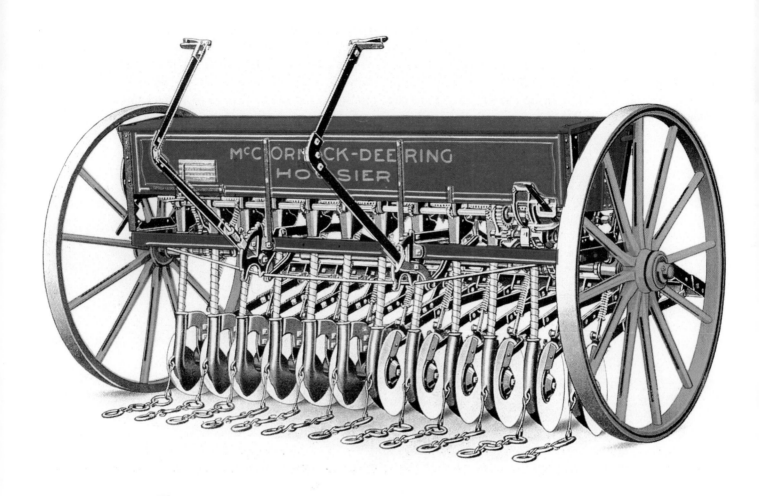

II: Planting & Cultivating Equipment

From the earliest days of recorded agriculture until the middle of the 19th century, seeds were planted by hand. The most popular, and fastest, method of sowing small grain and grass seed was to broadcast, or scatter it by hand. After the seedbed was prepared, a man slung a sack of seed over his shoulder with the mouth of the sack open at his front. As our intrepid sower strode across the field, he dipped into the sack with first one hand and then the other, tossing each handful of grain out in a semi-circle by a swinging motion of his hand and arm. The pace and motions of a skilled sower were smooth and unhurried, and he was able to distribute an even amount of seed over the entire surface. After broadcasting the seed, he ran a harrow over the ground to cover the seed. In a field that had been sown in such a manner, the plants came up willy-nilly, leaving no way to chop out the weeds without also chopping out a lot of good plants.

Although it was much slower, the dibble was used as well, and offered the advantage of placing seeds in rows, or drills, at regular intervals, thus allowing space between the plants for cultivation. A dibble was nothing more than a pointed tool pushed into the ground by hand to make a hole. The sower dropped one or more seeds into the hole and kicked dirt over it with his foot before moving on to the next hole. The dibble was popular for planting corn until the mid 1800s, and for potatoes until much later.

The 19th century was a time of great progress in mechanizing all aspects of farming, with thousands of new inventions in America and Europe. By the turn of the 20th century grain, corn, and potato planters, as well as machines to sow many other crops, were commonplace and closely resembled those in use today.

5 *Grain Drills and Seeders*

"One for the rook, one for the crow,
One to rot, and one to grow."

Ancient English farmer's verse

Until the mid 19th century most small grains were broadcast by hand and then covered by harrowing. This method practically guaranteed that much of the seed would be sown too deep, causing it to rot before germinating, or else too shallow, making it prey for the "rook and the crow."

Hieroglyphics of a Babylonian seed drill have been found dating to the 14th century BC, but mechanical grain drills didn't appear until the British agriculturist Jethro Tull experimented with the idea in the 1730s. Tull developed a wheeled, three-row machine with a seed hopper and a seed metering device for each row. The metering device consisted of a notched, wooden barrel that revolved inside the seed hopper, where it picked up the seeds and dropped them into a tube. Just ahead of the bottom end of each seed tube, a knife coulter made a slit in the soil into which the seeds fell. Shovel–like hoes at the rear of the machine covered the seeds. Farmers were reluctant to adopt Tull's machine, however, and grain drills didn't come into widespread use until almost a century and a half later.

A Vermont farmer named Eliakim Spooner patented a grain drill in 1799, but little is known about his machine. A seven–hoe drill was developed in 1841 by Samuel and Moses Pennock of Chester County, Pennsylvania. A rotating, flanged shaft running through the bottom of the seed hopper agitated the seeds and caused them to fall into the tubes that led to the hoes. Set for 9–inch rows, the hoes opened furrows in the soil into which the seeds fell. In loose soil, enough fell back into the furrow after the hoes had passed to cover the seeds.

In 1851 a force–feed mechanism to meter the quantity of seeds was developed, and in 1857 disc furrow openers, as well as chains or press wheels to cover the seeds, appeared. By the middle 1860s, grain drills that placed the seed into the ground at a uniform interval and depth, while covering the seed with an even layer of soil, were in common use on eastern and midwestern farms.

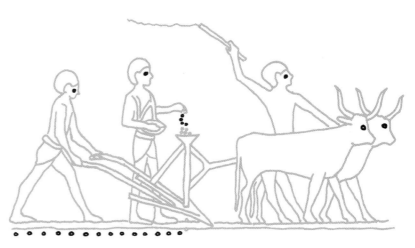

A Babylonian seed drill from the 14th century BC

Conventional Drills

The *grain drill* is a machine for planting small grain in evenly spaced rows, or drills. The machine forms a series of shallow trenches into which it drops evenly spaced seeds, then covers the seeds with a uniform layer of soil. Grain drills are built in many sizes and styles to meet the different conditions in every section of the country. Most modern drills use either single or double disc openers to make the trench, and apply a band of fertilizer in close proximity to each row of seeds. Many drills include an extra attachment that plants grass seed at the same time as the grain.

A 13x7 fertilizer–grain drill with a tractor hitch and power lift. Notice how the disc openers all throw the soil from the center toward the outside. *Deere & Co.*

Features of a Grain Drill

A grain drill consists of a main frame supported by a wheel at each end. The wheels—large diameter on early drills, small diameter on later versions—provide not only transport, but a ground drive for the planting mechanism. The larger wheels are placed directly on the axle, from which gears and sprockets drive the feed mechanisms and power lift, if provided. The smaller wheels are mounted on short stub axles that drive the main shaft through roller chains.

A long box, or hopper—made of wood on early machines, and steel on later ones—sits atop the frame to hold the seed. Many drills have additional boxes for fertilizer and grass seed. In the bottom of the boxes a series of feed devices meter the seed and fertilizer out of the hoppers in uniform quantities and drop them down the flexible seed tubes. The bottom of each feed tube ends in a boot, just behind a furrow opener that makes a trench in the soil for the seeds.

Furrow Openers

The furrow opener may be a hoe or a shoe, or a single or double disc. Each furrow opener has a draft link that's hinged at the front to either a horizontal drag bar or the drill's front frame. A vertical pressure rod and spring connects each opener to the lifting mechanism above it. The spring

pressure on these rods is adjustable to hold the opener at the proper depth, while allowing it to move back and up if it encounters an obstruction.

The furrow openers may be arranged in a straight side–to–side line or may be staggered, with every other one slightly ahead. In trashy ground the staggered arrangement offers more clearance between the openers for the trash to pass through. Disc openers with gauge wheels for a more accurate planting depth are available for most drills.

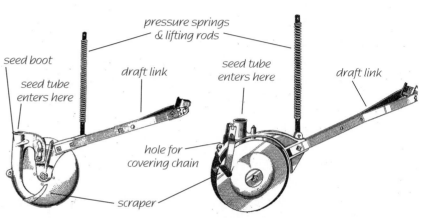

A single disc furrow opener with a rear seed delivery boot (left), and a double disc opener with a center delivery boot, both with scrapers to keep the discs free of sticky soil. The pressure springs hold the openers to the proper depth, even on rough ground, and allow them to ride up and over obstructions.

International Harvester

A pin break hoe style furrow opener (left) is designed so the pin breaks and allows the hoe to swing to the rear if an obstruction is encountered. Some hoe openers have a spring trip arrangement, rather than a wooden pin. On a shoe style furrow opener (right), a pressure spring holds the shoe at the proper planting depth, yet allows it to ride up over an obstruction.

International Harvester

Covering Chains and Press Wheels

Short large–link chains are usually dragged behind each disc opener to pull loose earth over the seeds. Some hoe and shoe openers rely on the natural tendency of loose dirt to fall back into the trench and cover the seed. In dry areas, a press wheel is mounted behind each opener to firm the soil over and around the seed, causing scarce moisture to more easily percolate up from below. Most modern drills use press wheels, although covering chains are available.

Depth Setting Lever

On older horse–drawn drills, raising, lowering, and setting the planting depth of the furrow openers is usually accomplished by means of a hand lever. Tractor drills and some horse drills use a mechanical power lift operated by a trip rope, with a hand crank to set the depth.

Planting and Cultivating Equiment

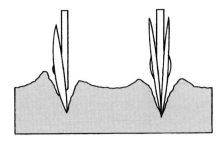

The single disc opener (far left) works well in hard or trashy ground, and doesn't clog easily in wet, sticky soil. It builds a higher furrow wall to protect the seedlings from wind. A double disc opener (left) makes a roomier furrow and can run at higher speeds while disturbing less soil. Single (right) and double gauge wheels (far right) assure accurate depth of planting and firm the soil.

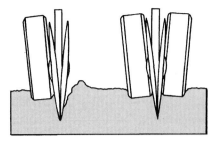

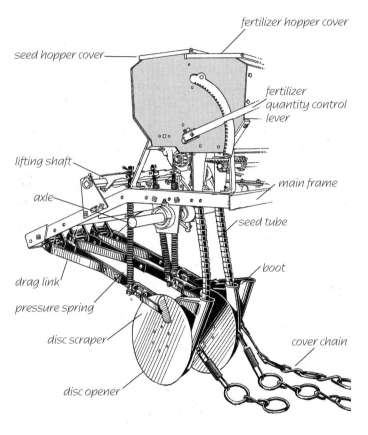

Left side view of a fluted feed grain drill, with the wheel removed for clarity.   *International Harvester*

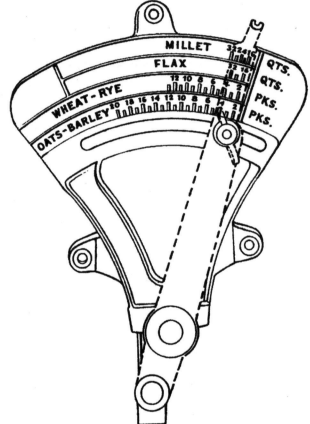

Levers or dials control the quantity of seed sown per acre, along with the rate of fertilizer application. Usually an acre meter, or land measurement device driven from the main axle or feed shaft, measures the number of acres covered by the drill. The seeding rate lever and quadrant shown here are from an older fluted feed drill; later fluted feed drills have a numbered quadrant with no printed seed names.

International Harvester

Wide Row Spacing

leave open only these feed holes—cover the rest with stops

drill size	21" row	28" row	35" row	42" row
9x7	3–6–9	1–5–9	3–8	2–8
11x7	3–6–9	2–6–10	1–6–11	3–9
13x7	1–4–7–10–13	1–5–9–13	2–7–12	1–7–13
15x7	1–4–7–10–13	2–6–10–14	3–8–13	1–7–13

From: *Farm Equipment & Machinery* by Harrison Pearson Smith

Modern drills are raised and lowered by a hydraulic cylinder. Each of the drives on a grain drill, including the seed, fertilizer, and grass seed, has its own clutch, which is automatically disengaged when the furrow openers are raised out of the ground to prevent the waste of seed or fertilizer when turning at the headlands or crossing grassed waterways.

Drill Size

The size of a grain drill is based on how many furrow openers it has and the spacing between the rows. A 12x6 drill plants 12 rows spaced 6 inches apart; a 16x7 drill has 16 furrow openers spaced 7 inches apart.

A drill may be used to plant wider spaced row crops by covering some of the feeds. Feed stops come as optional attachments for most grain drills, but if the originals aren't available you can improvise stops.

Stop both the seed and fertilizer feeds on the unused holes, although if you wish you may leave the fertilizer to flow between rows. Unused furrow openers may be left on the drill to work the soil between rows. For consistent row spacing, use row markers when planting row crops.

Feed Mechanisms

Grain drills use a force–feed mechanism to meter the right amount of seed from the hopper and drop it into the seed tube. These force–feed mechanisms are of two styles: fluted feed and double run feed. For many years most drill manufacturers offered both styles. Today's grain drills are predominately of the fluted feed style, using better materials and an easier method of setting the gates than in the past. All fluted feed drills are operated in the same manner.

The *fluted feed* consists of a feed roll, feed cutoff, feed cup, and adjustable gate for each row. The feeds are spaced along the bottom of the seed hopper and have angled baffles between them to cause the seed to slide into the feed cups. The feed roll turns with the square feed shaft, gathers the seeds in its fluted recesses, and forces them out over the feed gate, which is adjustable for seeds of different sizes. The feed cutoff and feed roll may be moved sideways on the shaft, exposing more or less of the feed roll to the seed in the feed cup. The more of the feed roll exposed, the more seed it will pick up and force through the gate, thus controlling the quantity of seed sown.

A *double run* feed consists of a feed wheel, a valve, and in some cases a feed gate. The wheel is double in having small cells on one side for planting small seeds, and a large cell on the other side for sowing larger seeds. A two–way valve on top of the seed cup directs the seed to either the large or the small side of the feed wheel. On some drills the two–way valve is a cast–iron flap with a centered hinge over each feed cup, and with the numeral one cast into one side and the numeral two on the other. When the one is showing, the small side of the double run feed is ready to use. When two is showing, the large side is in use. Other manufacturers use separate feed covers, held in place by spring–loaded latches that may be reversed to expose one side of the feed wheel or the other.

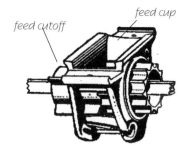
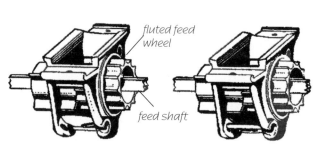

feed cutoff *feed cup* *fluted feed wheel* *feed shaft* *gate latch*

Set the gate in the highest position to sow wheat, oats, barley, rye, flax, rice, and similar seeds.

Set the gate in the middle position to drill small peas or soybeans, common beans, corn, or trashy oats.

Set the gate in the lowest position to plant large soybeans or peas, as well as kidney beans and lima beans.

To clean the feed cups, remove the seed tubes, shift the feed roll all the way to the left, and drop the gates.

A calibrated feed shaft shifter lever on the outside of the seed box controls the amount of seed drilled per acre by sliding the feed cutoff and the feed roll along the feed shaft. The more of the feed roll that is exposed inside the feed cup, the more seed will be picked up and sown. The adjustable gate allows the accurate planting of large, medium, or small sized seeds. A small lever at the side of the seed cup, or inside the cup on the gate itself, controls this setting. All the gates should be set to the same position.

Agricultural Machinery by J. Brownlee Davidson

Planting and Cultivating Equiment

A double run feed cup showing the large side of the feed wheel. The other side is the same, except the seed cells are smaller. *The Oliver Corp.*

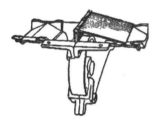 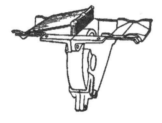

A cover in the No. 1 position (left) exposes the small side of the seed cup and wheel. When the cover is flipped to the No. 2 position (right) the large side comes into play. Covers on all the feed cups should be in the same position, as recommended by the grain sowing table found inside the seed box lid. *International Harvester*

The rate of seeding is adjusted by a lever that moves a sliding pinion along a face gear, or into mesh with one of a multiple cluster of gears of different diameters, causing the speed of the feed wheels to vary. When the sliding pinion is close to the center of the face gear, or in mesh with the largest of the cluster gears, the feed wheels turn slower and the amount of seed per acre is less. To increase the rate of seeding, move the sliding gear outward on the face gear, or into mesh with a smaller gear in the cluster, causing the feed wheels to turn faster and dispense more seeds.

The hand lever that moves the sliding gear to control the rate of feed is usually located beneath the seed box. It

consists of a short lever you press inward to unlock the sliding gear and allow it to be moved along a square shaft. A series of numbered grooves, or notches, allow the lever and gear to be locked into place. The numbers on these notches correspond to the numbers on the seeding chart on the inside of the seedbox cover and listed in the operator's manual. Some drills use compound gears, or different combinations of sprockets behind the face or cluster gear, to further control the seeding rate.

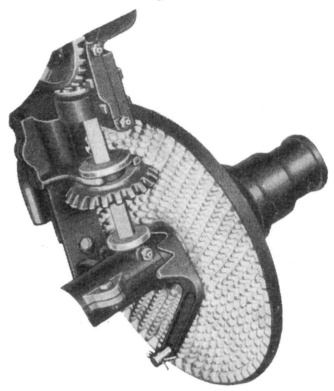

A typical face gear and sliding pinion—this one with 13 rows of teeth, allowing 13 different rates of sowing. *The Oliver Corp.*

Combination Fertilizer–Grain Drill
Many drills in use today are combination fertilizer–grain drills that open and till a trench, place the seeds and distribute the fertilizer, then cover both. These drills have two distributing units, one for seed and another for fertilizer. The drive for the fertilizing attachment is separate from that of the seed feeding mechanism and has its own controls for regulating the rate of application.

Star type feeder wheels rotate along the bottom of the fertilizer hopper, causing an even flow into the feeder tubes. The rate of fertilizer application can be varied

Double Run Feed Gates

To further regulate the size of the feed openings, some double–run feeds have adjustable gates inside the feed cups. A double–run drill with these gates will have a lock lever on each side of the feed cup that may be moved through several numbered notches. Each lever controls the gate associated with the side of the double–run mechanism in use at the time. Usually the higher the number in which the lock lever is set, the greater the amount of seed that will be sown.

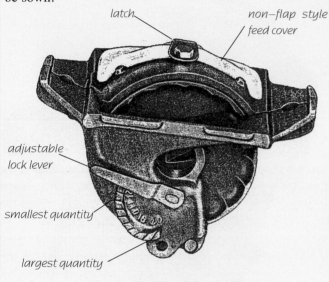

latch

non–flap style feed cover

adjustable lock lever

smallest quantity

largest quantity

Large Side of Feed Wheel

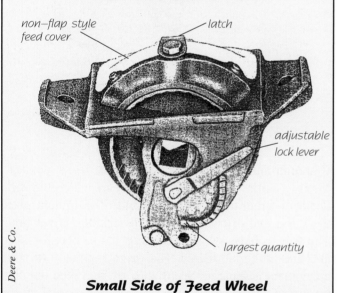

non–flap style feed cover

latch

adjustable lock lever

largest quantity

Deere & Co.

Small Side of Feed Wheel

Refer to the sowing chart for your particular drill and set these gates accordingly. For uniform seeding set all gates in the same position.

widely. Most machines have a lever on the outside of the fertilizer box that moves a series of slides to control the size of the openings through which the fertilizer falls onto the feed wheels. The speed of the feed wheels may be varied by another lever, as well, usually under the fertilizer hopper on the feed drive.

Some drills drop both the seeds and the fertilizer through the same tube to the opener, where they are placed together in the seed trench. With today's concentrated fertilizers, the band–seeding method is more prevalent. In band–seeding, the seeds drop down one tube to the opener where they are planted, while the fertilizer drops down a separate tube and is placed in a band a little off to one side and above the seeds.

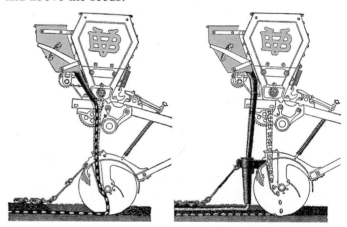

Some drills drop the fertilizer down the seed tube (left); most drills have a separate fertilizer tube for each row (right) that places the fertilizer in a band separate from the seed.
                                                                Deere & Co.

Grass Seeders

A grass seeding attachment available for most drills consists of a smaller hopper, usually mounted in front of the main hopper. This attachment is used to seed grass or legumes such as alfalfa, clover, timothy, and brome grass, either by themselves or in with small grains such as wheat. Most manufacturers use a fluted–type feed for the grass seed attachment, even though the main feed may be double run.

A shifter lever and quadrant are mounted on the seed box to set the seeding rate. The lever moves the fluted feed rolls into or out of the seed cups, and controls the amount of seed sown. The grass seed is fed into separate seed tubes that may be moved to either deposit the seed into the furrow, or scatter it behind the opener in front of the covering device. The grass seed attachment has its own clutch and drive from the main axle, and a seeding chart inside the hopper lid.

Operation, Adjustment and Care

The grain drill is a precision implement that requires careful adjustment and operation, regular and thorough lubrication, and a meticulous cleaning after each use. Before using a grain drill for the first time, especially if it is an older model, perform the following operations:

● Remove the seed and fertilizer tubes and thoroughly clean out the grain and fertilizer hoppers and all the feed cups.

● Make sure all feed shafts and gears move freely. Check them by using an adjustable wrench to turn the square feed shafts. If the feeds stick or turn hard, look for rust or foreign objects in the feeds (mice love to make their homes in grain drills), and liberally apply kerosene or diesel fuel to free up the moving parts. *When using diesel fuel or kerosene, be careful it doesn't ignite—use only in a well–ventilated area and away from sparks or open flames.*

● Check all drive chains for correct installation. Replace any chains that are badly worn.

● Remove the wheels from the main axles, and clean and lubricate the bearings. If the hub contains driving pawls (mechanisms that allow rotation in only one direction), make sure none of the pawls are broken or worn to the point of slipping. The driving surfaces of the pawls may be built up with weld, then filed to shape. Replace any broken pawl springs. When replacing hub caps, make sure the pawls are properly engaged in the wheel ratchets.

● Check the opener tension springs. Replace any springs that are broken. Adjust all springs to equal tension.

● Make sure all the connections of the drag links are tight and not badly worn.

● If the drill is equipped with disc openers, remove the discs and clean and lubricate the disc bearings. Replace any badly worn discs or bearings.

● Adjust the scrapers to conform to the surface of the discs.

● Adjust the lifting shaft helper spring(s) so the pressure helps raise the openers when they're raised, and helps to force them into the ground when they're lowered.

● Calibrate the drill. Even though the manufacturer may indicate on a scale or chart how to adjust the drill for different rates of seeding, variations in the weight, size, and character of seeds make calibration of the drill before use a wise course of action.

To calibrate a grain drill, first jack it up so the wheels turn freely. Place a tarpaulin under the furrow openers, or place a paper bag or other container under each seed tube, to catch the seeds.

Set the gates, valves, and feed shifters properly for the amount of seed you want to sow per acre, and fill the seed box with grain. To obtain the length of a strip necessary to plant one acre, divide 43,560 (the number of square feet in an acre) by the width of the strip sown by the drill. Then find the number of times the drill wheel must turn to plant that strip by dividing the length of the strip, in feet, by the circumference of the wheel. Divide this number by twenty to get the number of turns necessary to plant one–twentieth of an acre, which is sufficient for the test.

> **Example:**
> A 12x7 drill, which plants a strip about 7 feet wide, has 48–inch wheels with a circumference of 12.5 feet.
> 43,560 divided by 7 = 6223 feet traveled to plant one acre.
> 6,223 divided by 12.5 = 498 turns of the wheel to plant one acre.
> 498 divided by 20 = 25 turns to plant one–twentieth acre.

Place a chalk mark or tie a rag on the outside of the wheel and put the planting mechanism in gear. Turn the wheel by hand and count out enough revolutions (25 in the above example) to sow one–twentieth of an acre. After making the correct number of revolutions, measure the grain on the tarpaulin or in the bags, multiply by 20, and compare the resulting amount to your feed shifter scale or chart.

If your drill is set to sow five pounds, you should have one-quarter pound of grain (five divided by 20) on the tarpaulin. If the amount is more or less than it should be, adjust the feed shifter mechanism to correct the difference, or use the percentage of error in future calculations. To obtain the percentage of error, take the difference between the quantity of grain collected and the quantity indicated, and divide by the quantity indicated. Keep in mind that the actual amount of grain found on the tarp or in the bags is one-twentieth the amount needed to plant one acre.

> **Example:**
> The indicator is set to sow 8 pounds of seed, but only 6 pounds (the actual amount collected times 20) are collected, leaving a difference of 2 pounds. Dividing the 2 pound difference by the indicated 8 pounds, tells you the drill is under sowing by 25 percent, the figure you must use in future calculations by setting the indicator on the feed shifting mechanism to a 25 percent higher feeding rate than that desired.

Draft of a Grain Drill

The draft of a grain drill depends on soil conditions and depth of seeding, and therefore varies widely. One study indicates a draft of 6 to 20 pounds per inch of planting depth for each furrow opener. Planting depth is usually from one to three inches. Fertilizer and grass seed attachments, as well as press wheels, add to the draft. A drill with the hoppers full of seed and fertilizer will obviously pull harder than one that's nearly empty.

Hitching a Grain Drill

Grain drills are designed to be operated with the grain box level from front to rear. If the front of the pole is raised, the rear of the drill is lowered, causing the furrow openers to swing forward under the axle and resulting in too–deep furrows, too much covering soil over the seeds, and increased draft. If the front end of the pole is lowered, the opposite happens—the furrow openers swing back and up, the furrows are too shallow, and the seed is scattered and not properly covered.

Most horse–drawn drills have a vertical clevis at the rear of the tongue to accommodate teams of different sizes. Neck straps may also be adjusted to level a drill. The hitch on a tractor–drawn drill is also adjustable.

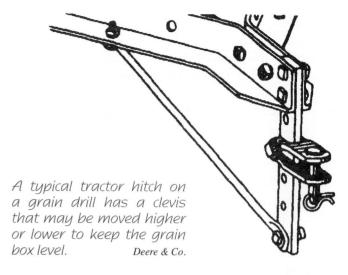

A typical tractor hitch on a grain drill has a clevis that may be moved higher or lower to keep the grain box level.   *Deere & Co.*

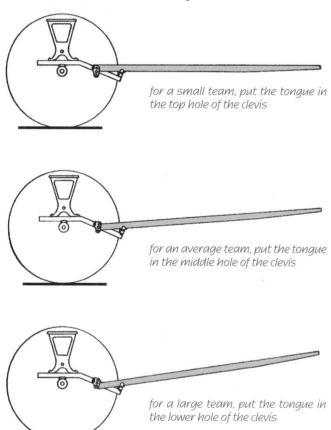

for a small team, put the tongue in the top hole of the clevis

for an average team, put the tongue in the middle hole of the clevis

for a large team, put the tongue in the lower hole of the clevis

Adjust the tongue on a horse–drawn grain drill to keep the grain box level from front to rear.   *International Harvester*

Filling Hoppers

Before filling the hoppers, you need to know how much seed and fertilizer to apply per acre, which will depend on many things including your climate, your soil's fertility, the size of the seed, and the expected yield. Once you decide on application rates, consult the seeding and fertilizer application charts provided with your drill to determine the necessary settings.

Fluted Feed Drills

To set the fluted feed drill to sow the desired quantity of seed per acre, adjust the feed shaft and the feed gates to suit the size and quantity of the seed to be sown. Before putting any seed in the hopper, open all the adjustable feed gates and clean out any old grain or debris. Make sure the seed tubes are clear of debris.

Close the gates and set them in the top notch to sow beets, all grain, and small seeds. Set the gates in the middle notch for coarser seed such as trashy oats, soybeans, corn, small peas, and common beans. Set gates in the bottom notches for large soybeans, kidney beans, or peas. To assure uniform planting, set the gates on all the feeds in the same position.

The feed adjustment lever may be on either the front or back of the hopper. It moves across a seed index quadrant marked off in pecks, quarts, or pounds per acre on older machines. Levers on later drills usually move across a notched and numbered seed index quadrant. Large drills have a separate control lever for each end of the hopper. Most drills have a chart inside the hopper lid that indicates the proper lever settings for various amounts of seed per acre, and the same information is usually in the operator's manual. On a fluted–feed drill, the lever moves the feed shaft sideways to expose more of each feed roll to the seed, thus increasing the amount of seed planted per acre.

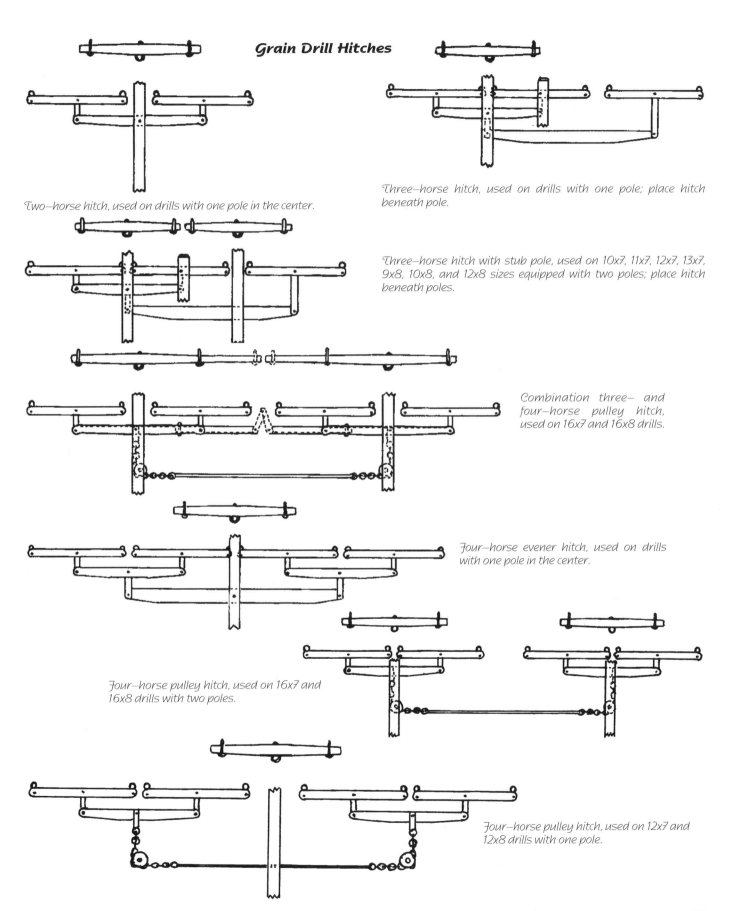

Grain Drill Hitches

Two-horse hitch, used on drills with one pole in the center.

Three-horse hitch, used on drills with one pole; place hitch beneath pole.

Three-horse hitch with stub pole, used on 10x7, 11x7, 12x7, 13x7, 9x8, 10x8, and 12x8 sizes equipped with two poles; place hitch beneath poles.

Combination three- and four-horse pulley hitch, used on 16x7 and 16x8 drills.

Four-horse evener hitch, used on drills with one pole in the center.

Four-horse pulley hitch, used on 16x7 and 16x8 drills with two poles.

Four-horse pulley hitch, used on 12x7 and 12x8 drills with one pole.

Grain Drills and Seeders

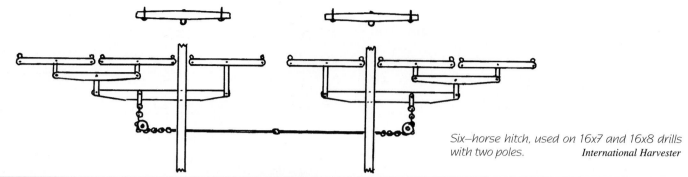

Six–horse hitch, used on 16x7 and 16x8 drills with two poles.   *International Harvester*

Sowing Table per Acre for a Double Run Grain Drill					
Sow through No. 1 opening					
figure on indicator*	wheat	treated wheat, rice, barley	rye, buckwheat	flax**	alfalfa, millet**
	pecks	quarts	quarts	pounds	pounds
1	2	14	14	13	5
2	2.5	17	18	17	6
3	3	21	22	20	7
4	3.5	25	26	23	8
5	4	28	30	27	9
6	4.5	32	34	30	10
7	5	35	38	33	11
8	5.5	39	42	37	12
9	6	42	46	40	13
10	6.5	46	50	43	14
11	7	49	54	47	15
12	7.5	53	58	50	16
13	8	56	62	54	17

** Many drills require a reducer for tiny seeds such as flax, alfalfa, or millet to limit their into the feed wheel.

Sow through No. 2 opening					
figure on indicator*	oats, spelt	wheat	dry treated wheat	rice, barley	rye, buckwheat	soybeans
	quarts	quarts	quarts	quarts	quarts	quarts
1	46	65	60	61	72	25
2	57	81	76	76	90	31
3	69	97	92	91	108	37
4	80	113	103	106	126	43
5	92	129	124	121	122	49
6	103	145	140	136		55
7	115	161	156	151		61
8	126			166		67
9	137			181		73
10	149			196		80
11	161					86
12	172					92
13	184					98

*Figures on the indicator represent rows of teeth on the speed disc, *not* the quantity of seed.   *From: The Oliver Corp*

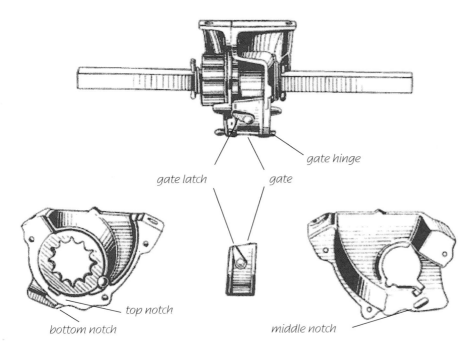

gate hinge

gate latch · gate

top notch

bottom notch · middle notch

At the bottom of the feed cup is a gate that is adjustable to three positions for seeds of different sizes. Latch gate into the top notch for small seeds and the bottom notch for large seeds. The middle notch, which is on the opposite side of the cup housing, is for medium seeds. Be sure the latches are firmly seated in the notches, and that all gates are set the same. Modern drills have an external lever on the outside of the seed cup that is latched into one of three notches for this adjustment. Unlatch the gate and drop it all the way down to clean out the feed cup and feed roll.   International Harvester

Double Run Feed Drills

Before putting seed in a double run feed drill, make sure the feed cups and tubes are clear of debris, and set all the flap valves the same way. The seeding chart will specify which side a given seed, or amount of seeds, should be sown through. Large seeds and large quantities of seed are sown through the large opening.

Most of these valves have the numeral 1 cast onto one side and 2 on the other. When number 1 is showing on the valve, the seed will be directed to the smaller side of the feed wheel. When number 2 is showing, larger seed may be planted. To ensure even planting, all the valves must be set the same way.

Inside the seed hopper lid is a chart that tells how to set the sliding pinion on the face gear to achieve different seeding rates per acre. Find on the chart the crop you wish to plant and your desired seeding rate. The chart will give you a number corresponding to a numbered notch on the sliding gear scale. (The numbers on the scale refer to rows of teeth on the face gear, not quantity of seed.) Press in on the thumb latch and move the gear until the latch drops into the desired notch.

TABLE FOR SLOW SPEED WITH BOTTOM OF CUP CLOSED

ZERO 24
16 32

QUARTS PER ACRE - MILLET

PECKS PER ACRE WHEAT - FLAX
12 16

PECKS PER ACRE BARLEY - OATS - RICE
12   16   20

FOR OTHER SEEDS SEE TABLE
IN INSTRUCTION BOOK

Grain indicator plate and fluted feed setting lever from an older model grain drill.

International Harvester

Example:
You wish to plant two bushels of treated wheat to the acre. Referring to the chart, you find that the columns for wheat call for pecks per acre. Four pecks make a bushel, so the seeding rate should be 8 pecks per acre. Look down the column for wheat until you come to 8. There you find that you should use the smaller, or No. 1 opening, and set the sliding pinion in the No. 13 notch on the scale.

Grain Drills and Seeders

CHART FOR DRILLING GRAIN IN POUNDS PER ACRE
FOR 10" FLUTED FEED DRILLS

N162687

NOTCHES ON SEED INDEX: 0 4 8 12 16 20 24 28 32 36 40 44 48 52 56 60

NOTCHES ON SEED INDEX	values (notch 0–28)	values (notch 32–60)
WHEAT	13 19 25 31 38 45 53 60 68 76 85 102	120 138 156 175 194 212
BARLEY	13 18 23 28 33 38 43 48 53 58 69	80 92 104 115 127 140 153
OATS OR SAFFLOWER	14 18 22 26 30 34 38 42 46 54	62 71 80 89 98 107 116 125
RYE	17 23 29 35 40 46 52 58 64 70 83	96 108 121 134 148 161 175
RICE—SHORT KERNEL	34 38 43 47 51 60	69 79 90 102 116
RICE—LONG KERNEL	28 32 36 40 44 52	60 69 79 90 102
PEAS	42 52 63 74 85 96 107 131	156 182 208 236 265 295 327
SOYBEANS OR NAVY BEANS	20 28 37 46 55 65 76 87 98 121	144 168 192 216 239 262 283 304
BUCKWHEAT	18 22 27 32 38 44 50 56 63 76	88 101 116
SORGHUM OR VETCH	12 17 22 28 34 40 47 54 61 68 76 91	
CRESTED WHEAT GRASS	6 8 10 11 13 15 17 19 21 25	
ALFALFA OR CANOLA	6 10 14 19 24 29 34 39	
MILLET	7 11 16 20 25 30 35 41	
FLAX OR SUDAN GRASS	9 14 18 23 28 33 38 43 48	

PLEASE CONSULT YOUR OPERATORS MANUAL FOR:

1. CHECKING QUANTITIES DRILLED
2. ADJUSTING FEED CUP GATES
3. METRIC CONVERSIONS
4. DRIVE SPROCKET AND GEAR CHANGES

IMPORTANT

CHARTS ARE ONLY A GUIDE. RATES ARE AFFECTED BY SEED SIZE AND QUALITY, WHEEL SLIPPAGE, TIRE TYPE AND AIR PRESSURE, ETC.

Grain seeding chart found inside the hopper lid of a modern grain drill.

Deere & Co.

Fertilizer Table, Pounds per Acre

From: International Harvester

number of notch	slow speed 7–inch	slow speed 8–inch	fast speed 7–inch	fast speed 8–inch
30	—	—	1,135	1,000
29	—	—	1,120	975
28	—	—	1,100	950
27	—	—	1,075	925
26	—	—	1,040	900
25	—	—	1,000	875
24	—	—	960	840
23	—	—	915	805
22	—	—	870	765
21	—	—	825	725
20	—	—	780	685
19	—	—	735	645
18	—	—	690	605
17	140	120	650	570
16	125	110	610	535
15	115	100	570	500
14	108	93	530	465
13	101	87	490	430
12	94	81	450	400
11	87	75	410	370
10	80	69	375	340
9	73	62	340	310
8	66	56	310	280
7	59	50	280	250
6	52	45	250	220
5	45	40	220	195
4	41	36	200	175
3	37	32	180	155
2	33	28	160	140
1	30	25	145	125

Planting and Cultivating Equiment

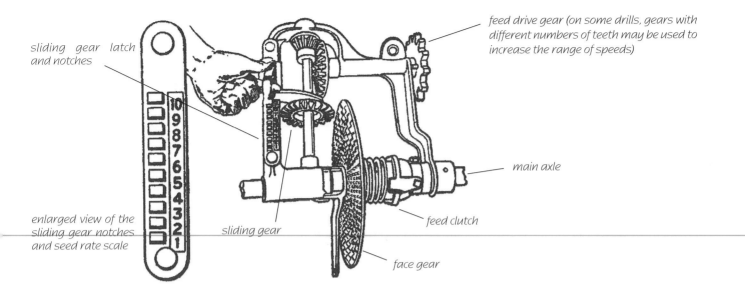

sliding gear latch and notches

feed drive gear (on some drills, gears with different numbers of teeth may be used to increase the range of speeds)

main axle

enlarged view of the sliding gear notches and seed rate scale

sliding gear

feed clutch

face gear

The feed rate on a double run drill is controlled by varying the speed at which the feed wheels turn in the seed cups, which is accomplished by moving a sliding pinion gear along a large face gear driven by the main axle. With the pinion at the outer edge of the face gear, the feed drive gear turns at a faster speed. When the pinion is near the center of the face gear, the feed gear turns slower and sows less seed. The sliding pinion may be locked into any of the numbered notches. The numbers correspond to the seeding rates listed in the grain sowing tables, and refer to the rows of teeth on the face gear, not quantity of seed—the face gear shown here has ten rows of teeth.

International Harvester

Fertilizer Drills

Fill the fertilizer hopper only in the field, to prevent packing and possible damage to the drive mechanism. Make sure the fertilizer drive is free by turning the square shaft with an adjustable wrench.

Most fertilizer drills have a chart inside the hopper lid, or in the operator's manual, to tell you how to set the regulating levers to obtain the desired application rate.

The quantity lever controls the size of the openings over the feed wheels; the speed lever controls the speed at which the feed wheels turn. Some drills use a face gear and sliding pinion to control the speed of the fertilizer feed, others use combination gears that may be shifted by a lever, or removed and placed in a different position.

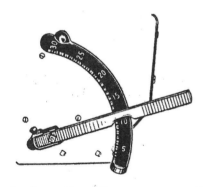

Quantity Lever

slow
out of gear
fast

slow speed

Speed Lever

slow
out of gear
fast

fast speed

Fertilizer drill regulating levers.

International Harvester

Grain Drills and Seeders

Field Operation

Most drills are equipped with a land measurer, or acre meter, to keep track of the number of acres covered by the drill. These measurers are mechanical devices driven from either the feed shaft or the main axle and should be reset to zero before a new field is started. Some acre meters are reset by pulling the spring loaded drive pinion away from the drive gear and then turning the pinion until the dial shows all zeros, or by loosening a wing nut and turning a pointer back to zero. Later versions are reset by turning a knob until all zeros are displayed.

The depth of seeding is controlled by the lifting levers on a hand lift drill, by a crank on power lift machines, or by the hydraulic control on machines equipped with hydraulic lift. Openers on grain drills are held to the preset depth of planting, regardless of undulations in the ground surface, by pressure springs. These springs, one for each opener, should be adjusted to all have the same amount of down pressure on each opener. Set scrapers on disc openers to just clear the disc surface.

Leave a headland, or turning strip at each end of the field. Lower the furrow openers at the inside edge of the headland and drive steadily and at an even speed across the field. When you reach the inside edge of the opposite headland, raise the furrow openers and turn the drill around, again dropping the furrow openers at the edge of the headland. To ensure that no ground is left unseeded, on each subsequent trip across the field drive so the inside wheel overlaps the previous wheel mark. Seed the headlands after the main part of the field has been planted. Do not turn the drill, or back up with the openers in the ground, or the seed boots will become clogged.

Thoroughly clean out the fertilizer hopper at the end of each day of use. Commercial fertilizers draw moisture and are quite corrosive, rapidly causing rust on any metal parts they contact. Never leave fertilizer in the hopper when the drill is not in use.

Lubricating a Drill

Grease all pressure fittings daily, with particular attention to the disc opener bearings. Wipe dirt from all grease fittings before greasing.

Before starting the drill after it has been idle for four hours or more, turn the feed shafts a few revolutions with an adjustable wrench. If the shafts stick or turn hard, squirt kerosene or diesel fuel on the drives and continue turning the shafts until they turn freely.

Cleaning and Storing a Drill

After each use of a grain drill, thoroughly clean the seed and fertilizer boxes. Detach the grain tubes, open the feed gates, and clear away any seeds or debris. Because of the corrosive action of fertilizer, take care to completely clean the fertilizer hopper and any related iron or steel parts. Thoroughly coat these cleaned parts with diesel fuel.

Remove and clean the grain, fertilizer, and grass seed tubes. If the tubes are made of steel, soak them in kerosene or diesel fuel to prevent rust. Most tubes today are made of rubber or plastic and should be washed out with soap and water and then stored inside the grain box..

Remove and clean feed shafts, gears and gear hangers, and any drive chains, check them for wear, and lubricate them before reassembling the drill. Clean and sharpen openers and coat them with heavy oil or grease to preserve their shine. Remove, clean, and oil the acre meter and its linkage. Make sure the power lift is cleaned and lubricated. Lubricate the entire machine, and replace any badly worn or damaged parts so the drill will be ready for use next season.

Store your cleaned and lubricated drill under cover. Never leave it outside in the weather.

No-Till Drills

Popular on many of today's farms are no–till, low–till, or minimum till practices, where little or no seedbed preparation precedes planting. Machines for planting seeds under these conditions are basically identical to earlier versions, with the exceptions of their row opening devices and their methods for covering seeds after planting. Seed, fertilizer, and grass seed hoppers are the same, and so are the feeding mechanisms, although virtually all modern drills use the fluted feed system. No-till drills are usually heavier than conventional drills to improve opener penetration in untilled soil.

Many parts, such as the fluted feed rolls and fertilizer star wheels, along with seed tubes, are made of up–to–date materials to provide more precise operation and fewer corrosion problems. Drive mechanisms have been improved by the use of high speed roller chains and modern materials. Speed change gear boxes and seed cup adjustment levers are easier to use and provide more accurate metering.

For true no-till planting use a straight single disc furrow opener to minimize soil distubance. In a minimum or low-till operation place a fluted coulter out in front of each furrow opener to cut through any trash, while loosening and stirring a narrow strip of soil. Behind the coulter is a double disc opener, usually with gauge wheels, that opens a trench in this narrow tilled strip. Tubes from the seed box, fertilizer hopper, and grass seed box, if provided, place their seed or fertilizer into the open trench in the angle between the two disc openers.

A small firming wheel may be provided to press the seed into the bottom of the trench. Bringing up the rear is a either pair of angled closing wheels or a single press wheel to cover and firm the soil over the seeds and fertilizer. A wide range of available fluted coulters and press wheels provide for different soil and trash conditions.

No–till drills are new enough that operator's manuals should be readily available. These manuals give detailed instructions on how to set up and operate the different machines. The operation and care of a no–till drill is exactly the same as for a conventional drill.

United Farm Tools' no–till grain drill, with fluted coulters in front. Note the right double disc furrow opener, with a press wheel behind it.

Broadcast Seeders

The *broadcast seeder* randomly drops or throws seeds onto the surface of the ground, where they are usually covered by harrowing. Broadcasting seeds is faster than drilling, and requires a less expensive machine, but has disadvantages. While a good broadcast seeder may distribute the seed evenly, the covering process with a harrow or cultivator results in some seeds being buried too deep and others being too shallow or not covered at all. Windy weather interferes with the even broadcasting of seed. In dry soil, broadcast seeding isn't as effective as drilling.

Hand Seeders

Hand seeders are of two styles, sack seeder and wheelbarrow. The *sack seeder* has a canvas bag holding two or three pecks of seed that is slung from the operator's shoulders so the machine is at the front or side of the body. Seed is fed through an adjustable valve in the bottom of the sack, and falls onto a star wheel or distributer that is rotated at high speed by gearing from a hand crank. Vertical ribs on the star wheel throw out the seed in an 8– to 36–foot circle as the operator walks steadily across the field. The quantity of seed thrown is regulated by the sliding valve and speed of cranking. The operator should walk at a steady pace and turn the crank at an even speed. Don't attempt to seed on a windy day.

A wheelbarrow seeder has a long seedbox across the handles, in place of the barrow box, and seed is dropped through holes along the bottom of the seedbox. The holes have an adjustable baffle that varies the opening size and regulates the amount of seed distributed. The wheelbarrow wheel drives a lengthwise vibrating device just above the holes in the box to keep the seed moving. Wheelbarrow seeders are usually from 12– to 16–feet wide. The wheelbarrow seeder is pushed steadily across the field, making sure the end drops seed next to the last pass so all the ground is covered.

With both styles of seeder a certain amount of experimentation is necessary to achieve the desired application rate. Lubricate gears and clean out a seeder after each use.

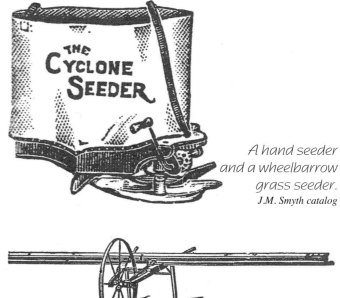

A hand seeder and a wheelbarrow grass seeder.
J.M. Smyth catalog

Endgate Seeders

The *endgate seeder* is mounted on the rear of a wagon or cart. The seeder consists of a seed hopper, under which is one or two star wheels or rotating distributers that receive rotary motion through a chain driven by one of the wagon or cart wheels. The seeder either clamps onto the wagon endgate or is mounted on a board that replaces the endgate.

The seed valve may be regulated to sow any desired quantity of seed. Some seeders may be set to half cast the seed to either the right or left of the wagon for sowing along fencerows or the edge of a field. Most seeders have a ratchet clutch on the drive shaft that allows the wagon to be backed without harming the distributing mechanism. The seed's weight determines the width of distribution. Average widths are 25 feet for clover, 40 feet for oats, and 50 feet for wheat. Some endgate spreaders may be used to also spread lime, salt, or fertilizer.

Seed is carried in the bed of the wagon or cart and is scooped into the hopper if loose, or dumped if in bags. Experimentation will reveal how to set the seed valve to achieve the desired rate of application. The team must be driven at a steady pace so all the ground is evenly covered with seed. The half cast feature, if provided, may be used when seeding along the edge of a field to avoid wasting seed by throwing it into the fence row.

Choose a calm day for seeding; because of the height of the seeder above the ground, wind has a great influence on

Oats being sown with a wheeled ground driven spreader built by Mullet's Repair Shop.

even seed distribution. Keep chains and gears lubricated and make sure the ratchet clutch is operating correctly. Clean out the seeder after use, taking special care if the machine has been used to spread fertilizer, salt, or lime.

Modern Broadcast Seeders

Modern seeders, or spreaders, may be used for broadcasting seed and spreading lime, fertilizer, and most granular chemicals. They are either 3–point hitch or mounted on wheels. A wheeled spreader may be ground or PTO driven, or have its own small gas engine, while 3–point hitch models are PTO or electrically driven.

A typical spreader consists of a cone–shaped steel or poly hopper with an adjustable feeding device and a distributing wheel. The spreading pattern may be regulated from right to left, or full width,. Spreading widths vary from 20 to 50 feet, depending on material and spreading pattern. Application rates are varied by adjusting the feed gate according to a feed chart usually found on the outside of the hopper. Hopper sizes vary from about 500 pounds to one–half ton.

The hopper is filled and the feed gate lever is set for the desired application rate. The spreader is then driven across the field at a steady pace and in a manner that covers all the ground with seed. Keep PTO shafts lubricated and gear boxes filled with oil. Clean out the spreader after each use.

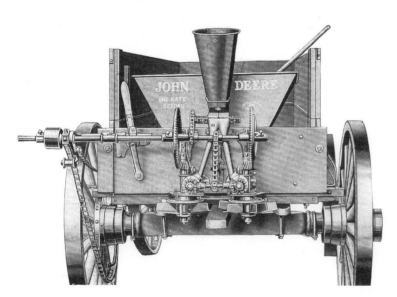

An endgate seeder attached to a wagon.   *Deere & Co.*

Planting and Cultivating Equiment

Some teamsters like to sit on the seed box; others prefer to walk behind or beside the drill; still others ride on the optional foot board.

Photos by Ruth Freeman (top)

Michael Lacivita (right)

Bonnie Nance (bottom)

Grain Drills and Seeders

6

Corn Planters

When the first European settlers arrived in America, they found Native Americans growing a plant called maize. The seeds of this wonderful plant could be pounded into meal, roasted, popped, parched, or boiled and could be made into bread, pudding, hominy cakes, and whiskey. It could be fed to animals and turned into hams, steaks, and drumsticks. Because of its food value, and because it out yields just about any other grain, maize— now known as corn— became America's foremost crop.

Native Americans planted, cultivated, and harvested their corn by hand. Their laborious methods were still in use at the middle of the 19th century, severely limiting the number of acres a farmer could plant to corn. Several Midwestern farmers experimented with corn planting machines during the 1850s. George Brown of Galesburg, Illinois, is credited with developing the rotary seed plate, the shoe furrow opener, and the lever drop method of regulating when seeds were released into the furrow. Later improvements included a row marker and an automatic checking device. By the end of the Civil War, successful horse–drawn corn planters were available.

Most corn planted today is *drilled,* meaning a continuous flow of seed is delivered to each seed tube, which drops it into a furrow made by the row opener. The spacing of seeds in the furrow is accomplished by using different seed plates or discs, along with changing the speed of the planting mechanism.

Before the days of chemical weed control, much corn was planted in hills of two, three, or four seeds. The hills were spaced to allow cross cultivation, a method called *check–row* planting, because each hill is set precisely at the intersection of imaginary parallel lines drawn across the field in both directions, like the lines on a checkerboard.

A third method is the *hill–drop,* which deposits groups of seeds at regularly spaced intervals along the row. Although this method is similar to the check–row method, it makes no effort to maintain a checked pattern, and cross cultivation isn't possible.

Both check–row and hill–drop planting have fallen out of favor with corn farmers because of their relative slowness, along with the fact that drilled corn allows an even flow of individual stalks into the harvesting machine without the shock that occurs each time a hill of several stalks hits the mechanism at the same time. Most corn planters sold during the check–row era could be set to operate in check–row, hill–drop, or drill mode.

A Pequea 3–row corn planter with a 12–volt hydraulic pump (the round black object just above and behind the forecart seat) for raising and lowering the planting units.

Features of a Corn Planter

Corn planters come in many sizes and styles, ranging from a single–row, walk–behind drill type, through trailed two–, four–, and six–row check–row machines, to today's huge 12– and 16–row pull type planters. Some planters are made to be mounted on a 3–point hitch.

A trailed corn planter consists of a frame supported by two or more wheels that serve to transport the machine, while providing a ground drive for the planting mechanism. The wheels on some planters also cover the seeds and firm the soil, while others have separate closing wheels. On the frame are mounted a seed can, or hopper, along with a furrow opener and closing device for each row. In each seed can is a rotating seed plate consisting of

Planting and Cultivating Equipment

a disc that meters the amount of seed and drops it into the seed tube. Most planters have a hopper and a distributing mechanism for fertilizer, as well as a way to mark a path for the next row or rows.

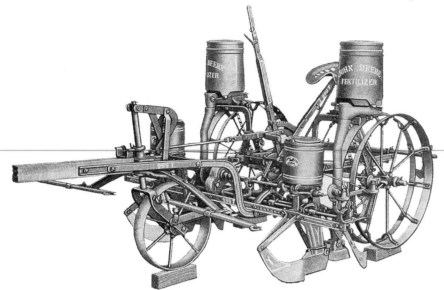

A horse–drawn two–row, check–row corn planter equipped with a fertilizer attachment and a caster–type tongue truck. Deere & Co.

Seed Plates

Corn planters built from about 1880 to 1970 have a horizontal revolving seed plate in the bottom of each seed can. The seed plate has a series of notches, or seed cells, around its outer circumference that pick up and count out the desired number of seeds per drop. These cells pass under a brush or a knocker that discharges the seed into a seed tube. The bottom of the seed hopper is shaped to channel the seeds into the cells of the seed plate as it is rotated by the drive mechanism. Some seed plates are called *full hill–drop,* and each cell or notch in the plate is sized to catch and drop the exact number of seeds desired in each hill.

A more common, as well as more accurate, method for planting in hills is the *cumulative drop,* where each cell picks up only one seed, but the seed plate has moved far enough each time a valve at the top of the seed tube opens to drop the desired number of seeds onto that valve. When the valve is then opened by the check wire or a mechanical trip, all the seeds necessary for a hill are dropped into the furrow at once. The distance moved by the plate between drops is usually controlled by a foot lever that has positions for dropping two, three, or four seeds per hill. During drilling the valves are locked open. A drill–only machine

has no valves; the cells drop a seed at regular intervals, as controlled by the seed cell spacing and the speed of the planter drive shaft.

Seed plate selection is one of the most important steps in achieving accurate seed placement. The seed should fit the cells in the plate. Seed plates are available for seed of any size from tiny celery seeds to lima beans. Seed corn dealers offer a full range of plates for handling the various strains of hybrid corn.

On most planters the hopper bottom plate, or a filler ring beneath the seed plate, is reversible. One side is flat and the opposite side has a circular groove right under the cells of the seed plate. If you use edge drop plates, the groove gives the cells extra depth to handle extra wide seeds. Edge drop plates are recommended for seeds that are relatively flat and generally of uniform size. On most planters the seed hoppers are hinged at the front and held at the rear by a wing nut. By loosening the wing nut, you can tip the whole hopper forward for easy access to the seed plate and easy cleaning of the container.

The number of cells on a plate, combined with the sprocket size on the drive chain, allow you to drill seeds almost any distance apart. Most planters have drive sprockets of two or three different sizes on the axle, as well as different driven sprockets on the planter drive shaft. Different drilling distances are attained by moving the drive chain to various combinations of drive and driven sprockets, as listed in a table usually included in the operator's manual issued by the manufacturer.

Examples: If you wish to plant corn 6½ inches apart in 40–inch rows, go down the drilling distance column to 6.5 on the accompanying table. Reading back, you find that the drive chain should be on the 13–tooth sprocket on the axle, and the 9–tooth sprocket on the planter drive shaft. With a 20–cell seed plate and a planting speed of 3.5 miles per hour, the planter should drop a seed kernel every 6½ inches. If you wish to plant 11½ pounds of sorghum per acre in 40–inch rows using a 108950 plate, the chain should be on the 13–tooth drive sprocket and the 6–tooth driven sprocket.

planting speed miles per hour	axle drive sprocket number of teeth	seed shaft sprocket number of teeth	planter travel per seed plate revolution inches	corn plate as required (20 cells) drilling distance, 9 inches	plate 108950 (40 cells)	sorghum plate 108951 (40 cells) pounds	plate 129912 (20 cells) per acre	plate 108953 (24 cells) in 40"	soy beans plate 121299 (24 cells)	navy beans plate 108958 (42 cells)
							pounds per acre in 40" rows			
2.5	13	6	87	4.4	11.5	21.3	5.0	54	111	36
3.5	13	9	130	6.5	7.7	14.2	3.4	37	77	24
4.0	8	6	141	7.1	7.1	13.1	3.1	34	72	22
4.5	7	6	162	8.1	6.2	11.4	2.7	30	63	19
5.0	13	12	174	8.7	5.8	10.6	2.5	28	59	18
6.0	6	9	212	10.6	5.8	8.7	2.0	23	49	15
7.0	7	9	242	12.1	5.2	7.6	1.8	20	43	13
7.0	8	12	282	14.2	3.6	6.8	1.5	17	37	11
7.0	7	12	324	16.2	3.1	5.7	1.4	15	33	10

From: Tractor and Implement Operations, Ford Motor Company

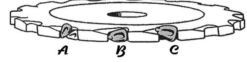

Edge–drop seed plate. Each seed should fit into a cell, as shown at B. The seeds at A and C fit imperfectly and will cause missed drops.

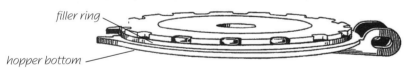

Flat–drop seed plate. Each seed should lay flat in its own cell. This plate is thinner than an edge–drop plate and requires a filler ring underneath.

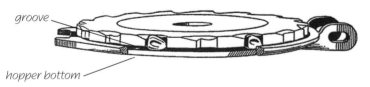

With an edge–drop plate, a grooved hopper bottom plate may be substituted for the regular plate to increase cell depth for extra wide seeds.

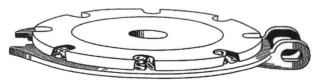

Whole–hill drop plate. Each seed cell is large enough to hold all the seeds needed for one hill.

International Harvester

Air and Vacuum Metering Systems

Modern planters no longer use the seed plate system of measuring the amount of seeds dropped down the tubes. A vertical seed disc, usually made of stainless steel and with rows of precisely shaped and sized seed cells, rotates inside a reservoir in each row unit. As each seed from the hopper enters the reservoir, it is gently held in one of the cells by vacuum or air pressure.

Once the seed is positioned above the seed delivery tube, the vacuum or air is cut off and a brush or ejector block ensures that the seed is dropped down the tube and into the furrow. The pumps to create the vacuum or air pressure are run by a hydraulic motor, PTO, or a small engine mounted on the planter. Due to the complexity of these metering systems, consult the operator's manual for your particular implement.

Planting and Cultivating Equipment

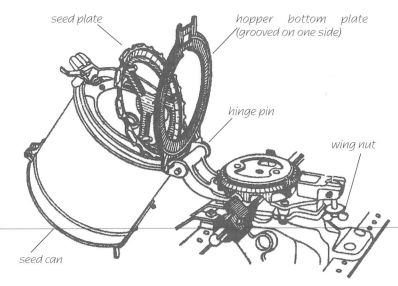

seed plate

hopper bottom plate
(grooved on one side)

hinge pin

wing nut

seed can

To change seed plates, loosen the wing nut, swing the locking bolt out of the way, and tilt the seed hopper forward. Pull out the hinge pin to reverse a reversible hopper bottom plate; place the grooved side up to enlarge the seed cell and accommodate wide seeds.   Oliver Farm Equipment Co.

Monosem two–row vacuum planter with a small gasoline engine mounted on the machine to drive the vacuum pump.

Fertilizer Attachments

Modern planters have optional liquid fertilizer attachments, as well as attachments for applying herbicides and insecticides. Most corn planters may be equipped with attachments to apply granular fertilizer at the time of planting. These attachments consist of tin or fiberglass hoppers, a feed mechanism, and flexible tubes to convey the fertilizer to the ground, where it is usually deposited in narrow bands on each side of the row of seeds.

On most planters a variable gate–type valve controls the rate of fertilizer application. The rate of flow through the valve varies with the type and condition of the fertilizer, so the control levers are usually not calibrated in pounds, but with reference numbers or marks only. The highest reference number or mark indicates the largest valve opening and the greatest rate of application. Some valves are adjusted by loosening and tightening screws with nuts or hand wheels. Sometimes different combinations of drive sprockets are used to control application rates. If you don't have an operator's manual, examine the base of the fertilizer hopper to determine how the adjustment is made.

Fertilizer application rates are usually expressed in pounds per acre. Adjustment for the desired rate is best attained by trial and error. Here's a useful way to calculate the fertilizer application rate before entering the field, based on a planter with 30–inch diameter drive wheels planting rows 40 inches apart: Jack up the planter and fill one fertilizer hopper. Rotate a drive wheel through 17 revolutions and catch and weigh the fertilizer delivered through the tube. Multiply this weight by 100 to determine the approximate number of pounds of fertilizer the planter will put down per acre for 40–inch rows. Adjust the valve and retest until you obtain the desired application rate. Different wheel diameters and row widths will give different results.

Pequea Planter's two–row corn planter with disc markers and a 12–volt hydraulic pump for raising the planting units out of the ground. The large hopper in front is for granular fertilizer, the smaller hoppers behind it are for seed and insecticide or herbicide.

Row Markers

To keep rows parallel and an equal distance apart, most planters are equipped with row markers consisting of an arm made of pipe, box section, or rod hinged to each side of the machine. The arm is usually telescoping to allow adjustment for different row widths. A hoe, shovel, or disc at the outer end of the arm digs a small furrow to indicate the proper location for the center of the planter during the next round. Before starting to plant, adjust the arm length so the disc or shovel falls exactly in the center of the next row.

At the end of each row, the marker is raised either by hand or automatically. After turning the machine, lower the marker toward the unplanted ground and drive the planter directly over the furrow the marker made on the previous trip.

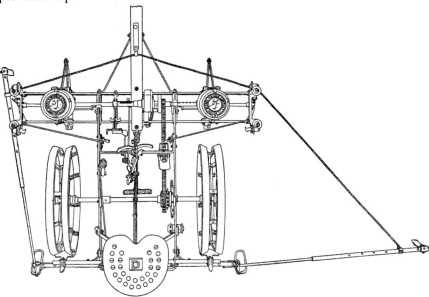

Overhead view of a corn planter with the right hoe–type marker extended.

Deere & Co.

Tongue Trucks

The caster–type tongue truck found on some horse–drawn corn planters has several advantages:

- It does away with any neck weight on the horses.
- It eliminates the planter's up and down movement when going over ridges or hollows, thus assuring a more even planting depth and better coverage of seed.
- It ensures a better job of check rowing, due to the elimination of pole whip and reduction of side slip on hills

Hitching and Draft

Hitch your team so the seed hoppers and planting mechanism are as level as possible while in operation.

Keep the neck yoke straps fairly short to facilitate straight driving. The draft of a two–row planter varies from 200 to 250 pounds—a light load for two horses.

Operation and Care

At the beginning of the season, clean your planter thoroughly, making sure nothing obstructs the feed tubes or valves. Wipe seed plates and fertilizer hopper bottoms dry of oil. Check and tighten all nuts and bolts. Grease and oil the planter.

When planting in wet or sticky soils, keep a close watch to see that the seed boots don't clog with mud. While planting, frequently inspect the boots and the dropping mechanism to ensure proper operation.

Lubricate the planter daily, but don't over lubricate the seed hopper bases, as excess grease and oil will collect dirt and may interfere with operation. Check the oil level in the gearbox. Make sure all bolts are tight and no parts are bent, broken, or worn out.

At the end of each season, replace any worn or broken parts. Clean out the seed and fertilizer hoppers, the spouts, and the boots. Lubricate the planter and coat the drive chains, feed plates, hopper bottoms, and openers with oil.

Check-Row Planters

Check rowing is a method of planting where each hill of three or four seeds is exactly the same distance from each adjoining hill. A field of check–row planted corn has the appearance of a checkerboard, with a hill of corn stalks at every point where the lines intersect. This method lets you cross cultivate the plants, which makes keeping a field free of weeds much easier.

Check–rowed corn is rarely seen today, having fallen out of favor with the advent of chemical weed control. Another deterrent is the huge amount of time planting requires. H.V. Hansen, in a 1944 article in *Agricultural Engineering*, wrote that approximately 50 percent of the time taken to plant a field with short rows of 20 rods was used up in handling the check wire and stakes. Even with long rows of 160 rods, 10 to 20 percent of planting time was consumed by laying out, moving, and picking up wire.

Planting and Cultivating Equipment

A two–row lever–drop corn planter from the 1870s. The ground was first marked with parallel lines by dragging a wooden marker across the field. The planter was then driven across the field at right angles to the marked lines. A second person, often a small boy, sat on the round seat and each time the planting shoes crossed one of the pre–marked lines in the dirt, he operated the wooden lever beside his seat. The lever released a hill of seeds from each seed box, which fell into the furrow created by the runner openers. The wide wheel rims covered and firmed soil over the seeds. Careful marking, and an attentive boy on the planter, resulted in an accurate check–row pattern.

Features of a Check-Row Planter

The check–row planter has a seed box or can for each row, with a revolving seed plate in the bottom of each box. The seed plate has a series of notches or cells around its circumference that pick up and count out the desired number of seeds per hill. These cells pass under a brush or a knocker that discharges the seed into a seed tube. Some planters use the full–hill drop method, but most use the more accurate cumulative drop method.

The distance moved by the plate between drops is usually controlled by a foot lever that has positions for dropping two, three, or four seeds per hill. In both full–hill and cumulative drop methods, the group of seeds falls onto a valve at the top of the seed tube. A second valve at the bottom of the seed tube works in conjunction with the upper valve, and both momentarily open each time a knot in the check wire trips the mechanism. The group of seeds on the bottom valve is deposited directly into the furrow, while the group above begins its journey down the tube where it is caught by the now closed bottom valve to await the next check wire trip.

Checking Head

At each side of the planter is a *checking head* consisting of two pairs of rollers and a checking fork. The rollers hold and guide the check wire as it slides through the checking fork. Each time a wire button reaches the fork, it forces the fork to the rear before sliding past the open end of the fork which then returns to its upright position.

Each time the fork is moved to the rear by a button, it opens the upper and lower valves in the seed tubes, and

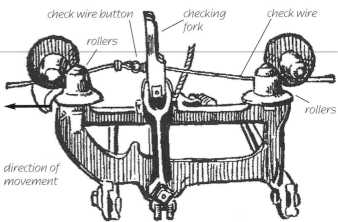

As the planter moves forward, the checking fork comes into contact with a wire button.

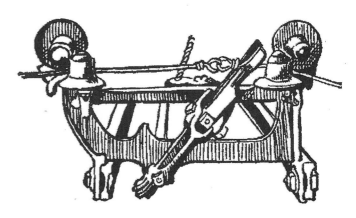

As the planter continues to move, the wire button forces the checking fork to the right, opening the valves and engaging the seed plate drive mechanism. The button then slips past the fork, which resets.

The check head is operated with a rope or a foot pedal that releases the check wire from the check head as the planter approaches the stake at the end of a row. Some planters release the wire automatically when the planting mechanism is raised at the row end.

Farm Machinery by Archie A. Stone

engages the clutch on the feed drive shaft (on some planters the feed shaft operates all the time). With both valves open, the seeds on the lower valve drop into the furrow, the seeds on the upper valve drop onto the lower valve, and the seed plates turn, measuring out the proper number of kernels onto the upper valve.

The valves may be locked open, allowing the planter to be used as a drill to plant a row of seeds at regular intervals, as spaced by the seed plate and the variable speed drive gears. Some planters may be set to power drop hills of several seeds at a time. The number of seeds per hill, as well as the distance between hills, is regulated by the foot lever, the seed plates, and the drive speed. No check wire is required in either drill or hill drop planting.

Wire Reel

Some planters carry the check wire reel under the seat at the center of the machine, others use a side reel that may be mounted on either side of the planter. Center mount reels are usually chain driven from the main axle and have a friction clutch so the tension for laying out the wire may be adjusted. Most reels also have an oscillating wire guide the operator manipulates to distribute the wire evenly on the reel when

it's being picked up. Side mount reels are driven by friction from the planter wheel and have a tensioning device for unwinding. Side reels are narrower than their rear mount counterparts and require no oscillating guide. Side mount reels should be removed while planting, but center mount reels may be left in place.

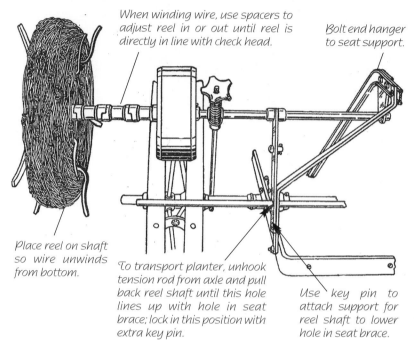

When winding wire, use spacers to adjust reel in or out until reel is directly in line with check head.

Bolt end hanger to seat support.

Place reel on shaft so wire unwinds from bottom.

To transport planter, unhook tension rod from axle and pull back reel shaft until this hole lines up with hole in seat brace; lock in this position with extra key pin.

Use key pin to attach support for reel shaft to lower hole in seat brace.

Side Mounted Check Wire Reel.

Oliver Farm Equipment Co.

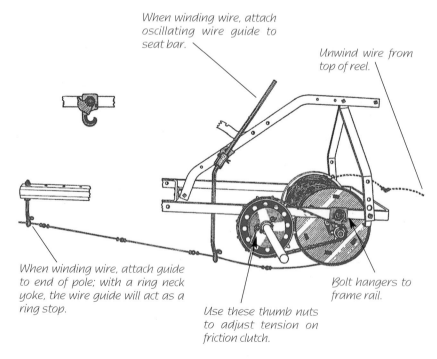

When winding wire, attach oscillating wire guide to seat bar.

Unwind wire from top of reel.

When winding wire, attach guide to end of pole; with a ring neck yoke, the wire guide will act as a ring stop.

Use these thumb nuts to adjust tension on friction clutch.

Bolt hangers to frame rail.

.Center Mounted Check Wire Reel.

Oliver Farm Equipment Co.

Successful Checking

Check wire is furnished in lengths of 80 rods, or one–quarter mile, because this length was common for a typical 40–acre field in the corn belt. Buttons are spaced along the wire at varying distances, depending on the desired row spacing. Typically 42–inch row spacing is used, although wire for any spacing from 30 to 48 inches was once available, but may be difficult to locate today.

Check wire needs to be broken at the edge of a field, or passed around a tree or other obstruction in the field, so every five or six rods a special button is placed so the wire may be easily taken apart and reconnected.

In operation the check wire is stretched across the field and anchored to a stake at each end. As the planter is driven forward, the wire slides through a fork that trips and opens the upper and lower valves each time a button catches the fork.

Planting and Cultivating Equipment

During use the check wire travels, meaning the buttons on the wire are a little farther north when the planter is traveling north than they are when the machine is moving south. If the planter was designed to drop the hills directly opposite the buttons, the hills across adjacent pairs of rows would be as far out of check as the travel of the wire. From experience, manufacturers determined that an 80–rod length of wire at the average tension setting travels about 3 inches. Check–row planters are therefore designed to drop the hill one and one half inches, or one half of the wire travel, behind the button. Consequently, half of the wire travel is offset by the planter when it moves one direction, and the other half on the return trip, resulting in a perfect check pattern, especially in the center of the field.

The length of the wire has a direct bearing on how much it travels; 40 rods of wire may travel only about 2 inches, while a 140–rod length may move 4 or 5 inches. The tautness of the check wire influences the amount of travel as well. The tighter the wire is pulled when the stakes are set, the less the wire will travel, so it's important to tighten the wire to the same tension each time you set a stake. When planting up and down a slope, however, pull the wire a little tighter at the upper stake than at the lower stake. By understanding and practicing these principles, you can easily adjust the planter to achieve a perfect check.

Laying out Wire

A poorly checked field can't be hidden. From the time the corn plants break through the ground until well into July, the field is a public demonstration of how much care was taken in laying out the wire and adjusting the planter. Here are the steps for planting a nicely checked field:

Step 1. In laying out wire, drive the planter to the edge of the field and place it in position to drive across the field where the first two rows are to be planted. Take the end of the wire from the reel's underside (some makes of planter feed from the top). Hook the wire on an anchor stake, leaving a few extra links back of the hook, then set the anchor stake to the rear of the planter in line with the outside check head, the one nearest the edge of the field.

Adjust the spring tension on the reel so it has just enough resistance to straighten out the kinks as the wire is being unwound. Now drive carefully straight across the field without lowering the planting mechanism, so the wheel marks may be used for a guide on the return trip when the first two rows are planted. At the far end of the field, uncouple the wire or remove the wire reel, leaving enough wire to reach the edge plus a few extra links, and turn the planter into position for planting the first two rows.

Step 2. Drive the planter far enough into the field to allow for about four buttons of wire between the rear of the planter and the edge of the field. These four buttons allow enough space at the headland to conveniently turn the rig and later drill four rows across the headland. Hook the wire

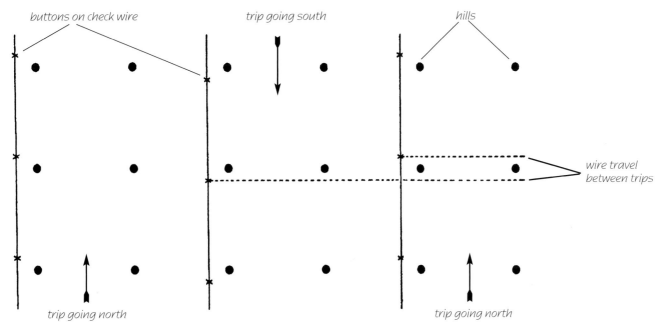

To compensate for check wire travel, drop the hills behind the buttons a distance equal to one half of the wire travel.

The Tractor Field Book, 1931

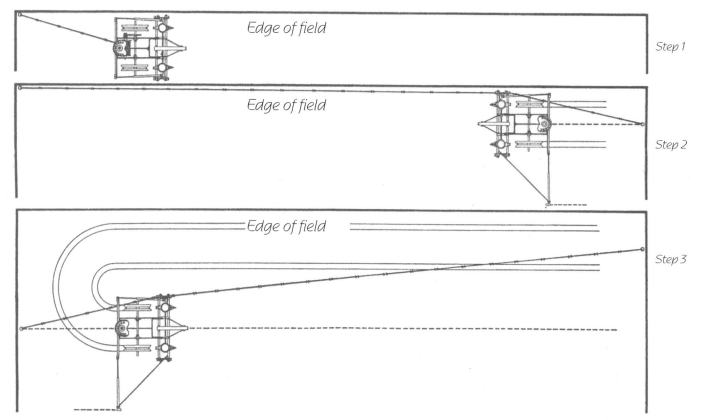

Steps in laying out check wire and beginning to plant.

Oliver Farm Equipment Co.

on another anchor stake, pull it fairly tight, and set the stake at the field edge directly behind the exact center of the planter.

Lower the row marker on the side toward the field, taking care to properly adjust it to conform to the width of the rows being planted. Place the check wire through the fork and pulleys and close the pulley holder. Set the lifting lever to allow the openers to go into the ground the desired depth and drive at a steady gait to the opposite end of the field, using the wheel marks as a guide.

Plant no closer to the end of a row than about four buttons before tripping the pulley holder and releasing the wire. This method not only relieves unnecessary strain on the wire, but leaves room for later drilling back and forth once along the edge to finish out the field. When the check head is about four buttons from the end of the row, release the wire and raise the planter and marker.

Step 3. Turn the team into position for starting the next row and stop at the edge of the headland with the planter tongue exactly over the furrow left by the row marker. Pull the anchor stake and move it until you are standing directly behind the check head. Pull on the wire and throw it toward the planter with an upward, circular, whipping motion, moving at least 50 buttons.

Thread the wire through the fork and pulleys and close the holder. Take up any slack and set the stake at the edge of the field, directly behind the center of the planter, making sure to maintain the correct tension. Lower the openers into the ground, lower the marker toward the unplanted side, and drive back across the field, keeping the planter tongue directly over the furrow made by the marker on the previous trip.

Continue this procedure back and forth until the field is planted. Then drill the headland rows.

If the field has a tree or other obstruction, handle it in the following way: Plant to the tree, then walk to the far end of the field and pull the stake to slacken the wire. Walk back to the planter, disconnect the wire at a convenient button, pull the two ends to the opposite side of the tree and rejoin the wire. Walk back to the end of the field, reset the stake in its hole and adjust the tension. Drive the team around the tree, put the wire back into the trip forks and resume planting.

Setting Anchor Stakes

Each time you set the anchor stakes, take care to maintain a uniform tension on the wire. Most anchor stakes are equipped with a ratchet and lever tensioning mechanism to

Planting and Cultivating Equipment

help achieve uniform tension. Each time you set a stake, make sure it is the same distance from the last hill planted. Stretch a line across the ends of the field and set a stake to the line each time you move it.

Securing a Good Check

To be sure of a good check, after planting a few rows across the field dig up at least eight hills, across rows, out some distance from the end of the field to see whether or not they are in check. In an average length field of 60 to 80 rods, you can attain a perfect check by carrying the planter's front frame level while the openers are in the ground in operating position. The hill will be deposited about 1½ inches behind the button on the check wire.

Should the hills show out of check, the distance of the out of check offset is twice the amount of adjustment required of the furrow opener heel to correct the error. For example, if the hills are 2 inches out of check, an adjustment of one inch of the heels will bring the rows into line. This adjustment is made on most horse–drawn planters by raising or lowering the front of the frame in relation to the pole, which changes the location of the furrow opener heel, or the spot where the seed is deposited, in relation to the check lever. On some planters the check lever mechanism itself may be adjusted forward or backward to accomplish the same thing.

To determine the planter's accuracy, dig up six or eight crossrows. Carefully uncover the corn to find the exact location of the kernels and sight along the uncovered hills to see the cross check.

If you find the seeds are dropped too soon, or too far before the check line, throw the heels of the openers forward by raising the front of the planter with the tongue adjustment. The seeds will then be carried a little farther before they are dropped. If the check head is adjustable, move it back a notch to cause the seed to be dropped a little later.

If the seeds are carried too far before dropping, or past the check line, throw the heels of the openers to the rear by lowering the front of the planter, or by moving the check head forward, thus dropping the seeds a little sooner.

These corrections, if not too great, may also be made by slightly raising or lowering the end of the pole with the breast straps. Do not rely solely on the breast strap method to secure an accurate check. Lengthening the straps too much may result in pole whipping. Adjust the planter for a good check, then adjust the breast straps to facilitate straight driving and keep the seed hoppers level.

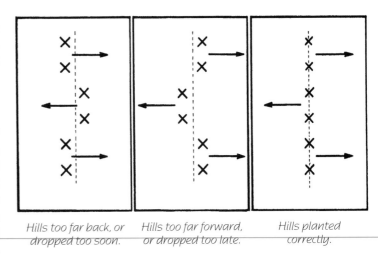

Hills too far back, or dropped too soon. *Hills too far forward, or dropped too late.* *Hills planted correctly.*

Determining Planter Accuracy.

Taking up Wire

With most planters, the wire may be wound on the reel as the last rows are planted. Place the reel attachment on the planter, thread the wire through the guide, and hook it to rewind from the front and over top of reel (on some planters the wire rewinds from the bottom of the reel). Adjust the reel tension so the wire will be kept tight in front of the reel when you drive across the field toward the anchor stake. Use the shifter, or oscillating wire guide, to distribute the wire evenly on the reel.

Finishing the Field

After you have planted all the checked rows and taken up the check wire, set the planter for drilling and plant back and forth once on each headland to finish up the field.

Drill Planters

Most check–row planters may be set to operate as drills, while many planters are drill–only machines. Different makes of check–row planters use different methods of setting to drill only. In all cases the valves are locked open and, of course, no check wire is required. The seed plates rotate continually, and each cell drops its seed directly through the tube and into the ground. Almost all corn planters in use today are drill machines.

The distance between seeds in a row is regulated by the number of cells on each seed plate, along with the selection of drive sprocket sizes to vary the speed of the feeder drive. Most horse–drawn planters use a combination of three different sized sprockets on the drive axle and the foot lever positions of two, three, or four to vary the drilling distance. Refer to the chart for the correct setting. If this chart isn't available, raise the furrow openers to their highest position and drive the planter across hard ground. Measure the distance between the seeds left behind, experimenting with different settings until you achieve the desired distance.

Modern vacuum and air planters rely on multiple gear boxes to give the different speeds required for varying seed spacing and population. Seed discs with cells of different sizes and shapes are available to plant most any size seed, from small sugar beets to large peanuts. They may, in addition, be equipped with an optional electronic monitor that keeps track of seed spacing and population, as well as row failures, ground speed, acreage, and a host of other functions on a display screen at the operator's station.

A good plan is to first plant one round at each end of the field to allow room for turning and to mark the point for raising and lowering the planter. Lower the row marker on the side toward the field, taking care to adjust it properly to conform to the width of the rows being planted. Lower the planter into the ground at the inside row planted earlier at each end, and set the lifting lever to allow the openers to run at the desired depth. Drive straight and at a steady gait to the opposite end of the field. Raise the planter and marker as you reach the inside end row and turn so the center of the planter is exactly over the marker furrow. Lower the planter and outside marker and drive straight across the field, keeping the planter tongue centered on the marker furrow.

Typical Drilling Distances
approximate drilling distances in inches

seed plate	shifting lever setting	low wheel				high wheel			
		large sprocket	medium sprocket	small sprocket	divided sprocket	large sprocket	medium sprocket	small sprocket	divided sprocket
2-cell	2	116	166	208	89	110	202	258	89
	3	77	112	139	59	73	135	172	59
	4	58	83	104	44.5	55	101	129	44.5
3-cell	2	77.5	111	139	59.5	73.5	135	172	59.5
	3	51.5	75	93	39.5	49	90	115	39.5
	4	39	55.5	69.5	30	37	67.5	86	30
4-cell	2	58	83	104	44.5	55	101	129	44.5
	3	38.5	56	69.5	29.5	36.5	67.5	86	29.5
	4	29	41.5	52	22	27.5	50.5	64.5	22
5-cell	2	46	66	83	35	44	81	103	35.5
	3	31	45	55.5	23.5	29	54	69	23.5
	4	23	33	41.5	17.5	22	40	51.5	18
6-cell	2	39	55.5	69.5	30	37	67.5	86	30
	3	26	37.5	46.5	20	24.5	45	57.5	20
	4	19.5	28	35	15	18.5	34	43	15
8-cell	2	29	41.5	52	22	27.5	50.5	64.5	23
	3	19	28	34.5	15	18	33.5	43	15
	4	14.5	20.5	26	11	13.5	25	32	11.5
12-cell	2	19.5	28	35	15	18.5	34	43	15
	3	13	19	23	10	12	22.5	28.5	10
	4	10	14	18	7.5	9	17	21.5	7.5
16-cell	2	14.5	21	26	11	13.5	25	32	11
	3	9.5	14	17	7.5	9	17	21.5	7.5
	4	7	10.5	13	5.5	7	12.5	16	5.5
20-cell	2	11.5	16.5	20.5	8.5	11	20	26	9
	3	7.5	11	14	5.5	7.5	12.5	17	6.5
	4	5.5	8.5	10.5	4	5.5	10	13	4.5
24-cell	2	9.5	14	17.5	7.5	9	17	21.5	7.5
	3	6.5	9	11.5	5	6	11	14.5	5
	4	4.5	7	8.5	3.5	4.5	8.5	10.5	3.5

To use a table such as this one, first decide how far apart in the row to plant your corn kernels. If you wish plant 7 inches apart with a low wheel planter, you can use a 16-cell seed plate with the chain on the large sprocket and the foot shifting lever set on 4. You can also use a 24 cell plate with the chain on the medium sprocket; the seeds will be closer together in the plate, but the plate will turn slower and dropped every 7 inches.

From: Deere & Co.

Planting and Cultivating Equipment

A Pequea 3—row corn planter, equipped with a liquid fertilizer tank, planting in sod. This machine uses John Deere planting units with gauge wheels, V—closing wheels, and wavy coulters that create a narrow seed bed for each row.

Common Planter Troubles

To avoid many planting problems, regularly and frequently inspect the dropping mechanism while planting to see that everything is operating correctly. It's annoying to finish up a field, only to discover one of the openers is clogged with soil and you have no way of knowing how long that particular row hasn't been planted. The problem becomes quite evident after the corn comes up, with one missed row after another. The most common planter problems are:

Inconsistent drop.
- Poorly graded corn of many different sizes—a problem not seen often with today's commercial seed corn.
- Wrong seed plate or disc. Make sure the cells in the plate or disc are the correct size for the seed you are planting.
- Seed brushes or knockers not working properly. Replace or readjust brushes or knockers as required.
- Plugged opener outlet, due to too—wet soil or having backed up the planter with the openers in the ground. Clear opener outlet.
- Obstruction in the seed hopper or tube.
- Broken drive chain, or broken or badly worn parts.

Poor cross check.
- Check head improperly adjusted or badly worn. Eliminate play in the check head operating rods. Repair or replace worn parts.

- Bent or misadjusted check forks. Pinched together check forks may bind the wire and drop corn between the hills. Adjust forks to have 1/4 inch clearance between them. Eliminate unnecessary play in the fork pivot and operating rod, while still allowing the fork to operate freely.
- Valves out of adjustment or binding. Upper and lower valves should operate at exactly the same time, and open and close without binding. Carefully examine the valve operating linkage to determine the necessary adjustments.
- Runners bent or misaligned. Repair or replace as required.
- Planter frame bent or twisted. Repair.
- Improper handling of check wire or anchor stakes. Carefully follow instructions.
- Planter not square with row when setting stake. Drive carefully into position.
- Stake not set in line with previous stakes. Use more care in setting stakes.
- Planter not a uniform distance from the stake when setting stake. Exercise care in stopping planter.
- Too much side draft on row marker, causing planter to run crooked. Readjust marker.
- Kinks or bad buttons on check wire. Repair.
- Seed drive shaft clutch worn or not engaging properly. Adjust, repair, or replace.

More seed in some rows than others.
- Incorrect sprocket combination.
- Wrong seed plate in one hopper.
- Foreign material in seed.
- Seed cutoff, brush or knocker not operating correctly in one planting unit.
- Incorrect or leaking air or vacuum pressure in one planting unit.

Cracking seed.
- Incorrect seed plate. Try a plate with larger or smaller seed cells.
- Problems with seed cutoff or knocker.

Planting depth not uniform.
- Inconsistent use of depth setting lever.
- Worn or bent openers.

John Deere's model 290 tractor corn planter, modified for use with horses by the addition of a tongue and seat, may be set up to drill beans, peanuts, sunflowers, and several other seeds in addition to corn.

Photo by Bonnie Nance

Planting and Cultivating Equipment

7

Potato Planters

"Only two things in this world are too serious to be jested on, potatoes and matrimony."

Irish saying

Potatoes have long been a staple food crop, and in the old days even farmers who didn't plan to sell potatoes planted an acre or two for their own use. For centuries potatoes were planted by hand using a hoe to dig a hole into which a section of potato containing at least one eye was dropped and then covered, again with the hoe. A dibble—a pointed tool that was thrust into the ground to make a hole—was sometimes used, and many different hand potato planters were put on the market as well.

Farmers often used a cultivator or a small plow to make a furrow into which they dropped potato seeds and covered them by hand. In about 1880 a machine was developed that opened a furrow, dropped the seed, and then covered the furrow. The mechanical potato planter not only saved time and labor, but gave better yields because of uniform planting depth and coverage of the seed. Many of these older mechanical potato planters are still in use.

Features of a Potato Planter

Potato planters use different methods to select each seed potato. Some require operator assistance, others are fully automatic.

Assisted-Feed Planters

Some early planters use one or two endless chains on which a series of cups are mounted. The chains are driven from the planter's axle and, as they travel upward through the seed hopper, each cup gathers a seed potato. At the top of their travel the chains turn over a pulley, or gear, and drop the seed potato into the planting tube, which carries it into the furrow created by the opener. The operator monitors the moving seed cups and manually fills any cup that fails to pick up a seed on its way through the hopper.

Other planters use a horizontal feed wheel with a series of pockets around its outer edge. An elevator wheel gathers the seed potatoes from the hopper, lifts them and drops them into the pockets of the feed wheel. The feed wheel revolves in front of the operator, who is responsible for

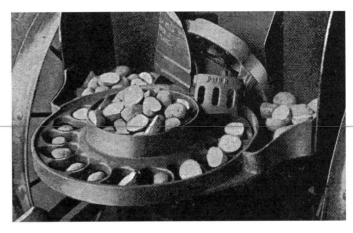

The feed wheel of an assisted feed planter. The seed pieces fall into the pockets of the wheel through the spout at the right front of the wheel. As the wheel rotates from right to left, the operator makes sure one seed is in each pocket. Under the wheel at the front, the seed is pushed into the seed spout where it falls into the furrow. The reservoir of seeds in the center of the wheel is for the operator's convenience. A.B. Farquhar Co.

seeing that each pocket contains only one seed potato. As each pocket reaches a position over the planting tube, an ejecting device pushes the seed off the feed wheel, whereupon it drops down the tube and into the furrow.

Such planters, called semi–automatic or assisted feed machines, assure an accurate rate of planting due to the efforts of the operator in making sure each seed cup is filled.

Automatic-Feed Planter

Later planters, called automatic–feed machines, use a picker mechanism to select each seed potato and require less attention from the operator. The heart of an automatic picker is a picker wheel with a series of three to 12 picker arms around its circumference. Each picker arm has two slender, sharp steel picks that protrude as the arms pass through the seed chamber, where each set of picker points impales a piece of seed potato. The seed piece is carried up and over the picker wheel. As it starts down the other side, the arm strikes a cam. The cam opens the picker arm and forces the seed off the points, dropping it into the seed spout, from which it is guided into the furrow made by the

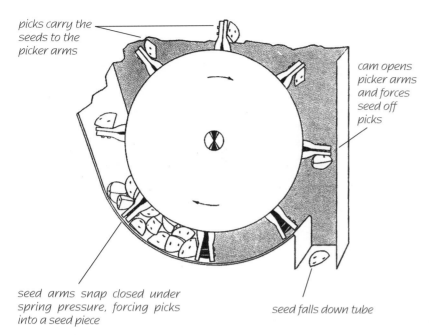

picks carry the seeds to the picker arms

cam opens picker arms and forces seed off picks

seed arms snap closed under spring pressure, forcing picks into a seed piece

seed falls down tube

Picker mechanism of an automatic–feed potato planter.

A.B. Farquhar Co.

Hitching a Potato Planter

Hitch a potato planter so the pole is carried such that the planter frame and hoppers are level when the machine is in operation. Make this adjustment with the neck yoke straps.

Operation and Adjustment

Plant potatoes in a deeply plowed and thoroughly pulverized seedbed. Seed potatoes, whether whole or cut, should be of a uniform size. Potatoes are usually drilled in rows 30 to 36 inches apart, with the seeds spaced from 8 to 15 inches apart in the rows.

Assisted-Feed Planting

Fill the seed hopper with seed potatoes or pieces. Fill fertilizer hopper, if provided, and adjust the fertilizer feed to distribute the desired amount of fertilizer per acre. Make sure the correct feed drive sprocket is selected to give the desired seed spacing.

Drive to the edge of the field where the first row is to be planted. Lower the row marker on the side toward the field. Make sure all the openings in the feed wheel, or all the feed cups, are filled with a seed piece. Lower the opener to the desired depth. Drive straight across the field at a steady

opener. The distance between seed pieces in the row is varied by changing the speed of rotation of the picker wheel. The flow of seed from the hopper into the picking chamber is also adjustable.

The distance between the seed pieces in the furrow is regulated by using different sized sprockets on the feed mechanism drive. Planters are usually furnished with several sprockets to give different seed spacings.

Planter Shoe and Attachments

Regardless of the style of feed, most potato planters have a shoe opener that opens a furrow into which the seed pieces are deposited. Double disc and V–plow openers are available, as well. Two angled discs behind the machine cover the seed with soil and are adjustable to provide the desired depth of coverage.

Fertilizer attachments are available that place a band of fertilizer on each side of the seed. A pair of angled discs ahead of the planter shoe opens a trench for the fertilizer. The depth of placement and rate of application may be varied as desired. Most planters have a marker, or markers, to mark the position for the next row.

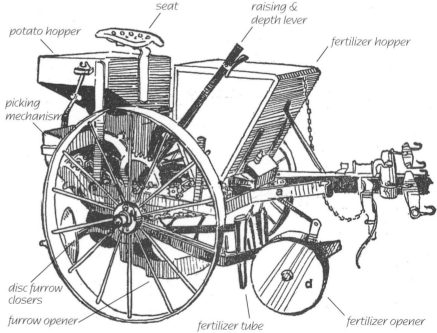

seat

raising & depth lever

potato hopper

fertilizer hopper

picking mechanism

disc furrow closers

furrow opener

fertilizer tube

fertilizer opener

Automatic–feed potato planter.

Farm Machinery, by Archie A. Stone

Planting and Cultivating Equipment

gait, while keeping an eye on the feed wheel pockets or cups to assure that each contains one seed piece.

When you get to the other end of the field, raise the opener and row marker and turn so the planter tongue is directly over the row mark. Lower the marker toward the field, start moving and lower the opener, keeping the planter tongue centered on the row mark. The furrow opener enters the ground more easily when the planter is moving forward. Don't back up with the opener in the ground or the seed outlet may become clogged.

Automatic-Feed Planting

The operation of an automatic–feed planter is much the same as for an assisted–feed machine, although less atention to the feeding mechanism is necessary. A gate between the seed hopper and the picking chamber may be adjusted to conform to seed pieces of different sizes. Set the gate so plenty of seed is always in the picking chamber. The picker points may be adjusted to accommodate different sizes of seed potatoes. Move the points to a position where they strike the seed nearly in the center. Keep the picker points straight, sharp, and shiny.

gear, but with the opener set in its highest position, and seed potatoes in the hopper. After driving a few feet, measure the distance between the seeds that have been dropped.

For best operation, the front of the opener shoe should run lower than the rear, resulting in a V trench with the seed pieces centered in the trench. Both the front and rear of the shoe may be adjusted vertically by moving the mounting brackets to different holes.

Both the angle and the distance apart of the covering discs may be varied to obtain the desired throw of soil. The discs are held into the ground by spring pressure, which must be adjusted to get proper penetration.

Most potato planters have a control lever to raise the shoe and discs, and shut off both the seed and fertilizer feed. The same lever controls the planting depth.

The depth of the fertilizer bands in relation to the seeds may be altered by adjusting the front disc coulters up or down on their mounting brackets. The fertilizer gate may be set to give the desired rate of application, usually by loosening a knob or wing nut, or by moving a hand lever.

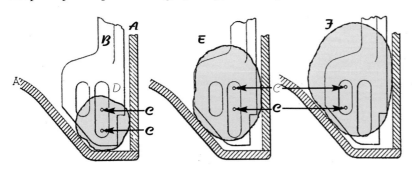

Position of seed (dotted line) in hopper throat.

Seed size (ounces)	1/2 – 1	1 – 1 1/2	1 1/2 – 2 1/2	2 1/2 – 4
Picks	short	long	long	long
Place picks in holes	1 + 2	2 + 3	2 + 5	4 + 5

D = Small
E = Medium
J = Large
A = hopper frame
B = picker arm
C–C = position of picks

A common method of adjusting picks for whole or cut seed of different sizes.

A.B. Farquhar Co.

Making Adjustments

The spacing of seed pieces in the row is changed by using different sprockets on the driving mechanism. These sprockets have varying numbers of teeth and drive the picker wheel, feeder wheel, or feeder cup chains at different speeds. Check the spacing by driving across a smooth, hard piece of ground with the planter in

Lubrication and Care

Lubricate all moving parts daily, and more often in dusty conditions, with particular attention to the clutch parts and the contact faces of the picker arms and releasing cam. Keep picker arm parts clean and oiled. Keep the picker bowl free of sprouts and other debris. Run chains tight enough to keep them from coming off, and lubricate them sparingly. At the end of each day, remove any fertilizer from the hopper, as it may pack and harden overnight.

At the end of the planting season, thoroughly clean and oil the fertilizer hopper, agitator, and feed parts to prevent rust. Clean all the seed out of the hopper and picker bowl. Clean the opening shoe, fertilizer discs, and covering discs of any sticking dirt, then coat them with grease. Thoroughly grease and oil the planter. Check and tighten all nuts and bolts. Replace any broken or worn parts. Store the planter under cover.

At the beginning of each season clean the planter and check for obstructions in the seed and fertilizer hoppers and the picker bowl. Before using the planter, wipe oil and grease off the potato picking parts and lubricate the planter.

A one-row three-point hitch potato planter, built by AFIVEPLUS, at work behind a Yard Hitch forecart.

Photo by Wendy Lawliss

Planting and Cultivating Equipment

Cultivators

"Now, with a span of horses,
and one of our best riding cultivators,
15 acres can be accomplished,
and this with almost as much ease
and comfort as a day's journey in a buggy."

*From the 1870 Report by the
United States Commissioner of Agriculture.*

The word cultivator may be applied to any implement that loosens and pulverizes the soil, without turning it as in plowing. Of the many kinds of cultivator, each is designed to meet the varying requirements posed by different crops and soils, as well as to attain the desired results. Proper cultivation of a growing row crop greatly enhances the crop's yield and quality. The destruction of weeds is the most important reason for cultivating, although the process also stirs and loosens the soil, creating a surface mulch that helps retain moisture.

Cultivation should begin as soon as the crop is up and the rows may be distinguished. The first time through, run the shovels deep so roots are not disturbed and the shields protect the plants. During subsequent cultivations, run the shovels and sweeps as shallow as possible to avoid pruning roots, especially when cultivating root crops such as potatoes or beets.

Shovel Cultivators

The most common style of cultivator uses shovels or sweeps to loosen the soil. Horse-drawn shovel cultivators are classified according to capacity and mode of operation.

One-Horse Cultivators

A *one-horse cultivator* is commonly used between rows to destroy weeds and loosen the soil. It consists of a triangular frame to which usually five or seven shanks are attached for holding the shovels or sweeps. An adjustable hitch at the front, or apex of the triangle, is provided, along with two handles at the rear. The frame is often equipped with a lever to vary the width to suit the distance between rows. A front gauge wheel may be used, and the shanks can be equipped with different styles of shovel, sweep, or point. The hitch may be adjusted vertically to obtain the desired penetration of the shovels or sweeps. If a gauge wheel is provided, it too may help control working depth.

One-horse, five-shovel cultivator with width adjusting lever.
International Harvester

Straddle-Row Cultivators

A *straddle-row cultivator* consists of a wheeled carriage that supports and controls the depth and direction of travel of the gangs, or rigs, of shovels that are drawn along both sides of a row. These machines are available in one-row walking and one-row riding versions that require two horses, as well as two- or four-row riding versions that need three or four horses. Two- and four-row cultivators are usually equipped with one or two caster wheels, either in front of or behind the frame, to eliminate weight on the horses' necks.

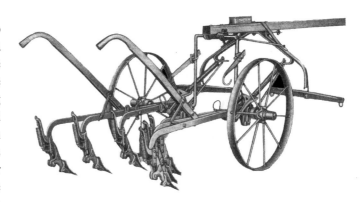

One-row walking cultivator with spring trip shovels.
Deere & Co.

One-Row Walking Cultivator

The shovel *rigs*, or *gangs*, on most one-row walking cultivators are controlled by handles that regulate depth and lateral movement. An adjustable depth stop screw on each gang allows you to easily return to the same cultivating depth each time you lower the rigs. Adjust the lifting spring on each rig so the shovels float at the desired depth without your having to exert much down pressure, yet you can still easily lift the rigs when necessary. A hang-up hook on each side holds the gangs in the raised position for transport. The rigs may be moved laterally for close cultivation or to dodge any out-of-line plants, by manipulating the handles.

Riding Cultivators

Riding cultivators, whether of one-, two-, or four-row capacity, share many features of construction. Two large wheels support a frame, from the front of which are suspended the arch (on a one-row machine) or arches. An arch is a substantial frame member to which the front end of each pair of gangs is attached, allowing the pair to act

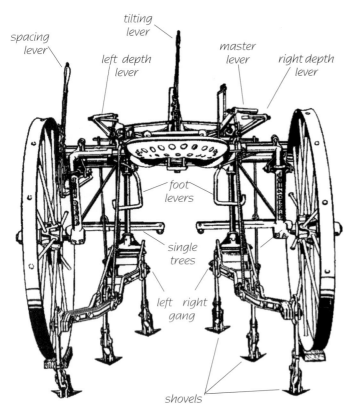

One-row riding cultivator equipped with pin break shanks, as well as foot levers to steer the gangs for close cultivating and dodging stray plants. *Deere & Co.*

as a unit. The wheels are mounted on pivots that, along with the lateral shifting mechanism of the cultivator rigs, are controlled by foot levers. These foot levers allow you to dodge plants that are out of line, or steer the wheels to maintain the cultivator's position when working on a side hill.

Several hand levers are provided for adjustment. The depth of each gang of shovels is controlled by a lever. A master lever raises all the gangs as a unit. Set the depth levers so as to cultivate at the desired depth, and use the master lever to raise and lower the gangs at the row ends. Some machines have a spacing lever to move the gangs closer to or farther from the row, other machines require a wrench to make this adjustment. A lever is sometimes provided to tilt the rear of the tongue in relation to the cultivator frame. This adjustment is handy for leveling the gangs to accommodate teams of different sizes, and for digging deeper or shallower with the front shovels than the rear ones.

Shovels, Sweeps and Gangs

A *gang* or *rig* consists of the coupling, the beam, the shanks, and the shovels all operating as a unit. A cultivator has one gang for each side of each row. The coupling at the forward end of the gang attaches to the arch and is flexible to allow both lateral and up and down movement. The pipe or I-bar beam extends to the rear and may have two, three, or four shanks attached.

The shovels or sweeps are bolted to the lower end of the shanks. The shanks must have some means of protection to prevent breakage when a shovel encounters a solid obstruction. Early cultivator shanks had a wooden pin that would break and allow the shovel to swing back if it hit a rock. The operator had to then whittle and insert a new pin, which gave the team a nice rest. Virtually all cultivators in use today have spring trip shanks, which allow the shovel to move to the rear and then reset itself after the obstruction is passed. The spring tension is adjustable and should be set just tight enough that the shovel doesn't trip during normal use.

Different styles of shovel and sweep meet different requirements. A *shovel* is considerably wide above the cutting edge to direct the stream of soil. A twisted shovel directs the stream of soil to one side while the point is set square with the direction of travel. A straight shovel directs the soil stream to both sides, unless the shovel is turned slightly to one side or the other. A double point shovel has a point at each end and may be reversed when one end is worn out. Shovels are usually from 1 to 4 inches wide.

A *sweep* has wide, low cutting wings that vary in width from 6 to 12 inches and cut below the surface without much lifting or throwing of the soil. Half sweeps with a wing on only one side are often used on the front shanks next to the plants to prevent damage to the stalks or roots.

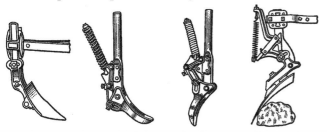

break pin spring trip two styles of spring trip operated by obstacle

Cultivator Shanks. Agricultural Machinery by J. Brownlee Davidson

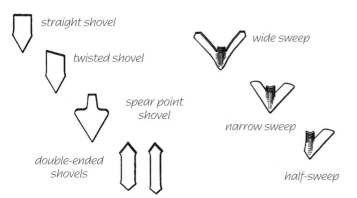

straight shovel
twisted shovel
spear point shovel
double-ended shovels
wide sweep
narrow sweep
half-sweep

Shovels and Sweeps. Agricultural Machinery by J. Brownlee Davidson

Operation and Adjustment

One-, two-, and four-row cultivators are all operated in pretty much the same way. Set the cultivator so the shovels penetrate well and run at the same depth without leading into or away from the row. Keep the shovels sharp, with a properly shaped point. Dull shovels do poor work, won't penetrate properly, and cause heavier draft.

Give the shovels the right inclination and side set. Shovel shanks are provided with an adjustment whereby you may change each shovel's pitch or angle. Shovels set too flat won't penetrate without being forced into the ground. Shovels set too straight, or without enough inclination, won't penetrate and will bounce along on the points. To ensure scouring, give the shovels just enough side set to turn the soil to one side without reducing pressure on the shovel.

Run all shovels at the same depth. Be sure all the shovels and shanks are set at a uniform depth on the beams. If the front shovels run deeper than the rear, raise the pole at the neck yoke or level the gangs with the tongue tilting lever. If the rear shovels run too deep, lower the pole at the neck yoke if your cultivator has no tongue tilting lever.

Use *shields* during the first cultivation, when growing plants are small enough to easily be covered. Shields, sometimes called fenders or guards, are attached to the cultivator gangs between the shovels and the plants to prevent the soil lifted by the shovels from falling onto and burying young plants. The shields may be sheet metal blades, closely spaced rods, or rolling discs or sprocket wheels. Sheet metal shields are the most common and should be set adjacent to the front two shovels. Set rolling shields slightly ahead of the front shovels, with their weight resting on the ground.

After the first cultivation plants usually reach enough height that shields are no longer needed. In subsequent cultivations the shovels therefore throw loose dirt among the plants, covering any weeds growing in the row.

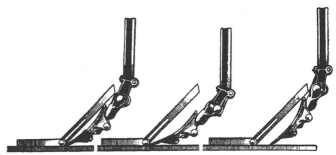

set correctly set too flat— won't penetrate set too straight— won't penetrate, and runs on the point

Setting shovel pitch. Farm Machinery by Archie Stone

rolling sheet metal open rod

Cultivator shields. Farm Machinery by Archie Stone

Hitching a Cultivator

A cultivator requires no horizontal adjustment. For vertical adjustment the singletree hangers have a series of holes. Hitching the singletrees high causes the front shovels to run deep and the rear shovels to run shallow. Hitching low has the opposite effect. The principle is similar to that of the line of draft on a plow (shown on page 10), except that the line of draft on a cultivator isn't as critical as for a plow, and sometimes you may want the front shovels to run deeper or shallower than the rear. For average conditions, however, the line of draft should extend in a straight line from the hames through the singletree hanger to a point on the ground just behind the front shovel.

Adjust the pole so the gangs run level. Most cultivators have a tongue tilting lever for this purpose, otherwise the adjustment must be made by raising or lowering the front of the tongue at the neck yoke straps.

Cultivating a Field

Before beginning to cultivate, adjust the machine to suit your size and weight: Set the axle crank adjustment or frame shift so the cultivator is balanced front to rear by your weight. Move the seat forward or back as necessary to help balance the machine.

Move the axles in or out on the frame until the distance between the wheels is the same as the distance between rows. Space the gangs so the front shovels work as close to the row as desired, usually closer for early cultivation, and farther away after the roots become larger. Use the individual gang levers to attain the desired penetration, deep during early cultivation, and shallower later on. After setting the correct depth use the master lever, if provided, to raise and lower the gangs.

Start cultivating by straddling the first row at the edge of the field. Drive straight across the field, operating the foot or hand levers to dodge plants. Keep the gangs free from trash by lifting the gang and shaking off any accumulation, or by stopping and clearing the machine. To take out weeds but not plants, drive slowly until you and your team are accustomed to the work

Avoid making the short turn necessary to return down the next row by using one of the following two systems:

● Skip one row every time you make a turn at each end of the field, thereby cultivating alternate rows. Then work back across the field in the opposite direction, cultivating the skipped rows.

● After cultivating the first row, return on the fourth row. Next cultivate the second row, and return on the sixth. Continue skipping one row each time you make the turn

into the uncultivated part of the field, and pick up the last skipped row when you go the other way.

Method of cultivating to eliminate short turns at the row ends.

Lubricating a Cultivator

Daily lubricate wheels and rolling shields, if provided. Occasionally oil the shank spring trip mechanisms to keep them from rusting tight. After each use, coat the shovels with grease to preserve their polish. At season's end tighten all bolts, lubricate the wheels, and grease the shovels well. Sharpen or replace dull shovels before the next season.

Disc Cultivators

Although they are not common, *disc cultivators* do a better job than shovel machines under some conditions. Especially weedy fields, where a shovel cultivator would clog, or fields with many stones or roots that could catch and damage shovels, are better worked with a disc cultivator. A disc cultivator can move a lot of soil away from or toward growing plants, and thus are handy for hilling crops.

Most riding cultivators may be converted from shovel to disc by changing the gangs. Three discs are usually on each side of the row, and they may be interchanged to throw the soil onto or away from the row.

The operation of a disc cultivator is virtually identical to that of a shovel machine. Lubricate the wheels and disc bearings daily, and clean the discs and coat them with grease after use.

Two-row rotary hoe.   Deere & Co.

Rear view of a disc cultivator with the gangs set to throw dirt away from the row.   Deere & Co.

Rotary Hoes

A rotary hoe may be used to advantage for cultivating and destroying grass and weeds around row crops when the plants are in the early stages of growth. It may also be used in small grain crops, and works well to break up the hard crust formed by heavy rain. A rotary hoe is operated directly over the plants, and lifts out tiny weed plants while not damaging the better rooted crop plants.

A rotary hoe consists of two gangs of rimless wheels, called hoes, on a frame supported by two wheels that double as transport and gauge wheels. The gangs are mounted one behind the other so the hoes on the rear gang work the land falling between the front hoes. The hoe wheels are about 18 inches in diameter and are set about 4 or 5 inches apart along each shaft. Each hoe wheel has 16 curved teeth that penetrate and stir the soil as they rotate. Hand levers adjust the carrying wheels up and down to control the depth of cultivation.

No special adjustments are required; just set the desired depth with the hand levers and drive your team so all the ground is covered. A rotary hoe is most effective at speeds above $2^1/2$ miles per hour. A two-row rotary hoe covers about 7 feet. The draft is about 50 pounds per foot of width when the hoe isn't weighted. Lubricate axle wheel bearings daily.

Spring-Tine Weeders

The most common weeder is the *spring-tine* type, which has many slender spring teeth spaced along three bars in a staggered manner. When the teeth contact the ground, they are 2 to 3 inches apart and penetrate the soil to a depth of 1 to 2 inches. The movement of the spring teeth through the soil sets up a vibrating motion in each tooth that helps uproot tiny weeds.

Riding weeders are supported on two wheels and are about 12-feet wide. Walk-behind weeders have two handles, but no wheels, and are typically 7- or 8-feet wide and equipped with shafts for a single horse. Used primarily for early cultivation of growing crops, the weeder is drawn directly over the crop and is effective in destroying young delicate weeds. These weeders are well adapted to mellow soil, but are not as effective in wet or heavy soil.

On a riding weeder, use the lever to set the depth, usually 1 or $1^1/2$ inches. Control the depth of a walk-behind weeder by exerting downward pressure on the handles. Spring-tine weeders are of light draft, about 25 to 35 pounds per foot of width. If wheels are present, lubricate them daily. The bearings of a rod weeder should be run dry because of running in the dirt. Oil the bearings thoroughly after use, and before storing the machine.

Two-horse spring-tine riding weeder.   Farm Tools, Inc.

A straddle-row cultivator equipped with wide sweeps for working market garden crops including carrots, leeks and onions on the left, and beets and broccoli on the right.

Photo by Anne Nordell

Planting and Cultivating Equipment

III: Hay Harvesting Machinery

Hay must be cut at just the right time—and carefully cured, handled, and stored—if its quality and nutritional value are to be preserved. In many areas hay making comes at the same time as rainy weather. If mown hay is rained on, nutrients leach out, the hay cures slowly, and it requires additional handling, which knocks off the leaves. Alfalfa, clover, and other legume hay contains most of its feed value in the leaves, which are easily shattered and lost through mishandling. Timothy, wild hay, and other meadow grasses aren't as perishable as legumes and require less care in handling.

The main purpose of each operation in curing and handling hay should be the production of a high quality and nutritious crop. Many tools in the horse farmer's arsenal are available to make good hay, allowing each farmer to choose the method that best fits the size of the operation, as well as the available amount of time and money. Good hay should retain all its leaves and its natural green color, and shouldn't be musty or moldy. Modern hay tools greatly ease the labor of making hay and, more important, speed up the operation. Grasses and legumes may thus be cut, cured, and put in the barn before weather related damage occurs.

Of the many tools for handling hay, some are old and some are not so old. Hay conditioners, pickup balers, and similar modern implements are complex machines, requiring careful adjustment and operation to attain the best results. This book offers general instructions and makes no attempt to describe every adjustment on every machine. The operator of any of these implements should have the operator's manual and study it before attempting to use the machine. Manuals for later models are usually available from the manufacturer.

Mowers

"There is a song that will inspire
Both man and boy and aged sire
With melody of tune.
This song requires a boy and team,
A graceful Buckeye for its theme
And a field of grass in June.

"Then as around the field they pass
Its lay will be the falling grass—
The gear will gently ring;
And as it speeds each pitman–beat
Will mark the chorus loud and sweet
And loud the boy will sing:

"'Oh thou friend of every farmer,
Glad I am to sing thy praise.
You are always true and faithful,
And unnumbered be thy days.'"

*Aultman–Miller Catalog for 1896,
extolling the virtues of the Buckeye mower*

Until well into the 19th century, farmers cut hay with a scythe or sickle. The first machine for mowing hay was patented in 1812, but it didn't work. Another unsuccessful mower, which had a horizontal revolving blade, was patented ten years later. William Manning of New Jersey came up with the idea of a reciprocating sickle blade and pointed guards in 1831, but his machine also failed. Obed Hussey, who battled Cyrus McCormick for years over who built the first successful reaper, improved on Manning's reciprocal knife and guard system on his combined reaper–mower. On July 10, 1847, William Ketchum of New York patented the first successful mower intended specifically for cutting hay. Ketchum's mower, with its single wheel and rigid cutter bar, became popular.

Later inventors, including Cyrenus Wheeler and Jonathan Haines, improved on the Ketchum patent. In 1854 Cornelius Aultman and Lewis Miller of Akron, Ohio, patented a much improved mower. The Buckeye mower, sold by Aultman–Miller starting about 1855, was similar to the horse–drawn mowers used today—with two wheels, front mounted pitman, and hinged cutter bar.

Mowing machines, commonly called mowers, are used in most parts of the country to cut meadow grasses and legumes that are to be used as hay. A mower also is handy

for weed control in pastures, and for keeping grass and weeds cut down along fence rows and roads. Mowers normally have a side–mounted cutter bar that is ground driven by the mower wheels, or by an engine or power take off. Cutter bars range in length from 3$\frac{1}{2}$ feet on a one–horse machine up to 9 or 10 feet on a mower designed for tractor use. Tractor mowers usually may be used with a powered forecart and are available as pull–type, semi–mounted, and mounted versions.

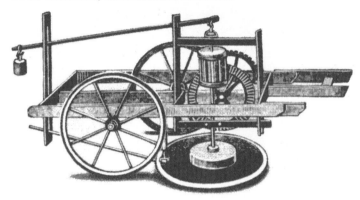

Mowing machine with revolving circular blade, patented in 1822. Farm Equipment Institute

Ketchum's successful mower of 1847. Farm Equipment Institute

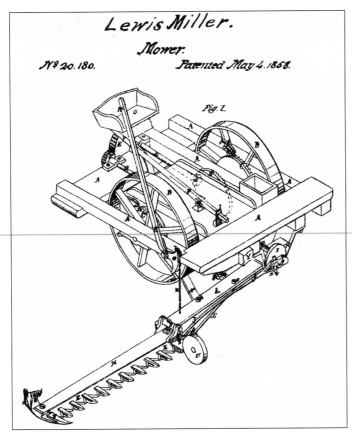

1858 patent drawing of an improved Buckeye mower.
US Patent Office

Mower Features

The horse–drawn mower has a cast–iron frame supported on two wheels. Most mowers have a live axle driven through a system of pawls and ratchets inside each wheel hub. The pawls and rachets allow the machine to be backed, and function as a differential when the mower makes a turn. Some late model mowers have a pawl–type differential inside the main gear case, rather than in each hub. The axle drives the pitman crank through several spur and bevel gears. A lever–operated clutch is provided to disengage the pitman drive.

A *pitman*, usually made of hickory wood, connects the crank or pitman wheel to the cutter bar knife, giving the knife a back and forth motion of about 3 inches. The seat extends behind the axle so the operator's weight offsets the tongue's weight on the horses' necks. A stub tongue and a tongue truck may be used to improve stability on uneven ground and eliminate any weight on the horses. The business end of the mower is the cutter bar, made up of the bar itself, a knife, inner and outside shoes, guards, ledger plates, wearing plates, and knife clips, along with a grass board and stick.

The *cutter bar* is a tapered flat steel bar, the same length as the width of cut, to which all the other parts of the cutting mechanism are connected. The *knife* is a flat steel bar called the *knife back*, to which the *knife head* and triangular *knife sections* are attached with rivets so they may be easily replaced. Three kinds of section are available.

1. Smooth sections are used for cutting fine–stemmed crops and are easily sharpened.

2. Top–serrated sections, the most common kind, are used to cut coarse crops. The serrations hold the stems so they cut cleanly. Although these sections cannot be sharpened, they hold their cutting edge for a long time.

3. Bottom–serrated sections work much the same as the top–serrated ones, but may be sharpened.

The *inner* or *inside shoe* is a large runner supporting the inner end of the cutter bar. It acts as half of the hinge between the mower frame and the cutter bar. It is provided with a replaceable *sole* that is adjustable to regulate the height of cut. An angled steel rod, or fender rod, is attached to the front of the inner shoe to guide the grass into the cutter bar.

The *outer* or *outside shoe* is a smaller runner supporting the outer end of the cutter bar. The outer shoe also has a replaceable and adjustable sole, as well as a ledger plate on which the end section of the knife works. The pointed end of the shoe acts as a divider and separates the standing grass from the grass to be cut.

The *guards* are bolted along the front edge of the cutter bar and hold the *ledger plates* in position. The guards protect the knife and divide the grass, forcing it into the knife to be cut. A ledger plate riveted to each guard forms the stationary half of the cutting unit, with a knife section acting as the moving half. Each knife section has a guard.

Knife clips, or *knife holders*, are provided to hold the knife sections down close to the ledger plates to maintain a shearing action. A *wearing plate* is held by the same bolts that hold the clips. The wearing plates support the rear side of the knife and hold the sections relative to the ledger plates so the crop is sheared off cleanly. Most wear plates have slotted holes so they may be moved forward to take up wear.

The *grass board* is bolted to the outer shoe with a flexible spring connection that allows it to follow the ground and to give when an obstruction is encountered. The grass board, which angles back and away from the uncut grass, throws the cut grass inward, leaving a clean strip for the inner shoe on the next round. The *grass stick* is bolted to the inside of the grass board and helps lay the cut grass into a neat swath.

A large hand lever is used to raise the cutter bar high off the ground when it's not cutting, or when it must clear an obstacle. On a regular lift mower, the inner shoe may be raised about a foot, while the outer end of the cutter bar will be about 3 feet high. On a vertical lift mower, the hand lever raises the cutter bar to a vertical position, automatically throwing the cutting mechanism out of gear. This feature is an advantage when mowing along roadways, or in a field with many stumps. After the obstruction is passed, the bar is lowered and the cutting mechanism must again be started. The hand lever may be latched in the raised position.

The foot lever also lifts the cutter bar off the ground, although it doesn't lift as high as the hand lever, nor is it equipped with a latch. The foot lever is used when turning a corner, or to quickly raise the bar over a rock or other obstruction.

The *tilting lever* regulates the angle between the front of the cutter bar and the ground. The guard points may be set parallel with the ground, inclined downward toward the ground, or inclined upward. A clutch lever, consisting of a short lever or foot pedal, is provided to engage or disengage the cutting mechanism from the drive wheels.

A horse–drawn mower doing good work in alfalfa hay.

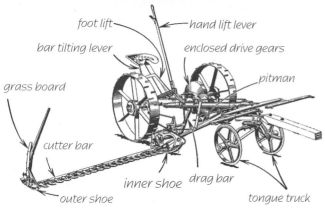

A horse–drawn 5–foot mower with a tongue truck

Deere & Co.

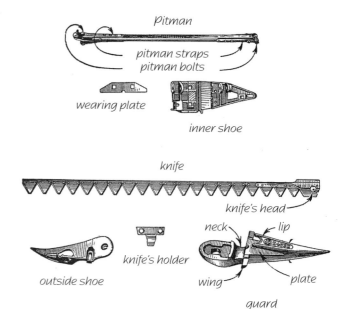

Cutter bar parts on a 5–foot mower.   *Deere & Co.*

Draft of a Mower

The mower's condition and the crop being cut both affect a mower's draft. A 5–foot cut mower pulled at 2$\frac{1}{2}$ miles per hour should vary from between 250 pounds and no more than 500 pounds. A dull knife or poorly adjusted cutter bar adds materially to the machine's draft.

Mower Draft	
Condition of Sickle Bar	*Pounds of Draft*
Knife in good condition	455 – 478
Knife 50 percent dull	538 – 562
Knife very dull.	560 – 622
Knife dull, guards bent,	
ledger plates rubbing	531 – 718
From a study by the University of Wisconsin in the 1920s.	

Hitching a Mower

Hitch a horse–drawn mower so the front end of the tongue is about 30 to 32 inches above the ground. Make this adjustment with the neckyoke straps. A too–wide evener will either force the off horse to walk in the uncut grass or the mower to take less than a full cut. Using a tongue truck will eliminate neck weight on the team.

Operating a Mower

To lower the cutter bar from the transport position, support the bar with one hand, while removing the tail nut from the end of the support rod. Lower the cutter bar into working position. *Keep your fingers out from between the guards.* The knife may shift while you are raising or lowering the cutter bar and easily remove a finger. Store the support rod in the clip on the tongue and put the tail nut in your tool box. Don't leave the tail nut on the rod, as it will vibrate off and get lost while you are mowing. Before you begin to cut, lubricate your mower, put it in gear, and operate it away from the crop to make sure everything is working as it should.

Mowing is done by driving around the field in a clockwise direction. Put the mower in gear and make sure the knife is moving before the cutter bar enters the grass, otherwise it will probably clog. The team and mower will likely have to be driven through the standing grass when making the first round. After you have made a couple of rounds, you can cut the grass left standing on the opening round by driving around the field in a counter–clockwise direction. Cut this backswath after only a couple of opening rounds, so the hay dries at about the same time. Some teamsters prefer to make the counter–clockwise round first, although they are less able to see any obstructions at the edges of the field.

A beginner may have some difficulty in turning at the corners without leaving tufts of uncut grass. Run the mower to the corner until the cutter bar has just left the standing grass. Stop the mower and raise the cutter bar with the foot lever. Turn and back your team so the full width of the cutter bar is ready to enter the hay. Drive forward and drop the cutter bar just before it enters the uncut grass. With practice, you will be turning corners in one smooth maneuver, leaving behind no ragged edges.

To regulate the height of cut, raise or lower the soles on the inner and outer shoes. Set the soles so the cutter bar is level. The cutter bar can be tilted forward with the tilting lever for cutting tangled and lodged or short grass, although tilting the bar should be done only on relatively smooth fields with no obstructions. When working in rough or stony fields tilt the guards upward.

Use the foot lever to raise the cutter bar when turning at corners and to quickly lift the cutter bar over stones and other relatively short obstacles. Use the lifting lever to raise the cutter bar over higher obstacles. On some mowers, especially the high–lift type, raising the bar with this lever disengages the clutch.

The grass board spring connection is usually set loose enough that it follows the ground contour, but not so loose the board flops down when the cutter bar is lifted. Set the grass stick so it lays the cut grass well away from the uncut hay. Raise the rear of the stick when cutting tall grass, and lower it for shorter grass.

When the cutter bar clogs, stop your team and throw the mower out of gear before dismounting. Never stand in front of the cutter bar in case your team spooks and lunges forward. A sharp cutter bar easily cuts through twigs as thick as a finger, and real fingers are no match at all for the knife.

To raise the cutter bar for transport, throw the mower out of gear and raise and latch the bar in its highest position, using the lifting lever. Turn the crank wheel by hand until the knife is in its inwardmost position. Lift the cutter bar by hand, *keeping your fingers out from between the guards.* Insert the threaded end of the support rod through the hole in the cutter bar and secure it with the tail nut.

Adjusting a Mower

Proper adjustment and timely repair of your mower go a long way toward ensuring it a long life doing good work. A smooth and quiet running mower that cuts cleanly will require the least power from your team and give you a lot of satisfaction. Avoid excessive wear and broken parts by having a regular program of lubrication, adjustment, and replacement of worn parts.

A mower's many different parts must work together to obtain good results. Any adjustment of one part may adversely affect several others. On any mowing machine, three important factors must be correct: the cutter bar's alignment, the knife's register, and the shear between knife sections and guard ledger plates.

Cutter Bar Alignment

When a mower is in operation, the pitman and knife should be in a straight line and at right angles to the machine's forward motion. The pressure of the grass being cut, along with friction from the soles riding on the ground, force the outer end of the cutter bar to the rear, especially as parts wear with use. To counteract this tendency, the outer end of an idle cutter bar should be ahead of, or lead, the inner end by about 1 1/4 inches on a 5–foot bar, 1 1/2 inches on a 6–foot, and 1 3/4 inches on a 7–foot bar.

Different manufacturers use different methods of adjusting cutter bar alignment. The most popular method for horse mowers is an eccentric bushing on the rear yoke pin. By removing a locking bolt and turning this eccentric, you can throw the outer end of the cutter bar either forward or backward as required. Some mowers provide for movement of the hinge yoke forward or back on the drag bar to correct the cutter bar alignment. Some drag bars are threaded at the rear end, and the lead is increased by first disconnecting the bar from the yoke, then turning it out of its socket enough to force the yoke forward. Your operator's manual, or a careful examination of your particular mower, should reveal how the adjustment is to be made.

Checking the Lead

To check the lead, park your mower on a level surface with the front end of the tongue blocked up to working height, about 32 inches. Tie a strong string to the oil cap or grease fitting on the pitman box at **A.** Run the string along the pitman and through the yoke, holding it taut at the outer end of the cutter bar. Hold the string so it is exactly over the center of the knifehead ball at **B.** Pull back on the end of the cutter bar to take up any slack from wear and, keeping the string tight, measure how much the center of the knife at its outer end either leads or lags the cord at **C.**

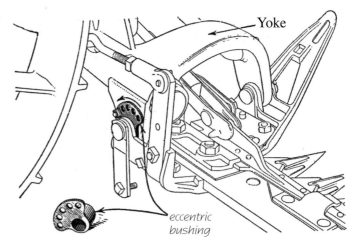

To increase the lead at the end of the cutter bar, turn the eccentric bushing to the left; to decrease lead, turn the eccentric to the right.   Deere & Co.

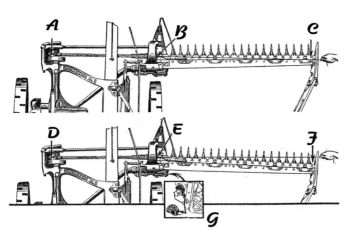

The upper illustration shows a 5–foot bar with the correct 1¼ inches of lead at C. The bar in the lower illustration exhibits nearly a 4–inch lag at F, a condition that would cause heavy draft and ragged cutting. Correct the lead by adjusting the eccentric bushing on the rear yoke pin at G.   Deere & Co.

centered, the cutter bar must be moved in or out until the desired setting is obtained.

On some mowers the register is changed by adjusting the length of the front brace bar, usually by screwing the threaded bar in or out at one end or the other. Other machines have a series of U–shaped washers or shims located where the hinge yoke connects to the front brace bar. Moving these shims from one side of the connection to the other moves the hinge toward or away from the crank wheel. A careful examination of your mower should reveal what you need to do to adjust the register.

Adjusting the knife register may affect the cutter bar lead, so check it again after setting the register. In some cases, especially if you use a homemade pitman, you may have to adjust the length of the pitman by drilling new holes for the pitman straps.

Knife Register

Knife *register* refers to the position of each knife section in relation to the guards. When the knife is at either end of its stroke, the point of each section should be centered on a guard. Incorrect register is a common problem with mowers, and can cause ragged cutting, clogging, and heavy draft.

To check for proper register, park your mower on a level surface and block the front end of the tongue to a height of 32 inches. Make sure the pitman straps are tight before making this test. Turn the crank wheel until the pitman is at the outer end of its stroke, at which time, each knife section should be centered in a guard. If the sections aren't

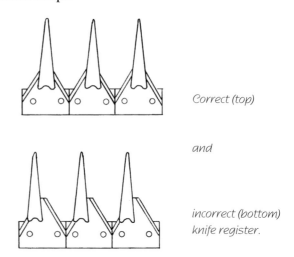

Correct (top)

and

incorrect (bottom) knife register.

Shear Cut

When all the cutter bar parts are correctly adjusted, every knife section rests smoothly on the ledger plate of a guard and is held in that position by the knife clips and wearing plates. This *shear* action ensures a clean, smooth cut with no clogging or missed hay. If the *shear cut* is lost and the grass is being chewed and torn off instead of cleanly cut, if your cutter bar frequently clogs, if your mower becomes hard to pull, or if parts become broken, check the cutter bar components.

● The guards are each held on the cutter bar by a single plow bolt that must be kept tight. Replace any broken or badly bent guard.

● The ledger plate is fastened to the guard with a single rivet, which must be tight. The sharpened edges of the ledger plates are serrated to keep grass from sliding out of the shears before it is cut. Replace any worn, broken, or dull ledger plate. A guard and knife repair block makes a quick, easy job of replacing ledger plates and knife sections. If you have no repair block, file or grind off the bottom end of the ledger plate rivet and drive it out with a punch. Universal guards, complete with ledger plates, are available at most equipment dealers and farm stores.

● Wearing plates support the rear edge of the cutter bar and, even though made of hardened steel, wear rapidly. When plates are worn, the rear of the knife drops and the section points lift off the ledger plates. Some wearing plates have slotted bolt holes so they can be slid forward to take up slop in the knife. Replace any plate worn enough to let the knife flop around.

● Knife clips hold the knife sections down against the ledger plates, maintaining the shear cut. The front tips of the clips can become worn badly enough to no longer hold down the sections, at which point the clips should be replaced.

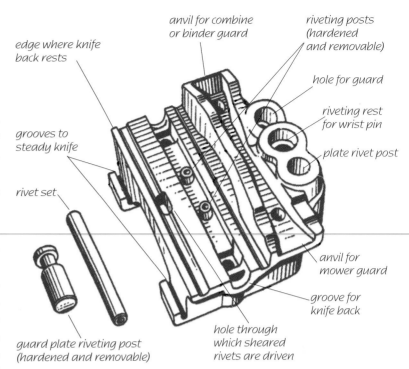

Guard and knife repair block.   *Deere & Co.*

● Knife sections are fastened to the knife bar with two rivets in each section. Made of hardened steel, these blades are sharp along the two angled sides and form the upper half of the shear cut. Sharpen or replace dull sections. Replace any that are broken or badly worn.

Repairing the Mower Knife

A dull or incorrectly ground knife increases draft, clogs easily, and cuts badly. The knife must be kept straight and sharp, and all the rivets must be tight. When sharpening the knife, maintain the original angle and bevel.

Most manufacturers of horse–drawn mowers furnished a knife grinder with a beveled stone. The hand–cranked machine grinds the edges of two adjacent sections at the same time, while maintaining the proper angle. Such grinders have become highly collectable and are hard to find. An angle grinder, or a stone on a flexible shaft, may be used to sharpen mower knives, but maintaining the right bevel and angle is difficult.

A common error is grinding away too much from the point and not enough from the heel. A section that has been sharpened a number of times with the correct angle and bevel may still not cut, because it has become too short to cut all the grass held by the guard.

The easiest way to replace worn or broken sections is with a guard and knife repair block. If none is available,

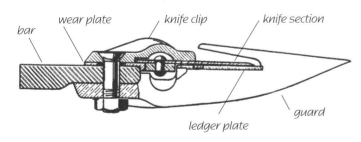

Cross section of a cutter bar showing the parts in correct alignment.   *International Harvester*

use a vise. Set the knife in the vise with the section points down and the edge of the knife back resting on the top of a jaw. Strike the back of the section, which sticks up beyond the knife back, a heavy blow with a hammer directly above a rivet. This blow will shear off the rivets and the section will drop off. Always shear off the rivets in this manner to avoid bending the knife or enlarging the rivet holes.

Put a new section in place and rivet it securely, using rivets of the correct length and thickness. Rivets should be large enough to completely fill the holes in the knife and the section to prevent the section from loosening in use. When riveting in new sections, use a solid base to keep from bending the knife back and to insure tight rivets.

Sight down the knife. If it is bent, straighten it on a flat surface by hammering.

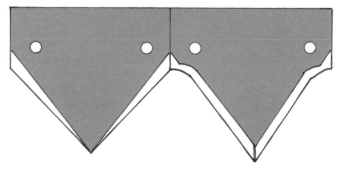

A properly sharpened knife section (right) compared to an incorrectly sharpened section.

Adjusting the Cutter Bar

Take time to align the guards so the ledger plates all are on the same plane. Pry up the knife clips slightly to provide clearance. Use a new knife, or one that is straight and not badly worn. Make sure the guard bolts are tight. Slide the knife into place and, while holding it down against the guards, note any that are too high or low. Using a heavy hammer, strike the guard at the thick part just in front of the ledger plate. Bend the guard up or down as required to obtain the shear cut between knife section and ledger plate. Don't hit the lips of the guard, as they are easily bent down, causing the knife to bind. Retighten each guard bolt after it is aligned. The guard wings should be aligned as well, making a smooth surface against which the knife back can work. Don't worry about misaligned guard points, as long as the plates and wings are in line. The points of the guards should be kept reasonably sharp.

Adjust or replace the wearing plates to take up any wear on the knife back and to reduce any play of the knife in the guards. The turned down front edges of the wearing plates must be in line to give the knife back a straight bearing surface all along its length.

The knife clips should hold the sections down against the ledger plates and wearing plates, but must not cause the knife to bind. The ideal clearance between the flattened front tip of the knife clips and the sections is about the thickness of a sheet of paper. Set the clips after the guards are aligned. Don't bend down a knife clip while a knife section is under it. Move the knife until the clip is between sections, tap down the clip, and test it by sliding the section back under the clip. If the clip is too tight, strike it between the bolts while the knife is under it. After setting the cutter bar, oil the guard plates and wearing plates and make sure the knife works freely.

Common Ground-Driven Mower Troubles

A ground driven mower doesn't work well when the grass is wet. The wheels will tend to slide on wet grass and the cutter bar will clog. If you're otherwise having problems with your mower, the following review should help you diagnose the trouble:

Heavy draft.
  lack of lubrication
  lagging of the cutter bar
  worn knife head, guides, knife clips, or wearing plates
  knife out of register
  guards loose
  guards out of line
  dull, broken, nicked, or loose sections
  dull, broken, nicked, or loose ledger plates
  knife clips binding
  cutter bar tilted too far forward
  lips of guards bent down
  not enough tension on lifting spring
Uneven stubble.
  guards loose
  guards out of line
  dull, broken, nicked, or loose sections
  dull, broken, nicked, or loose ledger plates
  worn knife head, guides, knife clips, or wearing plates
  knife out of register
  cutter bar lifting parts out of adjustment
  lifting spring out of adjustment
  knife clips binding
  uneven adjustment of shoe soles
Drive train bearings or pitman box overheating.
  lack of lubrication
  warped or twisted pitman

Hay Harvesting Machinery

crankwheel pin bent or badly worn
dirt or metal in bearings
cutter bar binding or in need of repair

Knife and knife head breakage.
worn knife head or guides, knife clips, or wearing plates
warped or twisted pitman
guards loose
guards out of line
broken, nicked, or dull sections and ledger plates
badly worn pitman box
crooked knife
lagging of cutter bar
guards tilted too far forward.

Choking or clogging.
lagging of cutter bar
knife out of register
lack of lubrication
guards loose
guards out of line
too much tilt of cutter bar
worn cutter bar parts
bar lifting parts or spring out of adjustment
knife head guide bolts loose
fender rod or grass stick not properly set
knife clips not properly set
dull knife

Adapting PTO Mowers

When a horse–drawn mower was first pulled behind a tractor is unknown, but it was probably as soon as the first tractors were in the field. By 1930 mowers designed for the harder use, as well as the higher speeds, of tractors had been developed. Some of these early tractor mowers were beefed up ground–driven horse mowers, but with the growing popularity of the tractor power take off, most were designed to be driven by a PTO shaft from the tractor.

Eventually all tractor mowers were power driven. Pull–behind, semi–mounted, and three–point hitch versions have been developed, each of which may be used with a powered forecart, although a three–point hitch mower obviously requires a cart with a three–point hitch. Tractor mowers that can be fully mounted on either the rear or the side of a tractor are difficult to adapt to a forecart and won't be discussed here.

A newer machine for cutting hay is the disc mower, which cuts with small, replaceable free–swinging knives on whirling discs. The suction of the spinning discs supposedly stands up lodged hay, and the free–swinging knives are less likely to break on stones. While disc mowers have some advantages over sickle bar machines, they require more horse power for a given width of mower than a sickle bar, and can be dangerous as well. The discs spin at high rates that are fast enough to cut off a steel fence post or send broken blades or stones out of the mower at deadly speeds. At least one manufacturer recommends they be used only on tractors with cabs. Although disc mowers can and have been used with PTO forecarts, they are not recommended for use with horses because of the potential for serious injury to team and teamster.

Features of a PTO Mower

A tractor mower has a frame, cutter bar, and control levers just the same as a horse–drawn machine. Of the several kinds of mower that may be used with horses and a forecart, the easiest to adapt is the trail–behind mower carried on its own two wheels and readily attached to the forecart drawbar by a conventional short tongue.

The frame of a semi–mounted mower is supported at the front by fastening it directly to the drawbar, while the rear rides on one or two caster wheels. The front mount is flexible, allowing the mower to follow the contour of the ground, and the caster wheel provides for short turns. Although this style of mower works well with a forecart, special mounting brackets may have to be fabricated and the mower is not easy to connect and disconnect.

To use either a semi–mounted or pull mower, the forecart must be motorized and have a standard power take off to drive the mower through its PTO shaft. If the forecart is equipped with both a PTO and a three–point hitch, a standard three–point tractor mower may be used. A three–point hitch mower is supported entirely by the hitch arms, and becomes an integral part of the forecart. On all tractor mowers, a shielded power take off shaft goes forward to the PTO drive on the forecart, and the power is transmitted to the crank wheel or counterbalance wheel by roller chain, gears, or V belts. If you strike an obstruction, a safety release allows the cutter bar to swing to the rear, while a snap or slip clutch is provided on the drive shaft to protect the drive and cutting components should the obstruction jam the knife.

The cutting parts are virtually the same as those of a ground driven mower, requiring the same care and adjustments. Until about 1952 all tractor mowers used a pitman to convert the crank wheel's rotary motion to the lateral movement of the knife. About that time, a pitmanless, balanced head drive was developed, and today most tractor mowers use this system. The balanced head design basically provides a weight that reciprocates in the opposite direction from the knife. This feature greatly reduces vibration, and allows faster knife speeds and greater mowing capacity. An additional feature of pitmanless drive is that the knife can operate at an angle ranging from 10 or 15 degrees below horizontal to almost vertical. For cutting heavy, matted crops, the double sickle cutter bar is useful. Instead of guards and ledger plates, the lower half of the shear cut is provided by a second knife that works back–to–back with the upper knife. No guards are used, and the two knives work in opposite directions.

Safety First!

☞ *Always* disengage the engine PTO shaft, shut off the engine, and take the key before dismounting from the forecart.

☞ *Never* try to clear a clogged cutter bar while the mower is operating.

☞ *Never* lubricate or adjust a mower while it is running.

☞ *Always* make sure all safety shields are in place, and stay clear of rotating parts.

A trail–behind power take off driven tractor mower.

Allis Chalmers

Operating a PTO Mower

Before operating any power take off driven mower, make sure the mower is properly hitched to the forecart and leveled from side to side. Connect the mower's telescoping PTO shaft to the engine power shaft, making sure the

connection is secure, and see that all safety shields are in place. Check the cutter bar for broken, bent, or damaged guards or sections, and see that the knife is sharp. Lubricate the mower and check for loose bolts and nuts. Lower the cutter bar *keeping your fingers out from between the guards,* stow the transport rod in its clips, and put the tail nut in your toolbox. Start the engine, put the PTO into gear, and slowly engage the clutch with the engine at idle. Check for loud noises, binding, and proper operation, while slowly bringing the engine up to operating speed. If excessive vibration or loud noises occur, immediately stop the engine and determine the cause.

Opening a field is usually done by driving around the field in a clockwise direction, keeping the mower close to the fence or field edge. After cutting a second round in this manner, turn and cut the backswath by driving counter–clockwise. Another opening method is to cut the first round in a counter–clockwise direction with the end of the cutter bar close to the fence or edge of the field. After this opening round, turn and cut the remainder of the field in a clockwise direction. Modern tractor mowers are designed to cut efficiently at speeds of 5 to 7 miles per hour, so don't be afraid you might drive too fast for the mower.

To make neat, square corners with a mounted or semi–mounted mower and forecart, follow the same procedure as for a horse drawn mower. Experience will soon show you when to start the turn with a trailed mower.

To do a clean mowing job, make field adjustments to suit the crop and field conditions. Be sure the cutter bar is floating and properly following the contours of the ground. Set the tilting lever so the cutter bar is parallel with the ground. In a rocky field tilt the guards up so the knife isn't damaged. If the field is smooth and free from rocks, the guard points may be tilted down to pick up a crop that is tangled or lodged.

Before raising and securing the cutter bar in the transport position, disengage the engine clutch, shut off the engine, and put the key in your pocket. Raise the cutter bar keeping *your fingers out from between the guards,* and secure it with the transport rod.

Adjustments

Set the float spring so the cutter bar follows the ground contour. Not enough spring tension allows the bar to drag heavily on the ground; too much tension keeps the bar from returning quickly to cutting height when lowered, and to bounce and cut unevenly on rough ground.

For smooth operation, the cutter bar must be at right angles to the mower's direction of travel. The resistance of

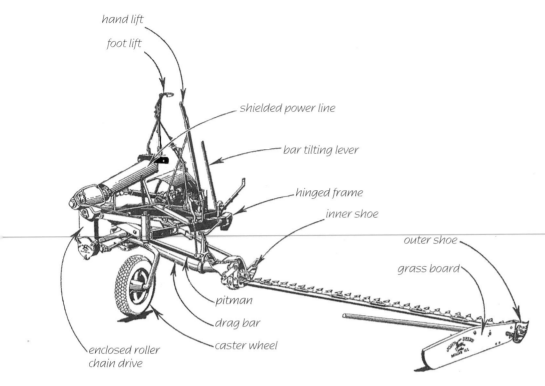

hand lift

foot lift

shielded power line

bar tilting lever

hinged frame

inner shoe

outer shoe

grass board

pitman

drag bar

caster wheel

enclosed roller chain drive

A semi-mounted power take off tractor mower.

Deere & Co.

the crop being cut causes the outer end of the cutterbar to be pushed to the rear. To offset this tendency, the outer end of the bar is designed to have a lead of $1/4$ inch for each foot of bar length. This lead allows the bar to be pushed back a little while the mower is in use and still be properly aligned. The lead may eventually be lost due to wear and should be periodically checked and corrected to keep the mower cutting efficiently. The lead on a pull–behind pitman tractor mower is checked and corrected the same way as a ground driven mower.

An easy way to check cutter bar lead on a semi–mounted or three– point hitch mower is to use a straight board. Park the forecart and attached mower on a level surface and lower the cutter bar to working position. Place a straight board in front of, and touching, both forecart wheels and extending the length of the cutter bar. The board must be as long as the cutter bar plus the width of the forecart. Measure the distance from the board to both the inner and outer ends of the cutter bar knife. The distance from the outer end of the knife should be $1/4$ inch per foot of cutter bar length shorter than the distance from the inner end (for example, $1 1/2$ inches for a 6–foot bar).

If the lead is incorrect, adjust it as directed in your operator's manual. Depending on your make and model,

adjusting the cutter bar lead might involve lengthening or shortening the pull bar or the drag bar, adjusting an eccentric on the cutter bar yoke hinge pin, or adjusting the breakaway linkage. If you don't have the operator's manual, closely examine the mower to find out how to make this adjustment.

Knife register on a pitman–type mower must be correct for good operation. To be in correct register, the knife sections should be centered on a guard at both ends of the knife stroke. On some mowers the knife stroke is less than the distance between the guards, while on others it is greater; refer to your operator's manual to adjust the register on these machines. Check and adjust the register the same as for a horse mower. Pitmanless mowers usually don't get out of register.

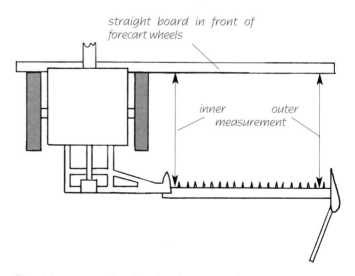

straight board in front of forecart wheels

inner measurement

outer measurement

Checking cutter bar lead using a straight board.

Maintenance

The cutter bar of a mower designed for tractor use requires more maintenance than a horse mower, but since cutter bar components haven't changed much, the procedure is the same. One difference is that the sections on the knives of many cutter bars are attached by bolts instead of rivets, and these bolts must be kept absolutely tight.

Whether you have a pitman or pitmanless machine, lubricate your mower regularly, with special attention to the high speed drive parts. Keep the sickle bar clean and lightly oiled, except for extremely dusty conditions, when it should not be oiled. Inspect bearings, belts, and chains along with the cutting parts, and replace any that are loose, worn, or broken. If hydraulic power is used on your mower, carefully inspect the hoses and cylinders.

Safety First!

 Hydraulic fluid escaping under high pressure can penetrate the skin. Any fluid injected into the skin must be surgically removed within a few hours, or gangrene may result.

Keep spare knife sections, guards, and ledger plates on hand, as well as a spare drive belt and pitman. Replace worn or broken parts as soon as they are detected.

At season's end, clean the mower thoroughly and paint any bare spots. Lubricate all fittings, and lightly coat the cutter bar with oil. Remove the tension from any drive belts and make sure they are clean. Store the mower under cover.

Common PTO Mower Troubles

Overheated bearings.
    lack of lubrication
    bearings too tight.
Cutterbar won't cut or plugs.
    loose, bent, or out of line guards
    missing or dull ledger plates
    dull or worn knife
    drive belt slipping
    bar too close to ground
    too much bar tilt
    incorrect cutter bar lead
    knife out of register
    knife clips not set correctly
    worn out wear plates

Cutter bar breaks back without hitting an obstruction.
    cutter bar plugs or won't cut (see above)
    too much weight on inner shoe
        due to loose float spring
    inner sole set too low
    outer shoe sole set too low
    breakaway latch worn
    breakaway latch set too loose
Plugging at inner shoe.
    grass board and stick missing
    grass board and stick incorrectly adjusted
    inner shoe too heavy due to loose float spring
    inner sole set too low
    bar too close to ground
    grass gathering on inner shoe due to missing
        or incorrectly adjusted fender rod
Plugging at outer shoe.
    outer shoe out of alignment
    outer shoe sole set too low
    ledger plate in outer shoe missing or worn
Knife breakage.
    guards loose or misaligned
    knife sections or ledger plates dull or missing
    worn knife head
    knife bent
    loose bolts
    PTO speed too fast
    slip clutch too tight
Uneven stubble.
    cutter bar not level due to incorrect
        shoe sole adjustment
    float spring too tight
Pitman breakage.
    loose pitman bolts
    incorrect lead adjustment
    PTO speed too fast
    slip clutch too tight
Slip clutch slips in normal mowing.
    binding of cutting mechanism due to
        breakage or clogging
    clutch adjustment too loose

A smooth and quiet running mower that cuts cleanly requires the least effort from a team and gives the teamster satisfaction.

10

Conditioners

"Save a day—Gain a cutting."
Slogan from a New Holland *Grassland Manual*

Hay, especially legume hay, must be cut at the proper time and cured with as little handling as possible to save its nutritious leaves. As sun cures the hay, the leaves dry first and some fall off and are lost, while the thicker stems are still too wet for safe storage. Someone discovered that crushing, or crimping the stems allowed them to dry at approximately the same rate as the leaves, thus greatly speeding the curing process and allowing the hay to be raked and baled much sooner.

Manufacturers started experimenting with machines to crush hay during the late 1940s, but the first successful hay conditioners didn't appear until ten years later. The hay conditioner follows closely behind the mower, picks up cut hay, and passes it between two rolls that crimp or crush the stems. A crimper crushes the stem at one to 3 inch intervals, while a crusher cracks, or bruises, the stem over its whole length. Today most conditioners in use are mower–conditioners that combine the cutter bar and the conditioning rollers into one machine.

The conditioning process cuts curing time by 30 to 50 percent, making a big difference in getting the hay in on time. Other advantages derived from conditioning include better hay color and reduced leaching of nutrients. Conditioned hay is also softer and much more palatable to livestock. Bales are more compact and easier to handle, allowing more hay to be stored in a smaller space.

Hay Conditioners

The typical hay conditioner is a pull–behind, power take off driven machine supported by a wheel at each side. Some machines use smooth rolls—one rubber and one steel, or both rubber—giving a continuous crushing action to the hay. Most rubber rolls have spiral grooves to aid in picking up the hay and feeding it between the rolls.

With smooth rolls, the hay is more likely to wrap, clogging the machine. To solve this problem some machines use a fluted or bar roll that presses against a smooth rubber roll. Others use corrugated, malleable iron rolls with tapered flutes that mesh together like gears. The hay is picked up from the ground and passed between the interlocking corrugated rolls.

Most hay conditioners are about 7–feet wide and are designed to condition one mower swath on each round. Adjustments are provided to set the roll height, the distance between the rolls, and roll tension. A safety slip clutch on the PTO shaft protects against broken parts if the rolls clog.

Action of corrugated rolls. The large drive roll picks up the hay and forces it between itself and the smaller driven roll. The crop passing between the interlocking rolls is not completely crushed, but is bent, crimped, and cracked all along its length.

A New Holland pull–type hay conditioner with grooved rubber rolls.

Operationing a Hay Conditioner

The average hay conditioner should be easily handled by a 20 horsepower, powered forecart. Hitch the conditioner tongue to the center hole of the drawbar and connect the power take off shaft, making sure the locking pin snaps into place. Be sure all safety shields are in place.

For best results use the conditioner just after the mower has cut the crop, and drive it so it picks up a single mower swath. Hay conditioners are designed for tractor speeds of 4 to 5 miles per hour, so don't worry about driving the team too fast.

In normal hay the rolls should be about 4 inches from the ground. Don't operate a hay conditioner empty, or the rolls may be damaged. Keep the drive chain tight enough not to slap or climb the sprockets. If the rolls become plugged or jammed by weeds, vines, heavy hay, or a foreign object, stop the PTO drive immediately and shut down the engine. Release the tension on the rolls and clear the jam. Don't forget to restore the roll tension after the rolls are cleaned out.

Adjustments

The height of the rolls above ground may be varied by means of a crank, or lever. The best height for an average crop is 4 inches. For a light or scattered crop, decrease the roll height; for heavy hay, increase it. Raise the rolls to their extreme height when transporting the machine.

Corrugated rolls should have a shallow mesh under normal conditions. If the hay tends to wrap on the rolls, increase the roll tension, and decrease the distance between rolls. The best roll tension will be determined by the crop and field conditions. Light crops require less tension than heavy crops. The goal is to positively crimp and crack the heavy stems, or stalks, while providing room for the small stems and the tender leaves to pass through the rolls without damage. A close examination of your hay conditioner should reveal the methods for making these adjustments.

Keep the safety clutch adjusted tight enough not to slip under normal operation in heavy hay, but not so tight it can't slip when the rolls become clogged.

Lubrication

At the beginning of each season drain the enclosed gear case and refill it with 90 weight gear oil. Check the oil level at least every 60 hours of operation and top up as needed.

Grease the high–pressure grease fittings twice a day, first wiping the fittings and the gun nozzle to make sure they are clean. Replace any missing grease fittings immediately.

Lubricate the drive chain once a day by brushing on medium weight oil. When conditions are extremely dusty or sandy, leave the chain dry.

Whenever you lubricate the machine, check all nuts and bolts for tightness. Check, too, for broken or damaged parts, particularly the rolls.

Mower-Conditioners

A cutter bar of a mower–conditioner is either a sickle bar or a rotary disc. The sickle cutter bar of a conditioner

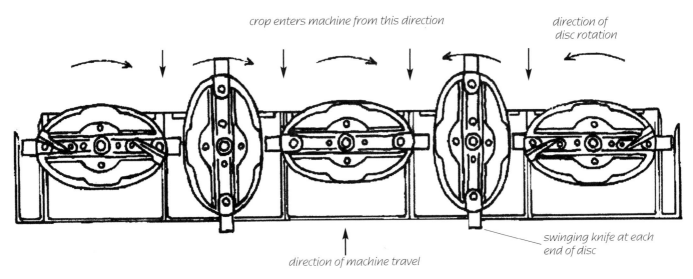

crop enters machine from this direction

direction of disc rotation

swinging knife at each end of disc

direction of machine travel

Top view of part of a rotary disc cutter bar.

operates exactly like that of a mower. A rotary disc cutter bar consists of a series of rapidly revolving, gear driven discs, to each of which is attached two replaceable horizontal knives. The discs on each half of the cutter bar rotate toward the center, and the knives overlap to cover the the entire width of the cutter bar.

Mower-Conditioner Drive

The width of the cutter bar is determined by the mower–conditioner's drive, which is either power take off or hydraulic. PTO driven models usually have a cutting width of 7 to 16 feet, and are hitched to the drawbar and PTO shaft of the power source. The PTO shaft, slip clutch, and gear box then drive the reel (if provided), cutter bar, and conditioning mechanism through a system of gears, belts, and chains.

A John Deere PTO mower–conditioner powered by a 25 horsepower Gateway forecart.

The same mower–conditioner, which John Deere calls a MoCo, laying the crop in a swath.

Hydraulically driven conditioners come with 12 to 16 foot cutter bars. Instead of a power take off shaft that runs from the power source to the machine, a hydraulic pump is mounted on the PTO. The pump runs hydraulic motors that, in turn, drive the chains, belts, and gears on the various mechanisms. The much greater flexibility of the hydraulic hoses, versus the PTO drive train, allows a wide range of adjustments and positions of the overhead pivot hitch, making turning and maneuvering the mower–conditioner much easier.

Safety First!

☞ Be extremely careful when working with hydraulic components. Hydraulic fluid escaping under pressure can penetrate the skin, causing serious injury. Before applying pressure, make sure all connections are tight. Relieve all pressure in the system before disconnecting hydraulic lines or working on a line or component. *Do not* feel for pinhole leaks with your hand—use a piece of paper or cardboard. *Any* hydraulic fluid injected into the skin must be surgically removed within a few hours, or gangrene may result.

Conditioning Mechanism

On both PTO and hydraulic machines the cutter, whether sickle or rotary, is in front of a full–width conditioning mechanism. Three different kinds of mechanisms condition hay in three different ways.

1. The *crimper* passes the hay between two corrugated steel or rubber rolls that mesh like gears. The rolls bend and kink the stems every one to 3 inches, causing cracks that allow the moisture in the stem to escape faster.

2. The *crusher* style of conditioner is the most common. It usually uses a pair of molded urethane rolls with wide intermeshing cleats that both crimp and crush the stems. Different manufacturers use cleats of different shapes, such as chevron, diagonal, and diamond block.

3. The *impeller system* of conditioning hay has free–swinging fingers on the rotor that pick up the hay and throw it against either a hood or a row of stationary comb–like teeth. The conditioning hood or comb teeth may be adjusted to provide more or less aggressive conditioning. The rubbing action of the hood, or the forcing of the crop through the comb teeth, bruises and removes the natural wax coating on the stems.

Mower-Conditioner Features

The mower–conditioner's platform carries the cutter bar, which may be either a sickle bar or a set of rotary discs. Most machines with sickle cutter bars have a *reel* as well. The reel forces the standing crop into the cutter bar, which cuts the hay. After the hay is cut, the reel helps move it into the conditioner mechanism. A mower–conditioner of the rotary disc type has no reel. The combination of the machine's forward motion and the action of rapidly revolving discs and knives is sufficient to cleanly cut even wet or tangled hay while moving the cut crop smoothly into the conditioner.

The mower–conditioner is carried by the mainframe and wheels. The platform is hinged to the front of the mainframe, and is supported by *float springs* that allow the cutter bar, and reel if provided, to follow uneven ground. The tongue, hitch, and power take off drive are attached to the main frame, as well. Provisions are made to keep the PTO shaft properly aligned with the power source while turning, to prevent chatter and breakage. The tongue may be shifted from the transport to the field position either mechanically or by hydraulic power. The conditioning rolls or impeller may be driven by gears, chains, or belts, depending on the model.

Windrow forming shields are located at the rear of the conditioner. These shields are adjustable to allow the crop to be left in a high–standing, narrow windrow, a wide, fast drying swath, or anywhere in between, depending on the drying conditions.

Operating a Mower-Conditioner

Since many different mower–conditioners are offered by several manufacturers, explaining the details of each model is not practical. For specific information on your particular model, consult the operator's manual. All mower–conditioners, however, follow the same general operating procedure.

Before Operation

Inspect and service your mower–conditioner before using it. Clean and lubricate the machine, and check it carefully for loose bolts, nuts, and set screws, as well as damaged or worn parts. Inspect the

Side view of the action of a pair of crushing rolls.

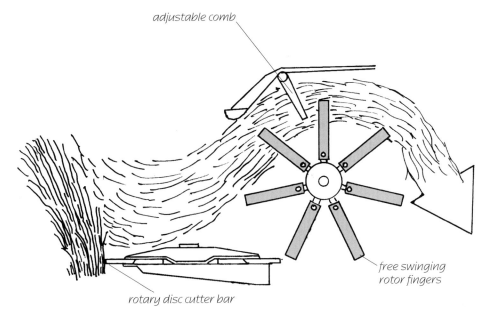

adjustable comb

free swinging
rotor fingers

rotary disc cutter bar

Side view of the action of an impeller conditioner with an adjustable comb.

drive system, and run the machine slowly at first to make sure everything operates correctly.

Hitch the tongue to the center of the forecart's drawbar, and move the jack to the transport position. Securely attach the powershaft to the engine PTO shaft and install all safety shields. Connect the hydraulic hoses to the breakaway couplers on the cart.

Adjust the platform float springs so the cutter bar is level with the ground. Too much tension causes the platform to bounce on rough ground and not return to the proper cutting height when dropped. Too little tension causes the platform to drag heavily on the ground. The tension springs are usually adjusted by means of crank handles.

The conditioning rolls must be timed so the ribs or cleats on one roll mesh in the exact center of the gap between the ribs or cleats on the other roll. If the timing is off, the hay won't be uniformly conditioned and the leaves may be

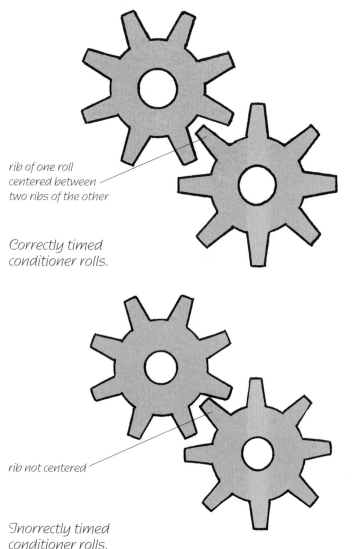

rib of one roll
centered between
two ribs of the other

*Correctly timed
conditioner rolls.*

rib not centered

*Incorrectly timed
conditioner rolls.*

pinched off and lost. If, on the other hand, the roll ribs are forced against each other as they turn, excessive wear and breakage may result.

Check and adjust all slip clutches. A slip clutch that is too tight won't slip when overloaded, causing damage to the machine. One that is set too loose will slip under normal conditions, causing inefficient operation and overheating.

Field Operation

After your mower–conditioner has been fully checked out, pull it into the field and change the hitch from transport to field position. Lower the platform, engage the PTO clutch, and bring the engine up to the rated PTO speed. Open the field by first cutting the swath next to the edge in a counter–clockwise direction. Turn around and cut the rest of the field in a clockwise direction. After a little experience to determine when to start a turn, you should be able to cut neat, square corners with your mower–conditioner.

Be prepared to make frequent field adjustments according to conditions. The normal pace of the horses should be okay for almost any crop condition, although a reduced ground speed may be necessary in lodged or tangled hay.

On a sickle bar mower–conditioner, the reel must be run just low enough to keep a steady flow of hay to the conditioner. In a tall, heavy crop set the reel forward and upward; in a short, light crop set it down and back. Reel speed should be set about 1.25 times faster than ground speed in a normal crop, and even faster to pick up a tangled or lodged crop. The reel should run just fast enough to lay the crop well back on the platform, but no faster. Changing the angle of the reel teeth affects the timing of the release of cut hay. Adjust for an earlier release in tall hay or to compensate for a fast reel speed. Adjust for a later release in short hay or to compensate for a slower reel speed.

The height of the crop being cut and condition of the terrain determine the cutting height. In tall hay or rocky fields the cutting height may have to be higher. Adjustable gauge shoes or turnbuckles are usually provided to adjust cutting height. Be sure to adjust each end of the platform equally. In most cases the cutter bar should be run level, although you may want to tilt it forward to pick up lodged hay or back in stony conditions.

Properly adjusted conditioning rolls will crack or break open the stem without squeezing out the juices, and will permit tender leaves to pass through the rolls without damage. Timothy and other grass hay generally requires most aggressive conditioning, while legume hay needs the least. Too much conditioning causes leaf loss; too little results in unopened stems and slow curing.

Corrugated rolls should have a shallow mesh under normal conditions. If the hay tends to wrap on the rolls, increase the roll tension, and decrease the distance between rolls. A heavy crop usually needs more tension than a light one. Ribbed rubber roll tension should be set about mid–range for most crops. For heavy or large stemmed crops, decrease the roll tension. In light small stemmed crops and grass hay, increase the roll tension.

To adjust the intensity of conditioning when using an impeller style machine, vary the impeller rotor speed and change the distance between the teeth and the conditioning hood. A slower rotor speed and increased hood clearance result in less aggressive conditioning. On mower–conditioners that use an impeller rotor in conjunction with a toothed comb, conditioning intensity is determined by the degree of overlap between the comb teeth and the rotor fingers. The angle of the comb teeth is changed with an adjusting lever to provide the desired intensity of conditioning.

The windrow–forming shields and swathboard are adjustable so the width of the windrows may be varied to meet the prevailing drying conditions. A lever controls the swathboard and the swath screens. In normal conditions adjust the lever to form a windrow of the correct width for the baler, without any need to subsequently rake the mown hay. If the ground is wet, a tall, narrow windrow may dry faster. In other cases leave the hay in a wide, fluffy swath so it can cure before subsequent raking.

If the cutter bar or rolls become plugged or jammed by weeds, vines, heavy hay, or a foreign object, disengage the PTO drive immediately, and shut off the engine, putting the key in your pocket before dismounting from the forecart. Release the tension on the rolls and clear the jam. Don't forget to restore the roll tension after the rolls are cleaned out.

Like any power take off driven machine, a hay conditioner is extremely dangerous. Hands, fingers, legs, and other body parts are no match for the power in a gasoline or diesel engine.

Before transporting the mower–conditioner, disengage the PTO clutch and shut off the engine. Raise the platform as high as possible, and adjust the tongue from the field to the transport position. When traveling on public roads, place a clearly visible Slow Moving Vehicle (SMV) emblem on the rear of the machine.

Common Mower-Conditioner Troubles

The cause of a problem running a mower–conditioner may depend on whether the machine has a sickle bar or rotary disc cutter. The following review will help you diagnose trouble.

Sickle Bar Mower–Conditioners

Plugged cutter bar.
    dull or broken knife sections
    bent or broken guards
    reel not adjusted correctly
    platform float springs not adjusted correctly
    drive belt slipping or broken

Broken reel teeth.
    reel set too low, allowing teeth to get caught in cutter bar

Excessive noise or vibration.
    PTO shaft out of alignment on turns
    damaged cutter bar
    rolls too close or out of time
    broken or damaged parts

Uneven or poor cutting.
    worn, bent, or broken cutter bar parts
    incorrect platform float spring adjustment
    loose cutter bar drive belt

Reel wrapping or carrying around crop.
   reel position not adjusted correctly
   reel speed set too fast
Shredded stems, or excessive leaf loss.
   conditioning adjustment too aggressive
   rolls out of time
   rolls set too close
   reel speed set too fast
Poorly formed windrows.
   swathboard and shields not set correctly
   reel teeth angle set incorrectly
   reel speed set too slow

Rotary Disc Mower–Conditioners
Excessive knife breakage.
   knives not mounted correctly

   incorrect float spring adjustment
   cutter bar set too low
Excessive noise or vibration.
   PTO shaft out of alignment on turns
   broken or missing knives
   rolls too close or out of time
   broken or damaged parts
Uneven or poor cutting.
   broken, missing, or dull knives
   incorrect cutting angle
   incorrect platform float adjustment
Shredded stems or excessive leaf loss.
   conditioning hood or comb teeth set too close
      to rotor
   rotor speed too fast

A New Holland mower-conditioner, which New Holland calls a Haybine, pulled by a 25 horsepower Pioneer forecart.

Hay Harvesting Machinery

11

Hay Rakes, Tedders and Loaders

Getting a field of grass or legumes cut and conditioned is
only the first step in the process of putting up good hay.
The crop must be gathered at just the right time, and stored
in such a way that it is protected from weather damage
until it is fed or sold. To accomplish these jobs many
implements and methods have been developed, including
hay rakes, tedders, and loaders.

Pitching hay onto a wagon by hand is slow, back
breaking work, and the first hayloader appeared in the late
1860s. Hayloaders were widely used in many parts of the
country until the lightweight pickup baler became popular
after World War II. In some parts of the country
sweeprakes were used to gather and transport windrowed
hay to a barn or stack. Sweeprakes, also known as
buckrakes or bullrakes, came into use late in the 19th
century and are still used to put up native prairie grass in
the northern Great Plains.

Eastern farmers stored their hay in barns with large
haymows built for the purpose. Putting hay into a mow was
hot, dirty, hard work. Around 1840 some enterprising
farmers began experimenting with large flat forks that were
lifted into the mow by a horse on the end of a rope and
pulley arrangement. Barn hayforks were perfected to
include large capacity grapple forks and hay slings that
could lift big chunks of a wagon load at a time. By about
1870 wheeled hayfork carriers that ran along a track in the
top of a barn came into use. These carriers saved the man in
the mow much labor, as the load of hay could be dropped at
any point along the track. Animal power was primarily used
to lift the hayforks, but gasoline and electric powered
winches could be used, as well as cars, trucks, or tractors.

Western farmers typically built smaller barns without
haymows and stored their hay outdoors in large stacks.
Hayforks and slings were used to lift the hay onto these
stacks, and were supported by more or less elaborate pole
and cable systems. Soon the overshot stacker, which looks
like a sweeprake on a big A–frame, came into use. The
stacker swung the sweep full of hay up and over, and
dumped the load atop the stack. To make it easier to build
higher stacks, hayslides were developed by hay growers in
the Great Plains. A portable angled slide was built of long,
peeled saplings. A toothed basket resembling a sweep rake
was mounted so it could be pulled up the angled poles by
animals or an engine. A sweeprake load of hay was
deposited on the basket's teeth, which then carried the hay
up the slide. When the top was reached, the basket flipped
over, dumping the load onto the stack. Hayslides are still in
use in some areas.

Putting hay into a barn with a traveling barn fork.

Hay Rakes

Before 1830 grass for forage was cut with a sickle or a
scythe, raked into piles by hand, and pitched onto a wagon
or cart by hand, using a pitchfork. As you can imagine, few
farmers put up more hay than was absolutely necessary to
get their animals through the winter. One of the first hay
handling tools to use animal power was a wooden rake that
could be pulled through a mown field by a horse. The
farmer guided the contraption with the handles and, when
the teeth were full of hay, stopped the horse and lifted the
handles to dump the load.

Hayrakes evolved as farmers and inventors sought a better way. The wooden rake grew an opposing set of teeth, which the operator allowed to revolve when full, dumping the rake on the fly. Wheeled sulky rakes with wooden, and then steel, teeth came on the scene. After the Civil War the side delivery rake was invented, and continues in use today, albeit in a much improved form.

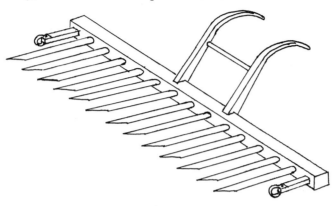

A simple wooden hayrake used during the early 19th century—ropes attached to the eye at each end of the rake were hitched to the horse's harness.

The Bob White brand revolving rake.   Polson Implement Co.

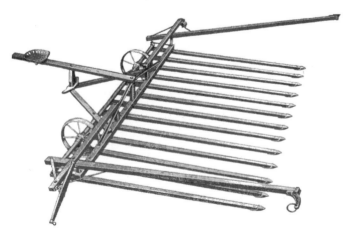

A John Deere sweep rake with teeth made of yellow pine tipped with iron. One horse was hitched at each side of the rake.
Deere & Co.

Dump Rakes

A *dump rake,* also called a *sulky rake,* is the simplest of the hay rakes, and the easiest to operate and adjust. Although this kind of rake is not widely used today, a few are still out there earning their keep.

Built in widths of 8 to 14 feet, the dump rake consists of a steel frame carried on a large diameter wheel at each end. The frame supports a hinged rake bar, along which are bolted a series of curved, steel teeth. The teeth, spaced about 4 inches apart, are made of 3/8– to 1/2–inch rods with either a rounded end called a pencil point, or a flattened end called a chisel point. A small coil near the top end of each tooth, where it is attached to the bar, give the tooth a spring action.

Stripping fingers protrude from the frame rearward between the raking teeth. These fingers strip the hay from the teeth when the rake is dumped. Dump the teeth by pressing your foot on the trip lever, usually located just in front of the seat support. This foot lever forces the outside ends of the trip rods into mesh with the rachets inside the wheel hubs and causes the teeth to raise, dumping the load of hay. As soon as the teeth are at their highest position, the dump rods retract and allow the teeth to fall back into raking position.

The teeth may be manually raised by a hand lever that can be hooked into the raised position for transporting the rake. A larger foot operated lever works in conjunction with the hand lever to hold the teeth against the ground while raking, hold the teeth in the raised position, or force the teeth down faster after they have started to drop.

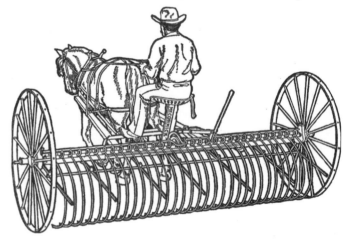

A McCormick all–steel self–dump sulky rake.
International Harvester

Dump rakes are usually equipped with a wooden two–piece pole. The two pieces may be used together as a tongue for two horses, or separately as shafts for a single horse. Solid wood or steel poles, tongue trucks, and tractor hitches came as options.

Hitching a Dump Rake

The correct hitching of a dump rake is critical to good operation. One horse can usually handle a rake of 8 to 10 feet in width; wider rakes are best pulled by a team. As a general rule, the front end of the pole or shafts should be carried at a height that causes the points of the teeth to run perpendicular to a line from the axle hub to the nearest tooth. If the tongue is too high, the hay will tend to stay on the teeth when dumping; if too low, the teeth won't rake clean.

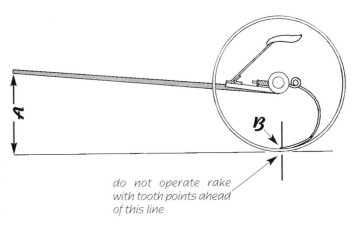

do not operate rake with tooth points ahead of this line

*Hitch a dump rake so the height above ground at **A** puts the points of the teeth directly beneath the center of the axle at **B**.*

Operating a Dump Rake

When a dump rake is adjusted and hitched properly, the teeth gather all the hay and rise quickly when tripped, without leaving behind a scattered windrow. Slight pressure on the foot lever holds the teeth against the ground to gather a larger windrow.

To dump, remove your foot from the foot lever and press the trip pedal, which is usually in front of the seat support. This action engages the dump rods in the wheel rachets and causes the teeth to rise. After the teeth have cleared the windrow and start to fall, they may be forced down more quickly by pressure on the foot lever. The teeth shouldn't dig into the ground, but should float on the surface. The tension spring may be adjusted to achieve this floating action (a small rake may not have a tension spring). If the rake repeats while being dumped, add tension to the trip spring. Use the hand lever to raise the teeth, and to hook them in the raised position for transport.

After the hay has been raked into long windrows, you may drive the rake lengthwise down the windrow to bunch the hay into piles for hand loading.

Adjustments and Maintenance

Most dump rakes have an adjustment behind the seat support to control how high the teeth lift when tripped. If the teeth rise too high and fail to return to working position quickly enough, especially

hand lever

stripper rod

foot trip lever

foot lever

singletree

two-piece tongue bolted to the outsides of the frame

A self–dump hay rake with two–piece pole arranged for one horse.

International Harvester

two-piece tongue bolted to the center of the frame

doubletree evener hitched to clevis

block bolted between front ends of shafts to extend the tongue length and provide an attaching point for the neck yoke

Two-piece pole arranged for two horses

International Harvester

Rakes, Tedders and Loaders

in light hay, turn the snubbing block bolt out, or turn the four–position trip stop so the longest arm is over the trip lever. To permit the teeth to rise higher when dumped, for heavy hay or bunching, turn the snubbing block bolt down, or place the shortest arm of the trip stop over the trip lever. In between adjustments may be made to suit other conditions.

Check all nuts and bolts at regular intervals and keep them tight. Replace badly worn or broken parts. Use oil liberally on all bearings and moving parts. If the automatic dump repeats when actuated, the ends of the dump rods or the ratchets in the wheel hubs have become worn, or the trip spring is too loose. The wheels may be reversed from one side to the other to present new latching surfaces. The dump rods on most rakes may be reversed as well, or built up by welding.

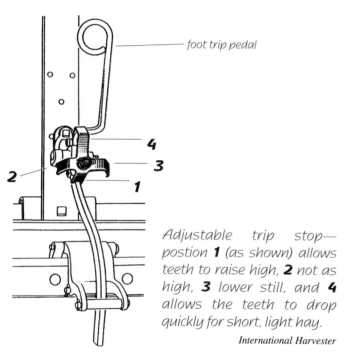

Adjustable trip stop— postion **1** (as shown) allows teeth to raise high, **2** not as high, **3** lower still, and **4** allows the teeth to drop quickly for short, light hay.

International Harvester

Side Delivery Rakes

Newly mown hay left to cure in the swath exposes the leaves to sunlight. If the hay is left in this position long enough for the thicker stems to dry, the leaves will get too dry, shatter, and fall off. A side delivery rake rolls the hay from a swath into a continuous loose, fluffy roll with the green leaves inside and the stems on the outside. The leaves are protected from the sun and are rapidly cured by air circulating through the loose windrow. The stems are on the outside and cure from direct exposure to the sun and circulating air. A heavy windrow, or one that has has been

rained on, may be inverted with the side delivery rake so the bottom will dry.

Four kinds of side delivery rake are commonly in use today—the cylindrical reel and similar parallel bar, the finger wheel, and the rotary rake.

Cylindrical Reel and Parallel Bar Rakes

The *cylindrical reel* rake has a four– or six–bar cylindrical reel suspended under an angle iron frame. The reel, which rotates in the opposite direction to rake travel, may be ground or power take off driven and is set at an angle of about 45 or 50 degrees to the direction of travel. A good rake allows the reel to follow any ground contours, dipping into low spots, and lifting over higher places without digging into the ground.

The rake teeth along the cylinder bars are held at an angle, with the points leading. This position imparts a pushing and lifting action to the hay, which moves and rolls along the front of the reel, and comes off the end in a loose roll. If the rake's direction of travel is the same as that of the mower, the heads end up inside the roll, while the thicker stems face the outside.

A series of semi–circular stripper bars form a basket around the lower part of the reel, and prevent the loose hay from being carried up and over the reel by the teeth. Hand levers are provided to raise and lower each end of the reel, as well as to change the angle of the teeth in relation to the ground. On many reel rakes, the direction of rotation can be reversed, so the rake may be used as a tedder.

The *parallel bar* rake is similar to the cylindrical reel rake in that it has four to six reel bars. These bars attach to two parallel plates, one at the front and one at the rear. These plates are set at right angles to the direction of travel, while the reel bars revolve within the bearing mounts on each of the plates at about a 65 degree angle. This motion keeps the teeth always in a vertical position, causing the hay to be moved to the side with less agitation than with the cylindrical reel. A pitch control tilts the entire reel, which is the only way to change the angle of the teeth. The height of the reel above the ground is usually controlled by one or two hand cranks.

Older side delivery rakes are of the cylindrical reel type and usually have a provision for sliding the tongue to either side of center so the horses can walk to the right, left, or center as the occasion demands. Use a long enough doubletree for the horses to walk in the paths made by the mower's swath board. Most of the newer rakes should be hitched in the center hole of the forecart drawbar. If the rake is PTO driven, be sure the PTO shaft is securely connected and all safety shields are in place. Disengage the PTO clutch before dismounting from the forecart to adjust the rake.

A side delivery rake normally follows the mower, raking in the same direction as the mower cut around the field. Raking in the same direction as the swaths were cut puts the heavy stems on the outside of the windrow where they can dry faster, with the tender leaves on the inside where they won't dry as quickly. The teeth should not scrape the ground, and should always be set as high as possible and still rake the hay clean. For loose, fluffy windrows set the front end of the reel slightly lower than the rear end.

The angle of the teeth in relation to the ground allows you to vary the shape and density of the windrow in different kinds of hay. In most cases angle the teeth to their most forward position so a loose, fluffy windrow results. If the hay tends to wrap, or if you want tighter windrows, use a little less tooth angularity.

On most drawn rakes, the height and tooth angle adjustments are controlled by hand levers or cranks. On some semi–integral rakes the tooth angle adjustment is changed by raising or lowering the rear caster wheels.

Always rake hay before the leaves dry out, and put the windrow onto clean dry stubble. If the hay has been left in the windrow overnight, or has been rained on, half turn the windrow after the top dries out to allow the bottom portion to dry in the sun and air.

To turn the windrow half over, drive along the windrow with the left wheel just to the inside, or right–hand edge, of the windrow. The tail end of the reel will then invert the windrow and the damp hay will be on top. Older rakes had a provision for shifting the left wheel in on the axle to allow the tail end of the reel to stick out far enough to accomplish

the windrow inversion. The wheels on newer rakes are usually behind the reel, which is wider than the wheel tread, and windrows may be turned by driving so the rear end of the reel catches the windrow. Two windrows may be thrown together if the hay is light or if larger windrows are needed for good bales.

Most older side delivery rakes double as tedders. A lever is thrown that reverses the drive and causes the reel to turn in the same direction as the wheels are turning, kicking the hay back and up. Adjust the angle of the teeth so they point toward the rear. Some rakes have a provision for raising the inside rear caster wheel so it doesn't run over the tedded hay. Set the teeth to run higher off the ground than when raking. Drive fast enough for the hay to fluff for faster curing.

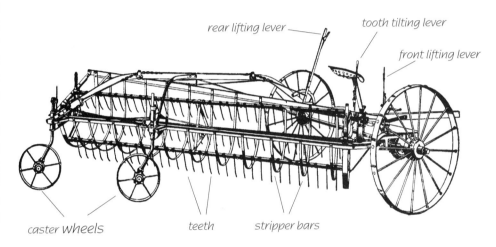

rear lifting lever — *tooth tilting lever*

front lifting lever

caster wheels *teeth* *stripper bars*

A cylindrical reel side delivery rake.

Deere & Co.

The action of a cylindrical reel rake.

Lubricate your rake daily. Put a coating of grease on open gears and oil drive chains, unless conditions are sandy or extremely dusty, when the gears and chains should be left dry. Periodically check the oil level in enclosed gear boxes.

A John Deere parallel bar side delivery rake.

Finger Wheel Rakes

The *finger wheel* hay rake is suitable for windrowing hay, straw, cornstalks, and the like. It consists of several 4½– to 5–foot diameter finger wheels attached to an angled frame. Wheel rakes are available in many sizes, from small models with four finger wheels that can rake a swath as narrow as 5½ feet to giant V–shaped machines with 14 finger wheels and a maximum width of 38 feet. Some rakes, especially the larger models, are supported on two or more wheels. On these pulled rakes, each finger wheel is attached to the main frame by a spring–loaded crank arm, allowing it to follow the contour of the ground without digging in at high spots or missing hay in low spots. The smaller rakes with four finger wheels are usually available as three–point hitch versions, and often have a single telescoping spring arm that provides the floating action to the frame on which all the rake wheels are mounted.

Each finger wheel has about 40 flexible steel fingers around its circumference, and is mounted so it overlaps the wheel next to it. The curved ends of the teeth contact the ground lightly and the wheels revolve as the rake moves forward. This dragging and turning action moves the hay to the side and rear, leaving

Method of adjusting the left wheel and turning over a windrow with a side delivery rake.   New Idea, Inc.

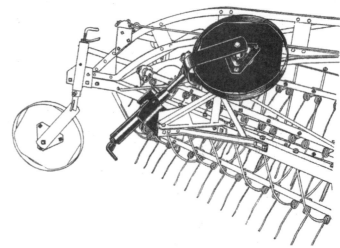

Inside rear caster wheel raised to use the side delivery rake as a tedder.   New Idea, Inc.

it in a windrow parallel to the direction of travel. Wheel rakes are simple and relatively inexpensive, and move the hay gently into high–standing, fluffy windrows that dry quickly. The dragging action sometimes leaves clumps of hay that may choke a small square baler, but have little effect on a round baler.

Before starting to rake, be sure the tooth bolts on all the rake wheels are torqued to 40 foot pounds, to prevent excessive tooth breakage. Adjust the hitch so the main frame of the rake is level, or parallel to the ground. The tips of the rake teeth should contact the ground with just enough pressure to keep the rake wheels turning.

A wheel rake has no designated height setting. Start off moving with the rake just barely off the ground, with the wheels at 90 degrees to the ground. Lower the wheels until the rake is doing the best raking with the least ground resistance. The best setting will produce the least amount of dirt and dust, while still getting all the hay. If the wheels are run too low the teeth will get bent or broken.

If the rake is clogging with grass, check for rust on the teeth ends and make sure the wheels are at 90 degrees to the ground. Don't back up with the rake lowered, as that will cause broken teeth. Grease all fittings daily, and before and after storage.

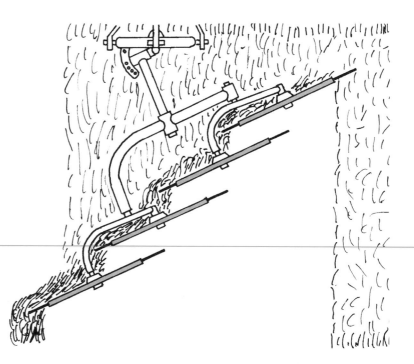

Top view of a four wheel 3–point hitch finger wheel rake.

A V–shaped 10 wheel rake by H&S Manufacturing can cover a swath of from 18 feet to 23 foot 3 inches and has an optional center kicker wheel to assure that all the hay is turned in.

Finger wheel.

Rotary Rakes

Most rotary rakes have a series of arms extending horizontally around a central hub. At the outer end of each tine arm are three or four sets of double spring–steel tines. On some models the tine arms may be removed and stored vertically on top of the rake, allowing the rake to be folded to a narrower width for transport and storage.

The central hub is usually power take off driven, although ground driven models are furnished by at least one manufacturer. When the hub rotates, the teeth gather the hay, lift it, and sweep it to the left and rear. As each arm reaches the left rear, it is rotated clockwise on its axis by a cam mechanism, which raises the teeth and releases the hay in a fluffy windrow.

You can use a rotary rake to windrow a mown crop, turn an existing windrow for better drying, or rake two windrows together. Most rotary rakes are equipped with an adjustable swath screen, or curtain, that helps form a good windrow. Windrow size and shape is controlled by the swath screen setting and the ground speed.

The rake tongue is normally hitched in the center hole of the forecart. If the rake is PTO driven, when connecting the PTO shaft make sure the connection is secure and all safety shields are in place.

Before raking, level the rotary rake. Park it on level ground and lower it to operating position. Measure the distance from the tips of the teeth to the ground on both sides of the machine. If the measurements are different, raise or lower the wheels to achieve the correct setting. Most machines have an adjustment mechanism for this purpose.

After reaching the field, lower the rake to working position. At the correct working height the tips of the teeth on both sides, as well as the front of the rake, just touch the top of the stubble. Move the swath screen in or out on its mounting bracket to control the windrow width. Screen height is also adjustable, and should be set so the bottom of the screen just touches the top of the stubble. When raking two windrows together, you may need to remove the screen and replace it upside down on the bracket.

The driveline of a PTO driven rake is protected from overload by a slip clutch. Engage the PTO slowly and at a low RPM to avoid slipping the overload clutch. If the crop shatters because the rotary speed of the rake is too fast, reduce engine speed somewhat. In areas where the crop is dense or wet, bring the PTO speed up to normal and reduce the ground speed. If the rake becomes clogged, stop immediately and disengage the PTO. Shut down the engine and put the key in your pocket before dismounting to clear the blockage. Before restarting the rake check for damage.

Keep the main gearbox full of oil, and grease all lubrication points every 8 hours. Every 5 to 10 hours of operation, check all bolts and nuts for tightness. If the rake

is equipped with rubber tires, check the tire pressure periodically. Immediately repair or replace any broken, damaged, or badly worn parts.

At season's end, clean and lubricate your rake. Repaint or coat shiny surfaces with grease. If the rake is equipped with a hydraulic cylinder, coat the cylinder rod with grease to prevent rusting. Store the rake under cover in a dry place.

A ground driven rotary rake from J&J Manufacturing.

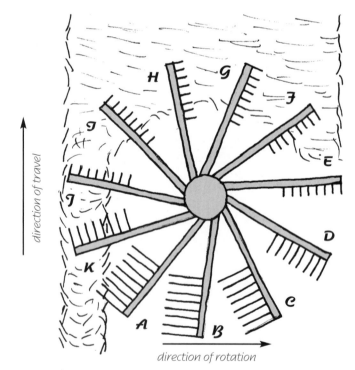

direction of travel

direction of rotation

*Rotary raking action—the tines at **A, B,** and **C** are in the raised position; the tines at **D** are descending to raking position; the tines **E, F, G, H, I** and **J** are raking; the tines at **K** are rising to release the raked hay into the windrow.*

Hay Tedders

Before raking hay into windrows, sometimes it's desirable to ted the hay by fluffing and aerating it to promote faster drying and more uniform curing. Tedding is especially useful if the hay has been rained on while in the swath. Rain beats the mown hay into the stubble, where it comes into contact with damp ground, preventing the bottom of the swath from drying properly. A tedder lifts and fluffs the hay so air can get through it freely. A tedder is equally valuable for spreading damp, matted windrows after a rain.

Modern hay tedders are either of the reel type or the rotary type. Many of the older cylindrical reel side delivery rakes have a provision for reversing the direction of the reel so the machines may be used for tedding.

Reel Tedders

A reel tedder has a four–bar reel suspended in a simple frame with a wheel at each end. Each of the four bars is equipped with rubber mounted steel fingers that lift and fluff the hay as the reel revolves in the same direction as the machine moves. Reel tedders come in 7–foot and 9–foot widths, and are available with either ground or power take off drive.

Set the height of the tines so the tips just clear the ground. The angle of the tines on the reel may be adjusted for either mild or aggressive tedding.

ends of which are mounted angled spring steel teeth. The rotors are driven by a power take off and turn at a high rate of speed to fluff and spread hay from either a swath or a windrow.

If your tedder is the kind that folds, unlock the outer ends and make sure the drive shafts line up before swinging the ends into position and locking them into place. Most rotary tedders may be adjusted for two kinds of working conditions:

An M&W rotary hay tedder powered by a homemade ground driven PTO cart.

A Pequea ground driven reel–style hay tedder.

Rotary Tedders

A rotary tedder consists of a series of rotors mounted side by side on a frame. Each rotor has several arms, on the

- For the normal position, which scatters hay evenly behind the tedder, the frame must be run at right angles to the direction of travel. Usually an adjustment device on the wheel supports may be set so the wheels run straight.
- To move hay away from a fence or ditch, adjust the wheels at an angle to the frame. Slant the frame to scatter the hay to either the left or right of the machine.

After setting the wheels, whether they are straight or angled, adjust the angle of the rotors with the adjusting screw crank handle until the tips of the tines just clear the ground when they are directly in front of the wheels. Lubricate your hay tedder daily to minimize wear and ensure its long working life.

Hay Loaders

For centuries loose hay was hand pitched onto wagons and carts and hauled to a barn or a stack for storage. During the years before the Civil War, several American inventors patented machines to mechanically gather the hay and lift it onto a wagon, and by the 1880s most farm equipment manufacturers offered a hay loader.

The more successful of the loaders to evolve from crude early experiments featured a cylindrical or reciprocal raking mechanism, along with a chain and slat conveyor—or, later, a system of reciprocating raker bars—that ran up a slanted framework to a height of about 10 feet.

The loader's frame is mounted on wheels and towed behind a wagon. As the wagon and loader are pulled lengthwise along a windrow, the hay is gathered and lifted onto the conveyor, or captured by the raker bars, which carries it up and deposits it on the rear of the wagon. A man with a pitchfork then moves the hay into position and builds a load on the wagon.

Hay loaders remained in wide use until pickup balers became popular. Since a hay loader takes up a fair amount of space, unused machines were usually parked outside in the weather and forgotten. Constructed with many parts made of wood, rope, and light sheet metal, these hay loaders soon deteriorated and were eventually scrapped. Most modern horse farmers use balers to handle hay, but a few hay loaders are still in use.

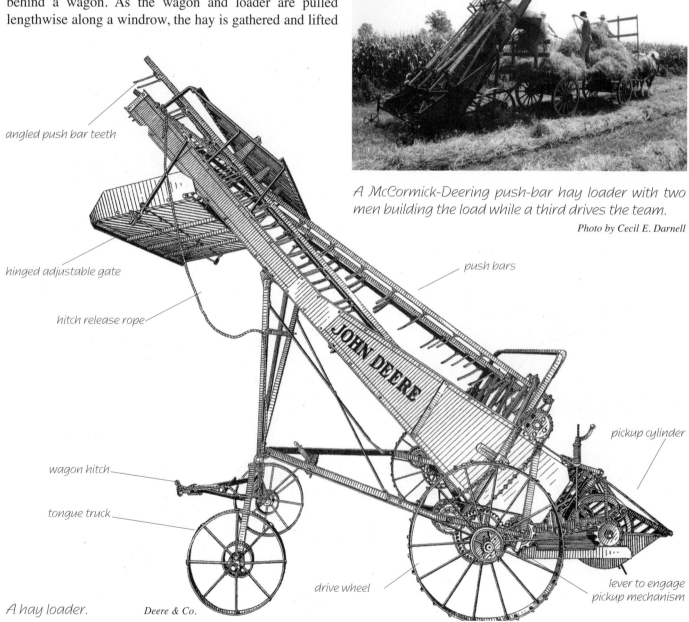

A McCormick-Deering push-bar hay loader with two men building the load while a third drives the team.

Photo by Cecil E. Darnell

angled push bar teeth

hinged adjustable gate

hitch release rope

push bars

pickup cylinder

wagon hitch

tongue truck

drive wheel

lever to engage pickup mechanism

JOHN DEERE

A hay loader.   *Deere & Co.*

Features of a Hay Loader

A hay loader is hitched close behind the hay wagon, with the top front of the angled deck overhanging the wagon. A floating gathering cylinder with teeth lifts hay from the windrow or swath and carries it into the lower ends of a series of crank–mounted push or raker bars.

The upward angled teeth on the push bars carry the hay up the slanting deck. The sheet metal floor of the deck on some raker bar loaders is formed in a series of horizontal ridges that help keep the hay from sliding back down the incline. At the top of the deck the hay is pushed off onto the wagon or hayrack, where a man with a pitchfork builds the load.

At the top of the deck is a hinged adjustable gate that may be let down when the load is started, so the hay doesn't have as far to fall onto the wagon. This gate is especially useful on windy days to prevent hay from being blown off the side of the wagon. As the load gets higher, the gate can be raised to provide more elevating height.

Some loaders have the large drive wheels toward the rear and a pivoting tongue truck supporting the front. On others

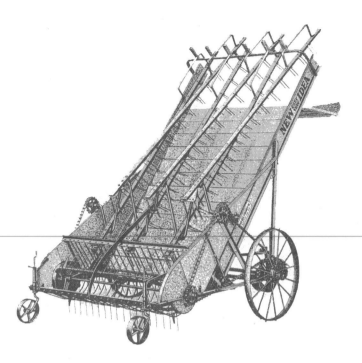

A push bar hay loader with rear caster wheels instead of a tongue truck.   New Idea Farm Equipment Co.

the drive wheels are set farther forward, and the rear of the machine is supported by two small caster wheels.

Operating a Hay Loader

For use as a hitch, an eyebolt and large ring are usually attached to the rear sill of the hayrack or wagon. Hitch the loader as close to the wagon or hayrack as possible without having the loader hit the wagon corners on a sharp turn. The point of hitch should not be too high on the wagon or rack. Otherwise, especially on loaders with rear caster wheels, the weight will be taken off the drive wheels, causing a loss of traction and erratic operation.

To put the pickup cylinder and push bars into gear, most loaders have a small lever on each drive wheel hub you must throw to engage the rachet pawls in the hub. Be sure to engage both sides before starting to operate the loader. Lower the hinged adjustable gate, or deck extension, into position for starting the load. Drive down the windrow with your team, wagon, and loader straddling the windrow.

The pickup cylinder should be adjusted just low enough to get all the hay. If it is too high, the cylinder will leave wisps of hay behind. If it is set too low, the cylinder teeth will dig into the ground and kick dirt and dust into the hay. On most loaders the height of the pickup cylinder may be adjusted by crank handles. On caster wheel type loaders, the adjusting cranks are on top of each caster shank. The

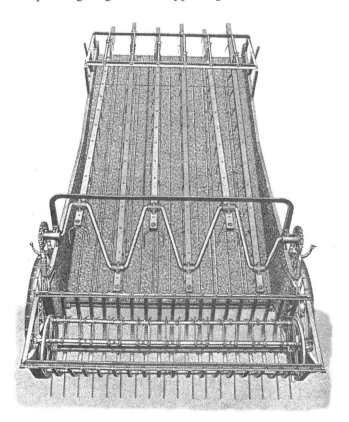

Rear view of a raker bar hay loader showing the crank motion of the six individual push bars. Both the pickup cylinder and the push bar crank turn in the opposite direction to the loader's forward motion.   Deere & Co.

pickup cylinder should be set in the highest position in which it will rake up all the hay, usually just touching the top of the stubble.

Most hay loaders will pick up hay from either a windrow or the swath, although a windrow gives you the best results, especially if the crop is light. A cleaner job of gathering all the hay will result if the loader follows the direction in which the hay was mowed and raked.

Begin building the load at the rear of the wagon or rack. As the height of the load reaches that of the lowered extension, raise it and complete the load. The extension may be gradually raised through several intermediate positions between full down and full up.

The loader hitch is provided with a rope you can reach from the top of the load. A tug on the rope will unhitch the loader from the wagon without the driver having to get

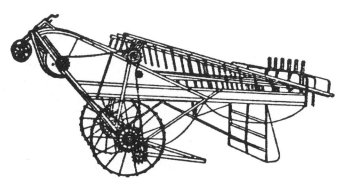

Lay down a caster wheeled hay loader to prevent it from being damaged by the wind.   *New Idea, Inc.*

down from atop the load of hay. Release the loader only on terrain where it won't run away after being unhitched.

At the end of the day's work, or if a storm threatens, a caster wheel–type loader should be laid down. Fore truck loaders are better balanced and less in danger from wind; nonetheless, most of them have a way to collapse the fore truck to lower the machine for windy conditions, hauling, or storage.

Maintaining a Hay Loader

Before using your loader check and tighten all bolts and nuts, particularly those on the push bars and crank bearings. See that the teeth on both the pickup cylinder and the push bars are not broken or bent.

Most loaders have a pair of crossed truss rods on the under side of the elevating deck. These rods keep the deck square to prevent binding between the upper and lower push bar cranks. Inspect the deck to make sure the cranks operate freely. If binding occurs on one side or the other, square up the deck by loosening and tightening the adjusting nuts on the truss rods.

Make sure the drive chains on each side are correctly routed and each chain contains the same number of links as its opposite number. The hook end of the chain links should always point in the direction of chain travel, with the open side of the hook to the outside.

Keep the loader's moving parts well lubricated. Oil the chains except in dusty conditions. Store your hay loader under cover. Left exposed to the elements, the wood and light sheet metal parts deteriorate quickly.

A New Holland parallel bar side delivery rake doing good work in heavy hay.   *Photo by Bonnie Nance*

12   *Hay Balers*

"To get the most money from your hay
   means you must bale it."
     J.I. Case Threshing Machine Company catalog, 1917

The prime impetus for devising a way to bale hay was the vast market that once existed in towns and cities for hay to feed city horses. Since loose hay was hard to handle, ship, and store, baled hay was much in demand and brought a premium price. Loose hay in a mow or stack, or shipped in a railroad car, weighs 4 to 5 pounds per cubic foot. Hay baled in a press averages 25 pounds per cubic foot, greatly reducing the storage or shipping space required. Then, too, baled hay is easier to handle, especially with modern implements.

About the middle of the 18th century hand–operated hay presses appeared. Then a man named Dederick built the beater press. It was a large, upright press and worked something like a piledriver, the baling being done by raising the beater, or plunger, to a certain height, where it tripped, descending with great force into the baling chamber. These presses made a bale about 24 by 42 by 42 inches and weighing from 300 to 400 pounds. The bale was fastened with wooden hoops, baling wire being unknown in those days. Later upright hay presses compressed the hay by horse power. These early presses made one bale at a time and were quite slow.

In 1872 P.K. Dederick of Albany, New York, introduced his perpetual press, which continually forced hay along a horizontal chamber, where it was divided and tied into bales. This system speeded up the operation and by the latter 1800s most presses were of the continuous type, similar to today's machines. The hay is fed into the feed chamber—by hand on the early balers and by mechanical means on modern machines—before being forced through a long, slightly tapered baling chamber by the force of a plunger. The plunger operating mechanism is arranged to force the plunger against the hay with a slow, powerful forward stroke and a quick return stroke.

On stationary presses, as well as early pickup balers, the stream of compressed hay is separated into bales by the insertion of grooved wooden blocks at the proper intervals. The bale is tied with two or three wires threaded through the grooves in the blocks. On modern balers each bale is separated by needles that penetrate the compressed hay stream. Each needle carries a strand of twine, which is automatically tied around the bale. The density of the bale is determined by the friction from the tapered sides of the bale case. This taper and friction may be varied by means

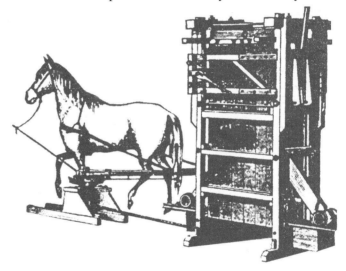

A vertical hay press operated by horse power.

                                  Farm Equipment Institute

An 1895 horizontal continuous feed press operated by horses, which had to back up at the end of each plunger stroke. Other presses allowed the team to walk in a continuous circle.   *1895 Farm Implement News*

of the tension spring screws at the rear of the case. Continuous hay presses were at first driven by horse power, but eventually were belted to engines or tractors, or driven by gasoline engines mounted directly on the baler.

Stationary Hay Presses

Few stationary hay presses or balers are used today for other than demonstration purposes. During operation a feed man stands on the platform and forks a charge of hay into the hopper while the feeder head is rising. When the feeder head falls, it forces the hay into the baling chamber, where it is compressed and pushed to the rear by the plunger.

Some hay presses have a tucker at the front of the bale case to fold in the ends of the hay or straw, ensuring a neat, square–ended bale. Adjustable spring tension at the rear of the bale case causes the hay to be tightly compressed.

The operator places a wooden divider block, with two or three grooves on each side, into the chamber at regular intervals to set the bale length and to allow tie wires to be poked through. A supply of wire ties, usually with a preformed loop at one end, and of the correct length for the size bales desired, is placed at one side of the bale case. The ends of the tie wires are pushed through the block grooves from one side and twisted securely around the bale from the other side. As the plunger pushes bales out the end of the bale case, the divider blocks are retrieved for reuse.

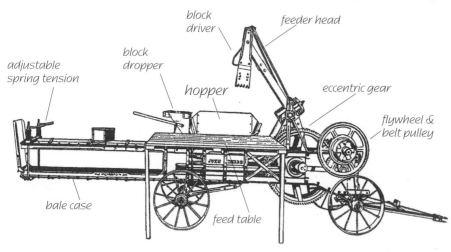

adjustable spring tension

block dropper

block driver

feeder head

hopper

eccentric gear

flywheel & belt pulley

bale case

feed table

A stationary hay press.

Deere & Co.

Operating a Hay Press

Before starting a stationary baler, turn it over by hand to make sure everything moves freely. Lubricate all moving parts, and see that no debris is in the bale chamber. Adjust the screw tension at the rear of the case so the height inside the case is $1/2$ to $3/4$ inch less than the height of a standard bale. The more tension, the heavier and tighter the bale will be.

When starting with an empty bale chamber, first insert a divider block. Fork a charge of hay into the hopper only when the feeder head is rising or at the top of its stroke. Each charge should be uniformly sized and separated before being placed into the feed chamber, to allow the feeder head to force the charge well to the bottom of the chamber. The feed man is responsible for making sure the feed chamber is clear of hay before the block is set. After the feed man breaks the stream of hay at the edge of the platform, a plunger stroke or two usually clears the feed chamber. If hay is in the chamber when the block is dropped, the block will be damaged or broken.

Under normal conditions only one man is required to handle the wire, although the job is easier with a man on each side of the bale case. Some large presses use three wires instead of two, and one man will have a difficult time keeping up with poking and tying on a three–wire machine.

More than one method is used to poke and tie the wires. A common method requires two men. As the first divider block comes into view in the bale case, the man on the left side of the baler pulls the looped ends of two tie wires (three, if using a three wire machine) from the bundle and pokes them through the block grooves toward the front of the baler. As feeding continues, that first block will be pushed through the case until it reaches the desired bale length, at which time a new divider block should be dropped. Some machines have a warning bell, or are marked in some way on the side or top of the bale case, to indicate when the desired length has been reached and a new block should be dropped. When the second block appears in sight in the bale case, the left–hand man pokes the straight ends of the previously placed tie wires through the block grooves toward the rear of the baler, and then pokes the loop ends of two new wires through the front grooves of the same block. The man on the right side of the baler pulls the wires tight and ties the bale.

Another method is for the right–hand man to poke the loop ends of the first wires back through the rear grooves, allowing the tie to be made on the left side of the chamber. This method is probably easier for a single wire man, as he can lean over the case from the left side and return the wires to himself.

The tie is made by placing the straight end of each tie wire through the loop on the other end, then bending the wire back and wrapping it two times around itself. The wrap is stopped at the correct point so the wire end lies snugly against the bale when the wire becomes tight as the bale leaves the bale case. Stopping the wrap at this point prevents the wire from unwrapping and positions the sharp wire end so as to prevent injury to anyone handling the bale. If the wires are too long, the ends may be cut off with a pair of sidecutters after they are tied. This method of tying the wires is recommended in baler manuals.

Some old–timers believe the only correct way to tie a bale is to make a square knot. This knot is made by taking the straight end of the wire through the loop, then around behind it, and back through the loop, thus forming a square knot before wrapping the end. This way of tying is a matter of preference (and considerable personal pride among its practitioners). While it undoubtedly makes a stronger tie, the operation requires more time and is unnecessary. If done properly, the wrapping method is quite adequate.

While the wires are being tied, they should be pulled reasonably tight around the bale with a uniform inch or so of slack, since the bale will expand and tighten the wires upon exiting the case. After a little practice, the correct amount of slack needed to make a tight but not too tight bale will become automatic. Banana–shaped bales exiting the case mean one wire is being pulled tighter than the other before they are tied.

One of the wire men, or whoever is carrying away the bales, is designated to retrieve the loose divider blocks as they emerge from the case, and place them into the dropper.

The wire men monitor the progress of the blocks through the case, so a new block can be inserted at the proper time. When the bell rings, or when the block reaches the mark, a new block is dropped (usually by the feed man), ensuring that all the bales are of the same length.

Take care to raise the block dropper into position only when the plunger is moving out of the bale chamber and the feeder head is rising. When the feeder head descends, the block driver on the head must strike the block squarely to set it into the chamber properly. Usually three blocks are provided—one waiting in the block dropper, and two passing through the case. As the new block is dropped into the chamber, the last one is being ejected from the case and can then be placed in the dropper. After making the first three or four bales, check them for tension and weight, and adjust the tension spring screws if necessary.

Maintaining a Hay Press

Lubricate all bearings at regular intervals during the day, and inspect the whole machine for loose bolts and worn parts before starting to bale each morning. If the press is to remain idle for any length of time, loosen the tension spring screws so the bale left in the chamber won't become locked. When baling is resumed, tighten the screws after the bale starts to move to the rear.

At the end of the season, loosen the tension spring screws and clean out the bale case and feed chamber. Coat the shiny inside of the bale chamber and case with oil to prevent rust, and lubricate the baler before storing it under cover. Store the wooden divider blocks and any unused baling wire in a dry place.

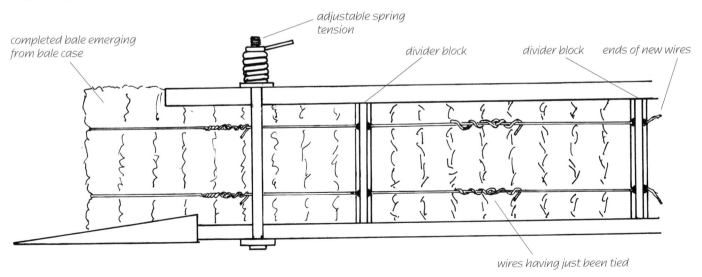

Side view of bale case showing how the wires run through the grooves in the divider blocks.

Method recommended in baler manuals for tying baling wire—two wraps with ends lying against bale.　　　J.I.Case Co.

An alternative method of tying baling wire— square knot and two wraps.

rectangular bales or large rectangular bales. Large rectangular balers usually require more than 100 horsepower on the PTO and therefore are unsuitable for use with horses. Another style, the round baler, rolls hay into firm square–shouldered round bales. These modern automatic pickup balers greatly reduce time and labor involved in handling a hay crop.

Early windrow pickup press with an engine attachment. The feed man stands on a platform behind the top of the pickup head and forks hay into the baling chamber. A seat and footrest are on each side of the bale case for the wire tiers.　　　*International Harvester*

Pickup Balers

Farmers in the early 20th century recognized the savings in time and labor by baling hay right from the windrow. Some manufacturers mounted engines on their smaller stationary balers, so they could be pulled through a hayfield and the loose hay pitched in. Many ingenious home–engineered rigs were cobbled together using stationary balers, hayloaders, and old car engines. These balers were heavy and cumbersome, and making them work required a large crew. In the 1930s manufacturers began experimenting with pickup hay presses, which were basically stationary balers with a pickup head and engine added, along with wooden seats for the two men (or more often boys) who poked and tied the wires.

By 1950 several comparatively lightweight one–man balers were on the market that automatically tied the bales with heavy twine. Instead of wooden block dividers, these machines use timed needles to carry the twine through the stream of compressed hay. One manufacturer produced a machine that made small rolled bales and wrapped them with binder twine.

Today several styles of pickup baler are available, including so–called square balers that make either small

Small Square Balers

Small twine–tie square balers have many variations from model to model, and from manufacturer to manufacturer, making it imperative that you obtain and carefully study the owner's manual for your particular machine. These balers are fully automatic and may be run by either a mounted gasoline engine or a medium duty PTO forecart. As the baler is pulled along the windrow, a number of components work together to gather the crop and move it into the bale chamber, where the plunger compresses and slices off the charge, which is then pushed into the bale case. Here the compressed bale slice is held against the bale being formed, while the plunger moves forward to get the next charge of hay. When the bale reaches the desired length, the tying mechanism is tripped and the bale is tied. As more hay enters the baling chamber, the completed bale is forced out the end of the bale case and drops to the ground, or is pushed or ejected onto a trailed wagon.

The *pickup head* is power driven—although a few older balers had ground driven pickups—about 5 feet wide, and adjustable in operating height. A *pickup lift crank* is located at the left end of the auger housing and should be adjusted so the pickup teeth are as high as possible, but still low enough to get all the crop. The pickup head has a floating action to allow it to conform to the ground. Strippers at the rear of the pickup head prevent wrapping around the reel, and provide a steady feed to the auger housing.

The *auger* receives the crop from the pickup fingers, and moves it sideways into the feeder. The auger floats against spring pressure so it provides steady feeding under heavy or light crop conditions. The *feeder* consists of a pair of teeth that lift and push the crop into the bale chamber.

The *plungerhead* compresses the bale. A sharp knife is mounted on the plungerhead, and on every stroke, each charge is sliced against a stationary knife and is then compressed against the bale being formed. Two retractable *hay dogs* firmly hold each bale slice while the plungerhead returns for another charge.

A toothed *bale measuring wheel* rides on top of the bale being formed, and trips the tying mechanism when the preset bale length is reached. Bales as short as 12 inches and as long as 50 inches may be made.

Two *tension cranks* at the rear of the bale case regulate bale density and weight. The greater the tension, the heavier the bales. Bale weight is also affected by windrow size, as well as the moisture content and quality of the crop. Bales that are too heavy may cause excessive baler wear, baler breakage, or twine breakage. Loosen the tension cranks at the end of each day.

The most common problem with an automatic pickup baler is untied bales. An occasional loose bale is to be expected, and can be easily rebaled, but a long line of loose hay stringing out behind the baler indicates a part has broken or worn out, or some adjustments are needed. To properly operate an automatic baler you must understand the tying cycle and the other adjustments that affect the tying process.

A pickup baler is a complex machine, requiring all its different parts and components to work in synchronization.

Tying the Knot

After each needle has been threaded, the ends of the two twine strands are held in the twine discs of the knotters by the twine holders, while each twine strand lays across its respective billhook:

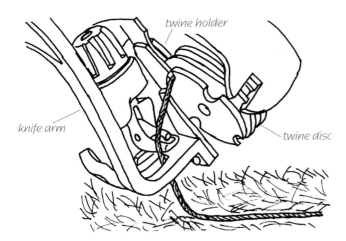

A bale moving through the case pulls twine from the twine box, thus surrounding the bale on three sides:

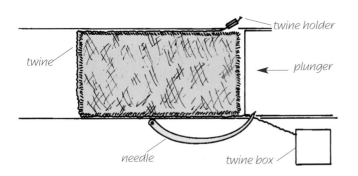

A toothed bale measuring wheel rides on top of the bale and turns as the bale is pushed through the chamber. When the bale reaches the desired length, the measuring wheel trips the tying mechanism. The needles move up through the bale chamber, through slots in the face of the plunger, each carrying a loop of twine, which is now around the bale. Each needle carries the twine through the guide on the knife arm, across the billhook, and into the twine disc:

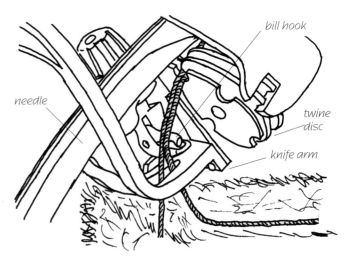

The twine disc driving pinion turns the disc far enough to allow the twine holder to tightly hold both the original twine end and the new twine. The billhook starts to revolve and its jaw to open:

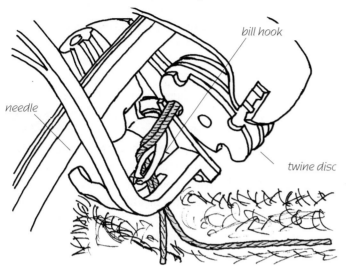

The revolving billhook forms a double loop of twine around the hook, and the knife starts to advance. At this point, the needle starts to retract, leaving the twine in the disc ready for the next bale:

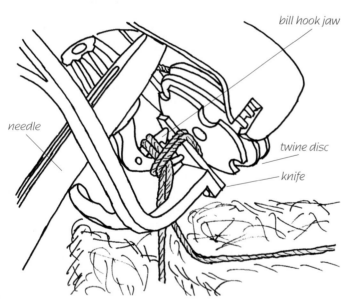

The knife cuts the twine between the billhook and the disc, and the billhook jaw closes tightly on the ends of the twine. The knife arm, with its built-in wiper, strips the looped twine from the billhook The billhook jaw tightly holds the cut ends of the twine, pulling them through the loop as it is stripped, thus forming the knot.

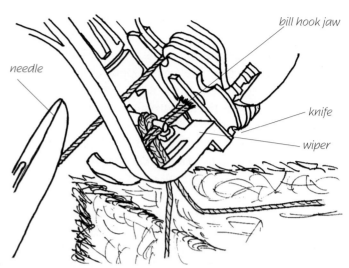

The movement of the completed bale to the rear under the impetus of the plunger pulls the knot tight, at which time the billhook jaws open and the bale is complete. The needles return to the home position, leaving the strands of twine extending from the twine discs through the bale chamber, ready to start the next bale.

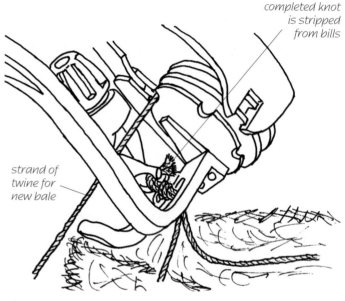

The movement of the completed bale to the rear under the impetus of the plunger pulls the knot tight, at which time the billhook jaws open and the bale is complete. The needles return to the home position, leaving the strands of twine extending from the twine discs through the bale chamber, ready to start the next bale.

Different makes and models have different instructions for loading the twine box, threading and adjusting the needles, timing the baler, adjusting the knotters, and all the other adjustments that must be correct for good hay baling. For these reasons, the instructions in the owners manual for the particular machine being operated must be studied and carefully followed. If the machine isn't badly worn, and meticulous attention is paid to *all* the recommended adjustments, a stream of well formed and tied bales should flow from the baler.

A New Holland pickup baler powered by a homemade ground driven PTO forecart.   Photo by Ted Rose

Operating a Square Baler

If the baler has been stored, remove the grease from the knotter mechanisms. Remove the grease or heavy oil from the bale case and drive chains. Make sure the gear case is filled with clean oil of the proper weight, as recommended in your operator's manual. Lubricate the entire machine. Tighten all bolts, nuts, and set screws. Check and adjust the timing of the entire baler per the manual. Check the air pressure in the tires. Make sure the slip clutches operate correctly.

Use twine of good quality and uniform size to ensure good knotter operation. Load the twine and thread the needles as described in your manual.

Start the baler and bring it up to the recommended speed; the plungerhead should be operating at 80 strokes per minute while under load. Listen for unusual noises and make sure the baler is functioning properly. When you start with an empty bale case the first few bales will be light and poorly shaped until enough crop has built up inside the bale case to provide sufficient compression.

The baler is operating efficiently when it takes 12 to 18 charges per bale. If the windrows aren't heavy enough to put 12 to 18 charges into a 36–inch bale, rake two or more windrows together. On the other hand, in heavy hay don't crowd the baler. If the auger drive belt slips, the baler is being overloaded, so drive slower or rake lighter windrows.

Periodically clean out the chaff and trash from around the tying mechanism and the plungerhead stop. If this accumulation gets wet, or the crop is high in moisture or gummy, the tying mechanism trip may not operate properly, causing long or untied bales, or broken parts.

Keep slip clutches and drive belts tight enough to do their work, but not so tight that parts break. Check these adjustments, and all the other adjustments in your manual, before putting the baler into use each season and anytime a malfunction occurs.

Regular and thorough lubrication is essential for the safe and efficient operation of a baler. Wipe the grease fittings clean before greasing, and wipe up any excess grease afterward. Replace any missing grease fittings immediately. Consult the lubrication charts in your operator's manual.

Troubleshooting

Most baler troubles are the result of either incorrect adjustments or the lack of service and lubrication. Poor quality twine is a major cause of knotter troubles. Make sure the problem isn't caused by a malfunction in some other part of the machine. A baler is a complex machine made up of many components that all have to work together, so trouble in one place may be the cause of a problem somewhere else. If a particular readjustment doesn't correct the problem, return that adjustment to its former position before trying something else. When problems occur, consult your operator's manual.

> *Safety First!*
>
> ☞ *Never* adjust, clean, or lubricate a baler while it is running.

Storing a Square Baler

At the end of each season thoroughly clean your baler inside and out. Clean the knotter mechanisms and apply a thick coat of grease. Lubricate the entire machine. Clean any drive chains by soaking them in kerosene or diesel fuel. Thoroughly dry the chains and coat them with heavy oil. Coat the shiny inside of the bale case with grease or heavy oil, and paint any other parts from which the paint has been worn. Check the baler for loose, worn, or broken parts and make repairs. Store your baler in a dry place, blocking it up to take the load off the tires.

Large Round Balers

Round hay bales have been around for a long time. A patent was granted to Ummo Franklin Luebben of Lincoln, Nebraska, on October 18th, 1910, for a baling press. Luebben's bales were round, formed by rolling the hay inside endless belts, and were tied with binder twine instead of wire. They were claimed to retain all of the plant leaves, and were said to be waterproof, allowing them to be piled in the field and left until ready for use.

Luebben's round baler never achieved much success and was largely forgotten until Harry Merritt of Allis–Chalmers bought the patent rights in 1940. In 1943 Allis–Chalmers announced a new one–man pickup baler that was billed as "an entirely new design," although it was based on the 1910 patent. The announcement said, "The baling operation is automatic and ordinary binder twine is used instead of wire. Bales are cylindrical in shape, the hay being rolled into a tight, compact bale, similar in appearance to a strip of carpet rolled and wrapped.. Since the stems are curved around the bale and tightly held, they serve to shed water and to reduce absorption, making the bale more resistant to weather." The bales were 36 inches long, from 14 to 22 inches in diameter, and weighed from 40 to 100 pounds.

During the late 1960s, engineers at Iowa State University experimented with a machine to make large round bales, and about 1971 the first of the big round balers we know today became practical. Some early balers formed the bale by rolling it along the ground before raising and wrapping it, but virtually all modern machines carry the bale in the bale chamber while it is being formed.

Features of a Round Baler

As with square balers, round balers vary from model to model, and from manufacturer to manufacturer, making it imperative that you obtain and carefully study an owners' manual for your particular machine. Two kinds of round balers are predominant—variable chamber and fixed chamber.

A *variable chamber* baler uses a series of forming belts that rotate and compress the incoming hay. As the hay is rotated within the chamber under the continuous

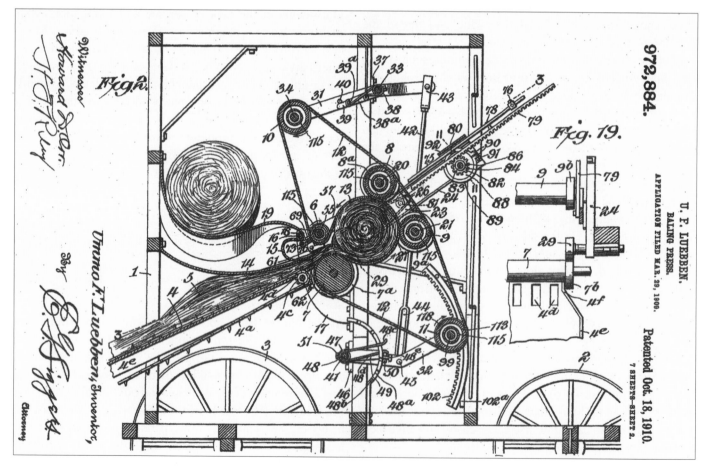

A 1910 patent drawing of Ummo Leubben's round hay baler, on which modern round balers are based.

compression of the belts, a relatively uniform density is maintained throughout the bale, although you can control the bale size and density. For making bale silage, which is considerably heavier than dry hay, a variable chamber baler is therefore the best choice. When a bale made in a variable chamber machine is viewed from the end, the tightly wrapped layers of hay may be seen progressing from the core to the outer edge, much like a rolled carpet.

The reel tines on the pickup head lift the crop from the windrow and carry it into the chamber, where the belts grab the hay and immediately start it turning to form a roll. The incoming hay is forced between the bottom of the rotating bale and the lower roller, and is thus compressed into a dense layer that is fed onto the revolving bale. As the bale size grows, it forces the continually turning belts upward under hydraulic pressure. This pressure maintains uniform bale density throughout the forming process.

Each baler has a visual or audible signal to indicate when the bale has reached the desired size. When this size has been reached, twine is fed into the chamber along with the hay, and forward travel is stopped. The bale is then wrapped with twine, either automatically or under manual control. Surface mesh or plastic wrap may be used on some models instead of twine. Surface wrapped bales retain their round shape better during storage and transport than those wrapped with twine. After the bale is wrapped, the hydraulically controlled rear gate is opened and the bale is ejected.

In a *fixed chamber* baler, also called a roll baler, hay enters the chamber until enough has accumulated for the rollers to start bale rotation. Additional hay is packed on the outside of the growing bale until the desired density is reached. The hay at the center is not compressed as tightly as that on the outside of the bale, and the bale size cannot be varied, although the density can. The core of a fixed chamber bale has a characteristic star shape when viewed from the end, while the outer shell is dense and well packed.

The crop is picked up by the pickup reel tines and fed directly into the baling chamber, where the rollers tumble the hay into a round bale. As the bale grows in size, it exerts more and more pressure on the rear door, which is held closed hydraulically. This pressure causes the outer shell of the bale to become packed hard, while the bale core is of medium density.

A pressure gauge is tapped into the hydraulic circuit of the rear door and monitors the pressure required to keep the door closed. The pressure gauge functions as an indicator of bale density and lets the operator know when to wrap and eject the bale.

The bale may be wrapped with twine or mesh any time after the hay in the chamber begins to roll, but the desired pressure should be reached on the pressure gauge before wrapping. Many balers have an audible signal, such as a horn, that alerts you when the desired pressure has been reached. At this point forward travel is stopped and the twine or mesh tie system is activated—whether electrically, hydraulically, or manually. After the bale has been wrapped it may be ejected from the chamber.

plastic mesh

A Claas Rollant fixed chamber round baler (powered by a Gateway 77 horsepower 4-wheel PTO cart) equipped to wrap bales with plastic mesh carried at the baler's top front; some brands carry the mesh roll at the rear of the bale chamber.

Setting up a Round Baler

A round baler isn't as mechanically complex as a square baler. It does, however have a lot of hydraulic and electrical components, rollers, belts, gears, and chains that must be kept in proper operation. Different makes and models have different instructions for preparing the twine or surface wrap mechanism, setting bale size and density, and all the other adjustments that must be correct for good hay baling. Poorly formed bales are the most common problem encountered in round baling and are most often caused by an inexperienced operator. The best place to find

A variable chamber baler discharging a completed bale. On the open door you can see the belts that form the bale.

these two belt rollers move to the right under hydraulic pressure to provide enough belt for the expanding bale

fixed belt rollers

hydraulic pressure maintains belt tension to create a tight, well-formed bale

In a variable chamber round baler, the incoming stream of hay is fed onto the outside of the rotating bale. Turning belts maintain hydraulic pressure on the bale, squeezing the hay into a compact and well-formed bale.

specific information for your particular machine is the owner's manual.

Your forecart must have adequate PTO power and hydraulics for the round baler you are using. Some machines also require a remote electrical outlet. The horse power of your team must also be matched to the total load. Your team may easily move the forecart and baler when the baler is empty, but as the bale grows inside the baler, the load's weight increases dramatically. A round baler needs a lot of hydraulic power; check your forecart's hydraulic system and add oil if necessary.

Safety First!

☞ Be extremely careful when working with hydraulic components. Hydraulic fluid escaping under pressure can penetrate the skin, causing serious injury. Before applying pressure, make sure all connections are tight. Relieve all pressure in the system before disconnecting hydraulic lines or working on a line or component. *Do not* feel for pinhole leaks with your hand—use a piece of paper or cardboard. *Any* hydraulic fluid injected into the skin must be surgically removed within a few hours, or gangrene may result.

To hitch the baler:

● Adjust the hitch jack up or down to match the height of your forecart's drawbar.

● Back the cart into position, align the holes, and insert and lock the safety hitch pin.

● Connect the baler power shaft to the cart's PTO.

● Connect the hydraulic hoses to the cart's breakaway outlets.

● Attach any electric control boxes, or manual control ropes to the cart so they are within easy reach.

● *Make sure all safety shields are in place.*

● Place the hitch jack in the transport position.

Before starting to bale:

● Lubricate the baler per your owner's manual.

● Check for loose nuts, bolts, and other parts, and for worn or broken parts.

A Gehl fixed chamber round baler. Note three of the large rollers that form the bale visible at the top front of the machine.

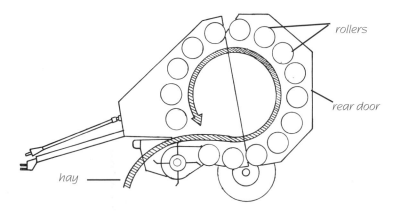

In a fixed chamber round baler, as the incoming stream of hay enters the chamber, rapidly spinning rollers tumble the hay into a round bale. The growing bale exerts increasing pressure on the rear door, which is held closed hydraulically. Pressure of the bale on the door causes the outer shell of the bale to become firmly packed.

The pressure gauge on a typical fixed chamber round baler.

- Inspect and adjust all belts and chains for wear and for proper tension.
- Clean out all dirt, weeds, chaff, and other debris from moving parts.
- Check tire pressure if appropriate. ● Check the hydraulic system again for leaks.
- Operate the rear gate and the other hydraulic components several times to purge the system of air and make sure everything operates properly. The hydraulic system must be in top condition, as it is essential in controlling bale density.
- Engage the PTO clutch and operate the baler for a short while to make sure all components are operating as they should.

To ready the twine bale wrapping system:
- Fill the twine box with balls of good quality twine.
- Thread the twine wrapping mechanism from the ball nearest the twine tube.
- Splice the balls of twine together, using a square knot in sisal twine, and a sheet bend knot in plastic. Pull the knots tight, and closely trim the ends, as the knots must be small enough to pass through the twine guides. Always tie the outside twine end of the first ball to the inside twine end of the next ball for continuous feeding.
- When adding new balls of twine, move the partly used ball to the compartment nearest the twine tube before splicing in the new balls.
- To thread the baler, refer to your operator's manual. Carry a length of wire in your toolbox and use it to pull the twine through the twine tubes, making sure the twine correctly passes through the twine guides. Secure the end of the twine in the cut–off assembly, as specified in your owner's manual.

Sheet bend knot for tying plastic twine. Pull the knot tight and trim off the loose ends.

Sisal versus Plastic

Sisal and plastic twine both work, but each has pros and cons. Sisal twine is cheaper, but deteriorates during storage, especially on the bottom of the bale. Plastic twine doesn't deteriorate and should be your choice if your bales will be handled several times or stored for a long time.

Remove all twine before feeding a bale. Plastic twine is indigestible to animals, and is hard on bearings when it gets wrapped up in equipment. All twine causes problems if it wraps on manure handling equipment, especially a spreader.

To prepare the surface wrap mechanism (for a baler so equipped):

- Open the rear cover over the roll holder.
- Pull out the pivoting support arms and place roll of wrapping material in position.
- Feed the loose end of the wrapping material through the feed rolls.
- Raise the roll to its final position.
- Close the rear cover.
- *Consult your operator's manual for specifics.*

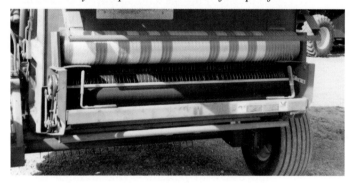

A roll of surface wrap material in place at the rear of a baler. Note the wrap feeder rolls visible below the roll of wrapping material.

To make preliminary adjustments:

- Set the pickup teeth as high above the ground as possible, while still getting all of the crop. The height adjustment is often made with a hand crank. The pickup head flotation spring tension should be set so the head floats over irregularities in the ground. Too much tension will cause the head to bounce on rough ground and not return to the proper height when dropped. Too little tension causes the platform to drag heavily on the ground. Adjust the tension springs by means of either crank handles or adjusting nuts.

- Check and adjust all slip clutches. A slip clutch that's too tight won't slip when overloaded, causing damage to the machine. One set too loose will slip under normal conditions, causing inefficient operation and overheating.
- Check belt and chain drives for correct tension.
- Make sure the twine wrap assembly is set for the proper twine tension, and the automatic twine cutter, as well as the number of wraps per bale are set as recommended in your operator's manual.
- If yours is a surface wrap machine, make sure the loose end of the wrapping material is fed into the rolls correctly, and that the cutting mechanism is properly set.

Safety First!

The hazard of fire is always present when dry hay is being baled.

☞ *Always* carry on your baler or forecart a pressurized water–type fire extinguisher of at least five gallons capacity.

☞ *Always* minimize the risk of fire by cleaning out all dirt, dust, and chaff buildup from inside the bale chamber, from the pickup head, and especially from behind the shields over the chain and belt drives.

☞ *Always* remove any buildup of hay wrapped around turning shafts—the friction from such a buildup easily creates enough heat to start a fire.

☞ *Always* stop immediately if a fire starts. Eject the bale, disengage the PTO clutch, and move the baler at least 30 feet away and upwind of the ejected bale. Shut off the engine and use the water–type extinguisher to douse any material burning inside the baler.

☞ *Never* use a water–type fire extinguisher on a fuel or electrical fire. Use only a dry chemical extinguisher for a fuel or electrical fire.

Operating a Round Baler

Before starting to bale, familiarize yourself with the operating controls—the remote hydraulic cylinder levers, the PTO clutch, and the controls for the manual twine wrap mechanism. Later machines have a bale monitor that senses bale shape and size, as well as an automatic tying mechanism. Mount the control or monitor box on your forecart within easy reach.

Proper raking of the crop to be baled is the most important first step toward consistently turning out bales of uniform size and density. The ideal windrow is even in height and as wide as the baler's pickup head. Drive straight down this windrow and you will have well–shaped bales. A windrow of the correct width, but with a high center, results in more material being fed into the center of the bale than the ends. The bale will have loose ends and be difficult to wrap with twine or surface wrap.

If the hay can't be raked into full–width windrows, the windrows should be no more than 24 inches wide. Avoid windrows between 24 inches and full width, because while you weave from side to side across the windrow to fill the ends of a bale, the center is continuously fed. The result is a barrel–shaped bale that is much denser at the center than at the ends.

If the windrows are too light, the bale will roll excessively in the chamber, increasing leaf loss. When your crop is light, rake more windrows together.

Making the bale. With a narrow windrow, start the bale carefully. First drive so as to feed hay into the center of the pickup head. As the core begins to form, weave from side to side across the windrow, so the crop is distributed evenly across the width of the baling chamber. For the last half of the bale, don't weave as often, but drive so the windrow enters the extreme sides of the pickup and cross over as quickly as possible. A bale made in this manner is more uniform than one made by continuous weaving during the entire cycle. On later machines the remote box monitors the bale's shape and indicates when you need to drive to the left or right to fill the bale ends tightly for a well–shaped bale.

Unplugging. If plugging occurs between the pickup head and the baling chamber, stop forward travel at once. Disengage the PTO, reduce engine speed, and slowly re–engage the PTO. This procedure often will clear the plug; if it doesn't, repeat the procedure several times. If the plug still doesn't respond, disengage the PTO, shut off the engine, put the key in your pocket, and manually clear the jam.

Wrapping the bale with twine. When a bale reaches the desired size, the size indicator—which might be a light, an audible signal, or a combination of both—alerts you not to add more hay. Most baler manufacturers offer an automatic tie system that is activated when the bale reaches a preset size and density. On an automatic tie machine, all you have to do is stop forward movement when signaled; the bale is automatically wrapped with twine, and the wrap is cut. Most bale monitor boxes also monitor the tying process, and some allow you to override the automatic system if necessary.

The manual tie system is controlled from the remote control box mounted on the forecart. Since the operation of manual tie systems varies from machine to machine, consult your owner's manual for the correct procedure. A typical procedure is as follows:

● When the bale reaches the preset size and density you will be signaled—visually, audibly, or both—at which time stop the forward movement of your team and baler.

● Using the actuator switch on the control box, move the twine tube to the bale center, bringing the twine end into position to enter the compression rolls.

● Drive the baler forward to take up a small amount of hay, which will carry the twine end into the compression rolls.

● Again stop forward movement.

● As the bale rotates, move the twine tube to the side of the bale opposite the twine knife.

● Hold the twine tube in this position until one full turn of twine goes around the end of the bale.

● Gradually move the twine tube across the bale, spacing the wraps 6 to 10 inches apart.

● When the twine tube reaches the bale end, make two full wraps of twine.

● At this point the twine is automatically cut on some machines; on others you must trip the cutoff mechanism.

● Disengage the PTO clutch and throttle back the engine.

Wrapping the bale with surface wrap. The wrapping mechanism on a surface wrap machine is automatic, and the bale monitor takes the place of a control box. A flashing light on the bale monitor warns you when the bale is nearing completion. As wrapping starts, the warning light stops flashing and goes steady, and a signal sounds. Immediately stop forward travel. An indicator on the bale monitor will show when wrapping is complete and the material has been cut off properly, all of which takes just a few seconds.

Ejecting the bale. If your baler is not equipped with a bale bumper, back the machine 10 or 15 feet. The bale bumper attachment is designed to roll a bale about 10 feet back of the baler on level ground. Backing is not required if a bale bumper is present.

Reengage the PTO clutch with the engine at idle speed. Fully open the rear door and the bale will fall to the ground. Note: Some manufacturers recommend opening the rear door *before* engaging the PTO.

If your baler is not equipped with a bale bumper, move the machine forward about 10 feet so the rear door won't hit the bale as it closes. Bring the engine up to operating speed, close the rear door, drive forward, and resume baling.

Field Adjustments. Change the pickup and wrapping assembly adjustments to match field conditions. Before transporting your baler, raise the pickup head as high as possible and be sure the rear door is closed.

Safety First!

Any power take off driven machine is extremely dangerous. Hands, fingers, legs, and other body parts are no match for the power in a gasoline or diesel engine.

☞ *Always* disengage the PTO, shut off the engine, and take the key before dismounting from a PTO forecart.

☞ *Never* attempt to clear a clogged machine while it is running.

Never clean, lubricate, or adjust a baler while it is running.

☞ *Always* stay clear of rotating power shafts, belts, pulleys, chains, and sprockets.

Always make sure all safety shields and covers are in position and properly secured before engaging the PTO.

☞ *Always* make certain everyone is clear of the machine before starting operation.

Always make sure everyone is clear of the baler's rear door before opening or closing it.

☞ *Never* eject or store round bales on uneven ground. A round bale is large and heavy, rolls easily, and can cause serious personal injury or property damage.

Common Round Baler Troubles

Pickup doesn't clean the crop off the field.
    windrow too heavy or too wet
    windrow too light
    pickup head set too high
    broken or missing pickup teeth

Hay won't enter the baling chamber.
    pickup drive belt loose or broken
    windrow too large
    pickup head set too low

Bale won't start to form.
    belts loose
    rear door open
    windrow too light and dry

Hydraulic pressure gauge reading drops suddenly.
    leak in the hydraulic system
    faulty hydraulic valve

Barrel–shaped bales or ends not square.
    windrow is too wide or too narrow
    windrow is high crowned in the center
    too much hay in the center of the bale due to
        weaving too often across the windrow, or
        not often enough
    too little hay packed into the sides of the
        baling chamber

Cone–shaped bales.
    broken or poorly adjusted compression spring
        on one side
    too little hay going into one end of the bale

Low bale density.
    hay is too dry
    hydraulic system is malfunctioning
    improper belt tension
    broken and slipping belts
    compression springs broken or maladjusted

Completed bale won't wrap.
    no incoming hay to catch the end of the twine
        or surface wrap
    twine or surface wrap not threaded correctly
    twine or surface wrap is jammed
    twine or surface wrap is used up

Insufficient twine bale wrap.
    twine tube moves across the bale too quickly
    twine mechanism clogged
    twine mechanism out of adjustment.

Ends of the twine wrap come off the completed bale.
    first and/or last wraps of twine placed too close
        to bale ends

Ends of the completed bale flare out
    first and/or last wraps of twine placed too far
        from bale ends

Twine or surface wrap not cut cleanly.
    cutter is dirty
    cutter is out of adjustment
    knife is dull

Bale won't eject.
    belts or clutch slipping
    rear of baler pointing uphill
    bale is too large

Maintaining a Round Baler

To keep your round baler operating efficiently, service it on a regular basis. Lubricate all grease fittings with a good quality lubricant at least once each day, and more often in dusty conditions.

On a variable chamber baler, the belts that form the bale must be in good repair and must function properly. Keep the belts clean and inspect them frequently for stretching, fraying, cuts, tears, or bruises that may cause problems. Always loosen belt tension when the baler will be idle for more than a couple of weeks. Make sure the belts are adjusted correctly during operation.

Inspect the pickup teeth each day. The teeth tend to bend and break.

Make sure the hydraulics of your baler and forecart are in good condition. Correct any leaks and replace kinked or frayed hoses. Keep the hydraulic reservoir full of oil, and inspect for leaking hoses or connections. Frequently check all hydraulic cylinders for leaks. When connecting or disconnecting the quick–disconnect hydraulic hoses be sure to wipe both ends clean—even a small amount of dirt can cause a hydraulic system to malfunction.

Before putting your baler away at the end of the season, remove all debris, dirt, dust, and chaff from the entire machine. Wash the baler and repaint any bare metal spots. Grease all fittings, as well as the telescoping PTO drive. Clean all drive chains in diesel fuel and apply a heavy coat of oil. Release the spring tension on all belts. Clean and oil the twine assembly. Retract all hydraulic cylinders and coat any exposed cylinder rods with grease. Repack the wheel bearings.

Store your baler under cover away from sunlight and weather. Keep the rear door closed during storage.

Baling straw with a John Deere 328 pickup baler powered by its own engine.

13 *Hay Handling Equipment*

"Cows can't get a square meal these days, what
with all these round bales."   *Old joke*

At first glance the large round bale method of putting up
hay may seem inappropriate for horse farmers, but that is
far from the case. Some horse farmers have motorized
forecarts capable of operating a round baler. Many more
hire custom operators to round bale their hay, or buy round
bales to feed their livestock.

An important use for round balers is to produce haylage,
or baleage, made by wilting a forage crop, such as alfalfa,
to 50 or 60 percent moisture content, then baling it, usually
with a big round baler, and ensiling the resulting bales
within a plastic cover. The same process of fermentation
takes place as in a conventional silo, resulting in high
quality feed. Since bale silage contains more moisture than
dry hay, the bales are significantly heavier. A 4-foot by 5-
foot bale of dry hay weighs approximately 850 pounds,
while the same-size bale of silage might be 1,300 pounds.
A number of machines have been developed for handling
large round bales.

> **Safety First!**
>
> ☞ *Always* be careful when moving and handling large
> round bales.

Bale Movers

Round bales are heavy and unwieldy, and being round can
easily get away and roll down a slope with potentially
disastrous results. Various machines make loading,
hauling, and unloading round bales easier and safer.

Bale movers come in dozens of different designs from
simple to complex. They may be three-point hitch
mounted or supported on wheels, and may carry a single
bale or several at once. They may be manually,
hydraulically, or electrically operated, and some may be
used also to unroll a bale for feeding. Most bale wrappers
may be used to move bales as well, either before or after
the bales are wrapped.

Three-Point Hitch Bale Movers

Three-point bale movers are quite popular with tractor
owners, with several different styles available that may be

used with a three-point hitch forecart. Many of these bale
movers have one large spear, and often a couple of smaller
spears, that penetrate the bale and then lift it for transport.
Some models have a clamp arm that goes on each side of a
bale, with a spear point on each arm to penetrate the center
of the ends of the bale. When the clamp arms are tightened
against the bale ends, these points not only lift the bale for
transport, but serve as an axle when unrolling the bale for
feeding. Other machines have two round arms that slide
under each side of a bale and cradle the bale for lifting. The
latter machine may be used to move wrapped bales without
damaging the plastic film.

When using a spear type mover, back up to the bale so
the spear fully penetrates the end of the bale as near the
center as possible.

When using a cradle type mover, back so the two arms
are under the long sides of the bale. The arms on most of
these movers may be moved sideways to accommodate
bales of different diameters. Set the arms close enough
together to support the bale, but far enough apart to cradle
the bale so it won't roll sideways off the arms.

A clamp arm type mover has a hydraulic cylinder to
move the arms sideways. Operate this cylinder so the arms
are at their widest point, and position the mover so it is
square with the bale. Back into the bale until the spikes on
the arm ends are positioned close to the center of each end
of the bale. Close the clamp arms to securely grip the bale
between them.

With the bale securely cradled or speared, raise the 3-
point hitch. The bale is ready for transport. To unload the
bale, lower it to the ground and pull away from the bale.
Open the clamp arms on that type of mover before
moving away.

Wheeled Bale Movers

Many different wheeled bale movers are on the market.
Some have two wheels, others have four or more. Some
wheeled machines have spears and cradle arms that are
much safer for use with horses than the three-point hitch
versions, since the weight of the bale is carried by the
mover rather than the forecart.

Some of the more elaborate wheeled bale movers have
hydraulic lifting forks to load bales, others rely on
mechanical means, such as hand or power winches and

A two-wheel three-point hitch forecart may not have enough weight to safely handle large bales. All the bale's weight is carried on the spears or arms of this machine, which is designed for use with a tractor having enough weight to counterbalance the bale's weight.

☞ *Always* make sure your forecart is heavy enough to counterbalance the weight of the bale you will be moving.

☞ *Always* keep the bale close to the ground. A heavy load can cause your forecart to tip over, especially on hilly ground.

☞ *Always* go slowly around turns.

☞ *Always* keep spectators at a distance.

☞ *Always* use caution while backing.

☞ *Always* be extremely careful when using three-point hitch equipment to move heavy bales.

A Yoder four-wheel multiple bale mover with a hydraulic loading fork at the front and a conveyor to move the bales back; it unloads by running the bales off the rear.

cables and grappling hooks. Most multiple bale machines have a power conveyor to move bales along the length of the bed. Some models have a platform at the rear that tilts sideways and rolls the rearmost bale off the side and onto the ground. Others just run the bale off the rear of the bed with the conveyor, or raise the front of the whole bed and tip the bale onto the ground at the rear. Still others have rollers on the bed so the bale may be pushed off easily.

Wheeled bale movers with spears and cradle arms are operated in the same way as three point hitch bale movers, and require the same precautions.

A Yoder wheeled spear type mover backs into a bale and lifts it for transport.

A Mascot cradle arm bale mover with a hand winch to raise the bale.

Multiple Bale Movers

Several manufacturers offer multiple bale movers with side mounted lift arms. Although they all operate similarly, they have enough variation to make consulting the operator's manual essential before using your particular machine.

To load a multiple bale mover with side mounted lift arms, lower the lifting fork to the ground as you approach the bale. Position the mover so an arm of the lifting fork is on each side of, and parallel to, the long side of the bale. Stop your team and raise the bale until it rolls onto the conveyor bed.

Using the conveyor, move the bale one bale length to the rear and proceed to the next bale to be picked up. Repeat this procedure until you have a full load of bales on the mover.

To unload, move the bale mover to your bale storage area. If your machine is equipped with a tilt table at the rear, tilt the table to roll the rearmost bale onto the ground.

Pull the mover ahead one bale length. Use the conveyor to move the next bale onto the tilting table and continue this procedure until all the bales are unloaded.

Release the brakes and pull forward, causing the mover frame to straighten and lift the bale onto the mover, while releasing the hook. The bale is now in transport position.

To unload the bale, back the mover into position to unload the bale to the rear. Make sure the hook is in its forward position and set the mover brakes. Continue to back, causing the mover frame to buckle upward and the bale to roll off. Release the brakes and drive away.

A bale has been loaded onto this Sunny Hollow Hay Equipment bale mover, and has been moved to the rear by the conveyor. A second bale is on the lift arms and is being lifted onto the conveyor. At the rear of the machine is a hydraulic platform that unloads a bale to the left side.

A Yoder Equipment grabber bale mover.

The rearmost bale is being unloaded by means of the tilting rear table.

The grabber isn't quite square with the bale, yet the frame has buckled upward and the hook arm has fallen and grabbed the bale.

Wheeled Single Bale Movers
One of the most popular wheeled single bale movers is the grabber style. To load one, back the mover up to a bale so it is against and square with the bale's long side. Set the brakes on the mover and continue backing, causing the mover frame to buckle upward in the center and the large hook arm to fall and grab the bale.

> **Safety First!**
>
> *Always* unload round bales on level ground where they cannot roll away. A loose rolling hay bale is dangerous and may cause property damage, serious injury, or death.

The driver moves forward, the grabber frame straightens and lifts the bale, and the hook is released. The weight of the bale is cradled between the bale mover's wheels and frame.

The driver sets the brakes and backs the team. The mover's frame buckles upward and the bale rolls onto the ground.

Maintaining a Bale Mover

Regular and thorough lubrication is essential for the safe and efficient operation of bale movers. Wipe the grease fittings clean before greasing, and wipe up any excess grease afterward. Periodically check all bolts for tightness. If applicable, check hydraulic hoses for leaks or wear and replace if necessary. Follow the instructions in the operator's manual for your specific machine. Don't let hay accumulate on conveyor gears or wind around rotating shafts. Replace badly worn or broken parts promptly.

At the season's end, thoroughly clean and lubricate the machine. Replace worn or broken parts and paint or cover any shiny metal with grease. Store your bale mover under cover.

Bale Unrollers

Unrolling hay bales for feeding, or straw bales for bedding, requires special equipment to perform the job easily and safely. Only bales made in a variable chamber baler will unroll; bales made in a fixed chamber baler cannot be unrolled.

Most of these machines consist of an arm that extends back from a crosspiece to the center of each end of the bale. A spike on the end of each arm is forced into the bale to act as an axle. All twine or netting is removed from the bale and, as the unroller is pulled forward, the bale rolls along the ground, unrolling the hay or straw in a long ribbon.

Unrolling Round Bales

Before attempting to unroll a large round bale, examine the bale to determine which way it is wrapped. Position the bale in the unroller so it will unroll from the bottom as it is moved forward along the ground. Unroll only as much of the bale as you need—partial bales may be set aside and unrolled later.

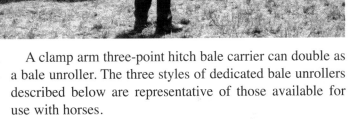

A clamp arm three-point hitch bale carrier can double as a bale unroller. The three styles of dedicated bale unrollers described below are representative of those available for use with horses.

Three-Point Hitch Unroller

A three-point hitch bale unroller has a main frame consisting of a crosspiece and an upright equipped with the necessary pins to connect to a standard category I or II three point hitch. Hinged to each end of the crosspiece is a rearward extending arm, at the end of which is a spinner plate with a spear in the center.

A double acting hydraulic cylinder is connected between the clamp arms by a linkage at the front of the arms near the crosspiece. The hydraulic cylinder furnishes the power to clamp the arms against the ends of a bale, while the spinner spears act as an axle on which the bale turns as it unrolls.

To use a three-point hitch unroller, be sure the bale will unroll in the proper direction. Using the hydraulic lever, open the grip arms to their widest position and back up to the bale so the unroller is square with the long side of the bale. Close the arms so the spears penetrate the bale ends as near the center as possible.

Keeping the bale in contact with the ground, drive slowly forward. If you don't need to unroll the entire bale, raise the three-point hitch; the bale will stop unrolling.

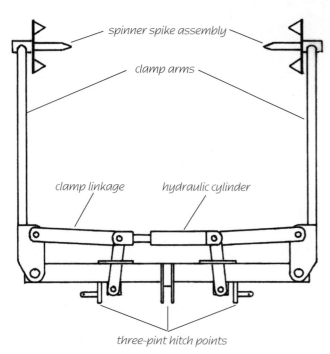

A three-point clamp arm bale carrier/unroller.

Wheeled Unroller

A wheeled bale unroller may be used to transport a bale as well as unroll it. This machine is made mostly of pipe had has two wheels set wider than the length of a bale. At each side, and extending to the rear, is an arm with a spinner and a short spear at the end. A lever swings the arms sideways.

Mounted on the tongue is a hand-crank winch, the cable of which goes to a pivoting overhead frame mounted crosswise over the axle. A chain from the outer end of each arm goes to the top of each side of the frame. By manipulating the winch, you can raise a round bale clear of the ground for transport or leave it on the ground for unrolling.

To use a wheeled unroller, be sure the bale will unroll in the proper direction. With the hand lever, open the grip arms to their widest position and back up to the bale so the unroller is square with the long side of the bale. Close the arms so the spears penetrate the bale ends as near to the center as possible and secure the hand lever in position.

While keeping slack in the winch cable, so the bale is resting on the ground, drive slowly forward, unrolling the bale. If you don't need to unroll the entire bale, use the hand winch to raise the bale and it will stop unrolling.

An EEW Sales wheeled clamp arm bale carrier that doubles as an unroller.

Non-Wheeled Bale Unroller

A non-wheeled bale unroller is a simple tool consisting of a crosspiece, a little longer than the bales to be unrolled, with a pulling ring or two on the front and an arm extending from each end to the rear. At the rear end of each arm is a spike that may be pushed through or withdrawn from the arm. This style of unroller may be used to move a tied bale by rolling it along the ground.

To use a non-wheeled unroller, carry the unroller to the bale and place it in position so the arms, with the spears pulled to their retracted position, are on each end of the bale. Be sure the bale will unroll in the proper direction before lifting the arms and pushing the spears into the center of each end of the bale.

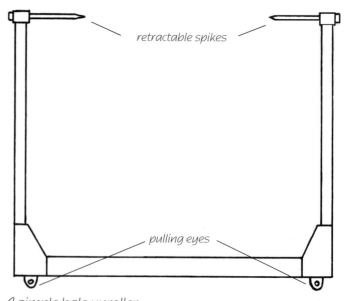

A simple bale unroller.

Hitch your team or forecart to the front pulling rings and drive slowly forward as the bale unrolls. If you don't need to unroll the entire bale, stop the team when enough has been unrolled.

Maintaining a Bale Unroller

Periodically lubricate pivot points and spinner assemblies. Check the bolts on a regular basis to be sure they're tight. If your unroller is equipped with hydraulics, check hydraulic hoses for wear and leaks and make corrections as necessary.

Bale Wrappers

A bale wrapper is a machine that tightly wraps several layers of plastic film around high moisture bales to create baleage for feeding cattle. Bale wrappers come in many sizes and configurations. Plastic for wrapping is one mil (0.001 inch) thick, and comes in rolls that are either 20 or 30 inches wide.

When properly stretched, the layers of film adhere to each other, forming a seal that excludes air. To create the best seal, each bale should be wrapped at least two times with a 50 percent overlap each time, resulting in a minimum of four layers.

A row of round bales wrapped with plastic film.

Hay Wrap System

The hay wrap system is probably the least expensive in terms of both the equipment needed and the amount of plastic film used. This method involves spearing the bale in the center of one flat end and spinning it on its axis while the plastic film is wrapped tightly around the bale's outer circumference and overlapping the ends by about 12 inches. The bales are then tightly packed flat end to flat end to

allow the overlapped plastic on one bale to stick to the next, forming an airtight seal. A bale wrapper may also be used to wrap dry hay to protect the bales from weather, in which case wrap just the circumference of the bale without overlapping the ends.

These machines are 3-point mounted, usually requiring a category II hitch, and are driven by a hydraulic motor connected to the remote outlets of the power source. The operator's manual for each model details the hydraulic requirements, as well as offering specific operating instructions for that model. To operate this style of bale wrapper:

1. Back up to the bale so the center spike of the wrapper penetrates as nearly at the center of one flat end as possible.

2. Raise the bale clear of the ground.

3. Take the free end of the plastic film to the outer end of the bale and tie it to the string around the bale.

4. Adjust the tension of the plastic feed roll to achieve the desired stretch in the film.

5. Start the bale rotating and move the slide that holds the plastic roll toward the inner end of the bale at a speed that results in a 50 percent overlap of the film. For best results, a minimum of two layers of 50 percent overlapped film are necessary. The slide may be angled at each end of the bale to allow the film to overlap the ends of the bale.

6. When wrapping is completed, stop rotation, cut or tear the film, and press the end against the bale. The film should adhere to itself.

7. Lower the bale to the ground, or move it into position for storage, and proceed to the next bale to be wrapped.

An Anderson turntable bale wrapper with a hydraulic lifting fork and a Honda engine to power the hydraulic system.

Turntable Machine

The most common bale wrapping method is with a table-type bale wrapper, designed to spin the bale in two directions at the same time while plastic film from a stationary roll is stretched and wrapped tightly around the bale. The result is an individual, completely wrapped, and tightly sealed package. Bales that will be moved before they are ready to be fed must be handled with equipment that won't puncture the plastic seal.

Features of a Turntable Wrapper

Many table-type wrappers have a heavy two-tine fork at one side that may be run under the bale while it's lying on the ground. The arm then hydraulically lifts the bale and places it in position on the turntable platform. The bale rests on two horizontal rollers connected by belts; a vertical roller at each end of the bale holds it in place. These rollers and belts roll the bale while the entire turntable rotates at the same time.

To the side of the turntable is a vertical device holding a roll of either 20- or 30-inch wide plastic film under tension. An applicator device holds the loose end of the plastic film in position to start the wrapping process and then cuts the film when the bale is finished.

These machines may be three-point mounted or trailer mounted. Hand levers on the front or side of the wrapper operate hydraulic valves that control the machine's various functions. Most bale wrappers have adjustments for wrapping bales of differing sizes, and for setting the tension on the plastic film.

On a turntable-type machine like this Kverneland/Taarup model, rollers and belts rotate the bale, which is held in position by vertical rollers. A roll of plastic film, the film tensioning rollers, and the automatic cutter/holder are at the left of the machine.

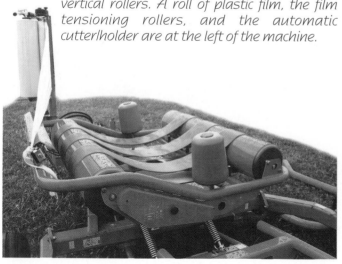

Many options are available, including automatic film holders and cutters, bale dumpers, mounted engines, and remote control consoles. Unless the wrapper has its own engine, it must be connected to the remote hydraulic outlets of the power source.

Operating a Turntable Wrapper

Refer to your operator's manual for the hydraulic requirements and operating instructions specific to your model. To operate a basic model, load a bale onto the turntable, either by using an integral lifting arm or some external means.

Tie the free end of the plastic film to a bale string. (This step isn't necessary if the wrapper is equipped with an automatic cutter/holder.) Adjust the pretensioner to provide a 55 to 65 percent film stretch, to ensure a good seal and eliminate air pockets between the bale and the film.

Operate the hand levers to start the bale rotating and spinning. Wrap the bale with at least two layers of film that overlap 50 percent, resulting in a minimum of four layers of film over the entire bale. When wrapping is complete, stop the rotation of the bale, at which time the film is cut. Most

An ELHO bale wrapper on its way to pick up a bale, with its hydraulic loading forks (on the right side of the machine) in raised position.

This wrapper has an automatic device to hold the free end of the plastic film. Here the bale has been picked up and wrapping is just beginning.

wrappers have a device that cuts the film and holds the free end of the roll in position for the next bale. Tip the turntable and lower the wrapped bale to the ground.

Wrapping proceeds as the bale both turns and spins on the turntable.

Wrapping has been completed and the automatic cutter/holder is cutting the film.

When the turntable is tipped, the wrapped bale rolls onto the ground.

Maintaining a Bale Wrapper

Regular and thorough lubrication is essential for the safe and efficient operation of bale wrappers. Wipe the grease fittings clean before greasing, and wipe up any excess grease afterward. Replace any missing grease fittings immediately. Keep all bolts tight. Follow the instructions in the operator's manual for your specific machine.

Check hydraulic hoses and cylinders for leaks and wear, and correct any deficiencies. Keep belts clean and replace any that are excessively frayed or cracked. Don't let hay wind around rotating shafts, as it may become hot from the friction and catch fire. Replace badly worn or broken parts promptly.

At the season's end, thoroughly clean and lubricate the machine. Replace worn or broken parts and paint or cover any shiny metal with grease. Store your bale wrapper under cover.

> **Safety First!**
>
> ☞ *Never* clean, lubricate, or adjust a bale wrapper while it is running.

Storing Wrapped Bales

If you find holes in the wrapping, patch them as soon as possible. Otherwise wind will get into the holes and billow the plastic, causing most of the bale's outer layer to spoil. Use only tape made for this purpose. Duct tape and masking tape are not satisfactory substitutes.

If possible, store bagged or wrapped bales on a slope with a northern exposure to avoid extreme temperature fluctuations. Remove any nearby weeds that may harbor rodents and insects. Clear the ground of stubble or sharp objects that may pierce the covering. An old piece of plastic may be laid on the ground before placing the bales. Don't cover the bales with tarps or plastic, which would provide an ideal nesting place for gnawing rodents.

A multiple round bale mover, like this one from Brandywine Welding, makes moving unwieldy bales easier and safer.

Hay Harvesting Machinery

IV: Harvesting Machinery

The most important food source for three-fourths of the world population is grain. Most grains belong to the grass family and are grown because of their large edible seeds, which are widely used as food for humans. Chief among these food grains are wheat, barley, rye, oats, corn, and rice. The grain may be pounded or ground into meal and flour with which to make bread, pudding, cakes, and pies. It may be roasted, popped, parched, or boiled and even made into whiskey. Corn, barley, and oats are also fed to livestock and poultry, to be turned into hams, steaks, and drumsticks.

All the labor and expense that go into tilling, planting, and cultivating these crops would be wasted were it not possible to harvest them at their peak. Because each crop must be cut, picked, dug, or processed at its proper time to avoid losses, harvest season is the busiest time of year. Each implement used for harvesting must be in good condition and tuned up before it is needed. Equipment used for harvesting is complicated. By knowing how to make the necessary adjustments and repairs, you can get the most from each implement.

14

Grain Binders

"It was a marvelous machine to me. It waited until the horses had drawn the thing along so far as to accumulate enough of the cut grain to make a sheaf, and then reached over with a metal finger carrying the twine, compressed the gavel into a sheaf, knotted the twine about the bundle and kicked it off into a bundle carrier. It was a triumph of mechanical genius."

Herbert Quick in One Man's Life, 1925

The twine tie grain binder evolved naturally from the reaper. Developed in the 1830s by men such as Cyrus McCormick and Obed Hussey, the reaper cut grain faster, and with less manpower, than a cradle scythe, but left the cut grain laying in the field in gavels, where it had to be tied into sheaves. Tying sheaves by hand was slow and labor intensive, requiring as many men (or women and children) as the scythe cutting.

A major step toward the modern binder was made in 1858 by the Marsh Brothers of DeKalb County, Illinois. To an ordinary reaper the brothers added endless canvas belts that carried the cut grain sideways, and up and over the large drive wheel, where it fell onto a table. Two men standing on an attached platform gathered the grain from the table and tied it into sheaves, allowing two binders to tie as much grain as four or five men following a reaper.

The first successful automatic wire binder was developed by Sylvanus Locke of Janesville, Wisconsin, in 1872. Locke teamed up with the Walter A. Wood Company to produce the machine, and soon both the McCormick and

Front view (top) and rear view of an 8–foot grain binder with a 4–horse hitch and tongue truck. Interional Harvester

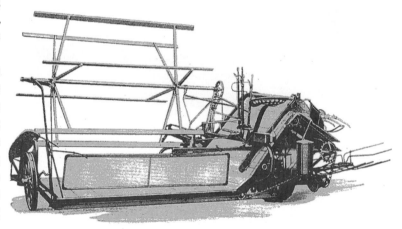

the Deering Companies were building wire binders. Millers complained about bits of wire in the threshed grain, and any cow hapless enough to swallow a piece of wire usually died.

In 1875 a Wisconsin man named John Appleby patented a successful device to wrap a piece of twine around a sheaf and tie it with a knot. By 1890 nearly every binder used in the United States was a twine tie machine.

Features of a Grain Binder

A grain binder—with all its gears, chains, cams, rollers, and pitmans—is one of the more complicated farm machines. These components must all work simultaneously, or in the proper sequence, to cleanly cut standing grain, tie it into neat bundles, and deposit the

An early twine tie binder. Aultman, Miller & Co.

Harvesting Machinery

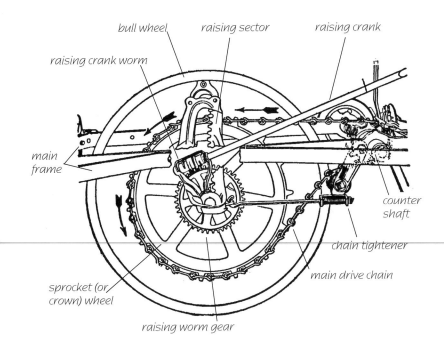

bundles, or sheaves, in windrows where they may be easily gathered for shocking. Many adjustments are provided, both for taking up wear between parts and for setting the machine to do good work. Ground–driven grain binders are usually made in 6–, 7–, and 8–foot cut sizes; power take off (PTO) driven binders are normally 8– or 10–foot cut.

Drive

A large main drive wheel, often called a *bull wheel,* carries most of the machine's weight. The bull wheel's rim is equipped with cleats to provide the necessary traction for driving the mechanism through a system of sprockets, chains, and gears. Some late model grain binders are equipped with a lugged rubber tire on the bull wheel.

Detail of bull wheel and main drive chain.   Farm Machinery, Archie A. Stone

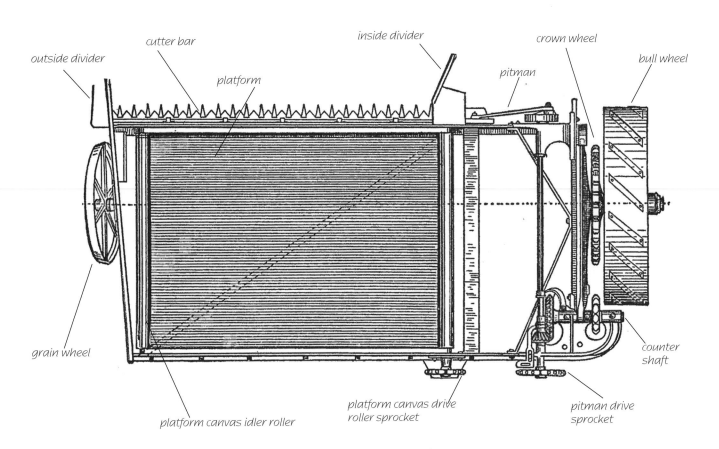

Relationship between cutter bar, platform, wheels, and other parts of the binder.   Aultman, Miller & Co.

Grain Binders   149

A ground–driven grain binder gets power for operating the machine from the bull wheel. A large sprocket, often called a *crown wheel,* is attached to the inside of the bull wheel. The crown wheel drives a heavy flat–link or pintle chain. A PTO–driven grain binder is similar, except the large wheel serves only to carry the machine's weight. The power is distributed throughout the machine by various combinations of sprockets, chains, and gears. Adjustable chain tension tighteners are provided for each chain.

Cutting Mechanism

The cutting mechanism consists of a reciprocating knife driven by a pitman, and finger guards to hold the grain stalks while they are being cut. A small *grain wheel* carries the weight of the outer end of the cutting mechanism and platform.

The cutter bar, consisting of the knife and guard fingers, is carried along the leading edge of the *grain platform.* The knife is equipped with serrated–edge sections to easily cut dry grain stalks. The height of cut is initially set by raising or lowering the grain and bull wheels. As the machine encounters different heights of grain in the field, the cutting height may be quickly adjusted by tilting the platform forward or backward with the *tongue tilting lever.*

Reel

A reel gently pushes the standing grain into the cutting mechanism and then causes it to fall evenly onto the platform canvas. The reel also helps pick up lodged and tangled grain. The reel usually has six thin wooden bats supported by wooden arms that are held in place by a metal spider at each end. As the reel revolves, the bats contact the standing grain and sweep it into the knife and onto the platform canvas. The position of the reel is adjustable— up and down by the *reel lifting lever,* and forward and back in relation to the cutter bar by means of the *reel tilting lever.* The reel must be properly positioned to collect all the grain and place it evenly on the platform canvas.

Canvases

An *elevating system* carries the cut grain across the platform and up and over the bull wheel, where it is evenly deposited onto a sloping table called the *binding deck.* The grain is moved through the elevating system by three endless *canvases,* sometimes called *drapers.* To carry the grain, the canvases have hardwood slats or

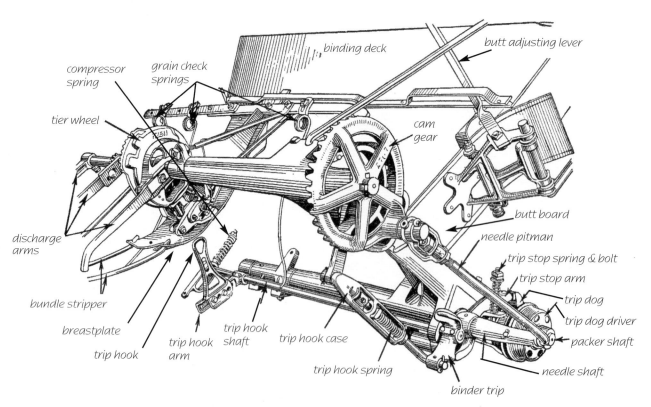

A common binding attachment.

U. of Saskatchewan Bulletin 67

Harvesting Machinery

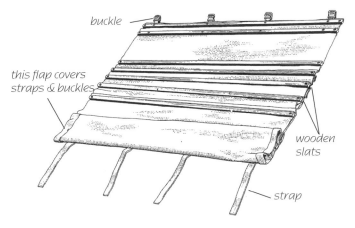

buckle

this flap covers
straps & buckles

wooden
slats

strap

A typical binder canvas.   *International Harvester*

cleats, and each canvas is fastened around its pair of rollers by four webbed straps and buckles. A tensioning device on one roller of each pair allows for tension changes and loosening of the canvases while the machine is idle. The canvases must be buckled so they run square with the rollers or the slats may be torn off or broken. The frame supporting each pair of rollers is adjustable to keep the rollers square with each other.

Binding Mechanism

The *binding* or *tying* mechanism is the heart of a grain binder. It collects the cut grain and ties it into bundles with a band of twine. Modern binder twine is made of biodegradable material available from many farm supply stores. Baler twine is much heavier and thicker, and will not work reliably in a grain binder.

After each bundle is tied, the binder ejects it to the side of the machine away from the standing grain. The binding mechanism is rather complicated, and its process may be divided into five steps:

1. After the machine is threaded, the free end of the twine, called the disc end, is held in the twine disc. The twine extends from the disc back over the knotter *bill hook* jaw, down through the breastplate, to the eye of the curved needle. From the needle eye, the twine runs back through the

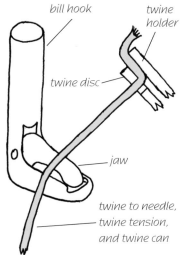

bill hook

twine disc

jaw

twine holder

twine to needle,
twine tension,
and twine can

The bill hook and twine in rest position.

twine tension—the purpose of which is to keep slack from forming in the twine between the needle and the twine can—to the ball in the twine can.

2. The cut grain is delivered by the elevating canvases onto the binding deck, where it is gathered, formed into a bundle, and held in place by two or three oscillating fingers called *packers*. The accumulating grain eventually reaches enough mass to trip the *trip hook*, which sets the tying mechanism into operation. The needle pitman advances the curved needle, bringing the bight of twine around the bundle and placing the other end, called the needle end, over the knotter bill hook and into the same notch of the twine disc as the disc end. The twine disc turns slightly, holding fast both ends of the twine. The twine band now extends from the disc end, across the bill hook, around the bundle, and back across the bill to the twine disc. A disc spring provides the tension to hold the twine ends and may be adjusted to control the amount of pull required to release the twine from the disc.

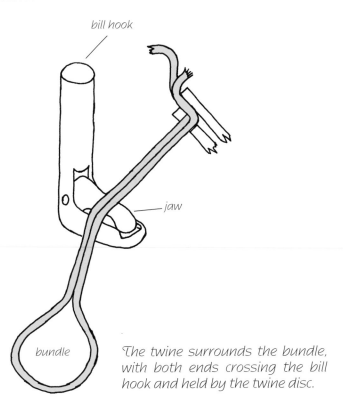

bill hook

jaw

bundle

The twine surrounds the bundle, with both ends crossing the bill hook and held by the twine disc.

3. The needle remains up and the disc holds both ends of the twine band, while the knotter bill hook revolves to make a loop in the twine and open the upper bill, or *jaw*. As the bill hook continues to turn, the open jaw closes, grasping the two strands tightly. The jaws are held closed on the string by the bill hook cam spring.

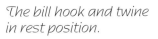

Grain Binders

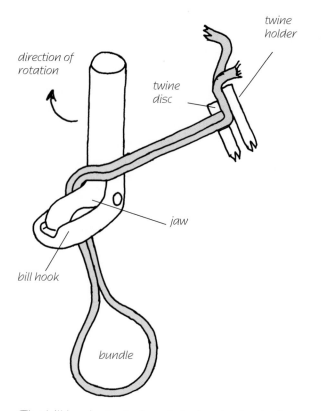

The bill hook starts to rotate, beginning to form a loop.

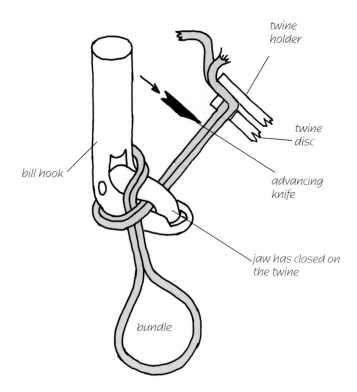

The bill hook completes its revolution and the jaw closes on the strands of twine, as the knife starts moving toward the string.

4. The knife advances and cuts the twine strands between the bill hook and the twine disc, while the *knife arm* is stripping the twine loop from the bill hook. The cut ends of the twine are grasped by the bill hook jaw.

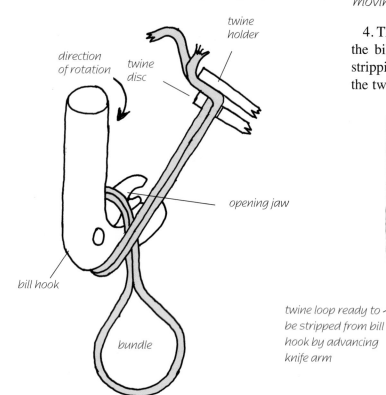

The bill hook continues rotating to form a loop, while the jaw opens.

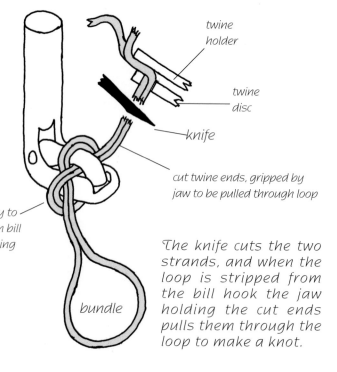

The knife cuts the two strands, and when the loop is stripped from the bill hook the jaw holding the cut ends pulls them through the loop to make a knot.

Harvesting Machinery

5. As the knife cuts the twine, the *discharge arms,* which have been turning throughout the tying operation, strike the bundle and the knife arm strips the twine loop from the bill hook. The loop is pulled from the bill hook, while the closed jaw pulls the twine ends through the loop to complete the knot. The momentum and weight of the bundle being discharged onto the bundle carrier pulls the knot tight and pulls the twine ends from the grasp of the bill hook jaws. The needle returns to its idle position, leaving the disc end of the twine in the twine holder disc, and leaving a strand of twine across the bill hook and binding deck ready for another bundle. In heavy grain, the bundles accumulate so fast the discharge arms are in almost continuous motion, kicking out bundles with hardly a pause between them.

bundle

Completed knot before being pulled tight.

Bundle Carrier

The *bundle carrier,* consisting of a series of steel fingers mounted just below the binding deck, is where a bundle lands after it is kicked from the tying mechanism by the discharge arms. The bundle carrier can carry four to six bundles, until they are dropped by the operation of a foot pedal. Dropping the bundles into windrows makes life easier for the shockers, who don't have to walk so far to collect the bundles, and helps keep bundles away from corners, where they may be trampled by the binder turning on the next round. Most bundle carriers fold for transport.

Transport Truck

Since a grain binder is too wide to easily pass through gates and readily transport on roads, provisions are made for narrowing the implement for easy travel between fields. Two wheels with stub axles fit under the frame, one in front of, and one behind, the bull wheel. For transport, the tongue is removed from the front of the binder and reconnected to the end of the platform, allowing the machine to be pulled endwise to its normal direction of travel.

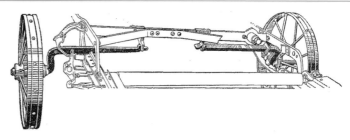

Transport trucks in position.   *International Harvester*

Tongue Truck

A tongue truck is an extra cost option, and money well spent. Because of a grain binder's weight and side–draft, especially on a wide cut machine, a tongue truck helps relieve the team of a lot of effort, as well as making square turns easier at the corners.

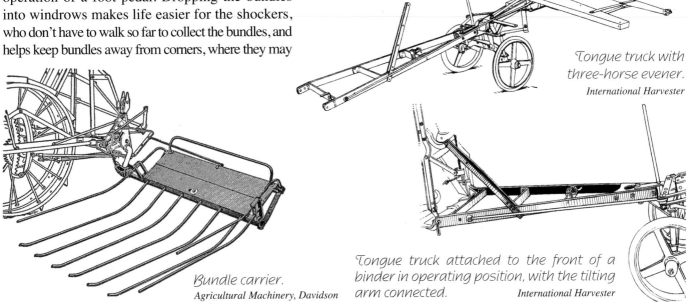

Tongue truck with three-horse evener.
International Harvester

Bundle carrier.
Agricultural Machinery, Davidson

Tongue truck attached to the front of a binder in operating position, with the tilting arm connected.   *International Harvester*

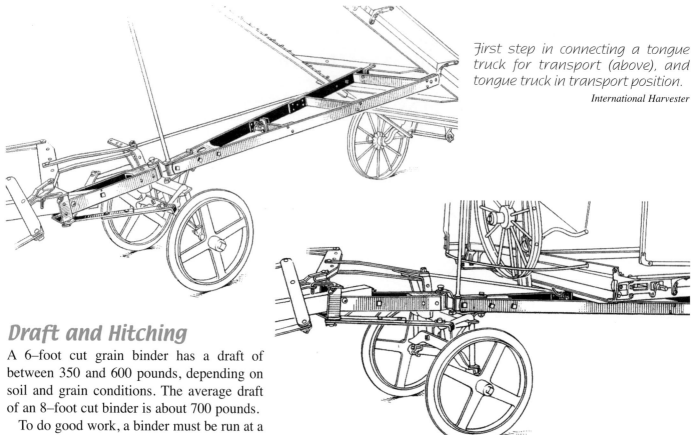

Draft and Hitching

A 6–foot cut grain binder has a draft of between 350 and 600 pounds, depending on soil and grain conditions. The average draft of an 8–foot cut binder is about 700 pounds.

To do good work, a binder must be run at a more constant speed than most other field machinery, which is hard on horses and requires frequent changes to fresh horses. The binder should always cut a full swath, but if you use a tongue truck cutting a full swath is sometimes difficult to accomplish. If you have to walk the inside horse in the standing grain to cut a full swath, set the tongue truck wheels to lead slightly into the grain. If the binder tends to run into the grain too much, set the truck wheels to lead away from the grain. This adjustment is made either under the tongue, where it attaches to the truck, or on the braces holding the wheels in position.

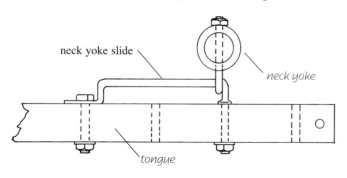

To prevent the tongue truck from tipping when turning corners, position the neck yoke at the front of the neck yoke slide when the team is moving forward.

A tongue truck may tip when turning at the corners. To overcome this problem, adjust the neck yoke slide so the neck yoke works at the front end of the slide when the team is pulling forward. In a turn, the neck yoke can then slide back freely. If the neck yoke doesn't slide back, the pole team pulls back and down on the tongue while turning, causing the truck to tip.

Operating a Grain Binder

Each make of grain binder varies in some of its details, but the operation is similar from one to the other. Knotters, especially, are virtually identical, since most manufacturers used one of only two similar types, M and D. McCormick–Deering binders used both styles, depending on their ancestry—the type M knotter was used by the McCormick Harvesting Machine Company, while the type D came from the Deering Harvester Company. The McCormick and Deering firms were principals in the 1902 merger that formed the International Harvester Company and resulted in the McCormick–Deering trade name for IHC implements. Both knotters work almost exactly alike, the main differences being the knotter frames and the placement of the components.

Harvesting Machinery

Your particular grain binder may vary from the following generic description. When in doubt, consult the owner's manual for your model. Before taking the binder to the field, make sure it is in working order, particularly with respect to the following points:

• Carefully check the entire machine for loose nuts and bolts, and badly worn or broken parts. Tighten, repair, or replace as necessary.

• Thoroughly lubricate the binder. Older machines have oil cups and oil holes, while newer models are equipped with grease cups and fittings. Look for lubrication fittings at any point where one mechanical component moves against another. A main drive chain of the pintle type has an oil hole in each link. The main drive gears on some late–model machines are completely encased and run in a bath of heavy oil. A plug in the gear case is provided for checking the oil level.

• Install the canvases, starting with the lower elevator canvas, then the upper elevator canvas, and last the platform canvas. When you face the rear of a left–hand cut binder, the platform canvas and lower elevator canvas turn in a clockwise direction, while the upper elevator canvas turns in a counter–clockwise direction. If the binder happens to have right–hand cut, the reverse is true.

Before installing the canvases, release the tensioning device for each one. Position each canvas so the buckles lead in the direction of travel and the flaps, which cover the straps, follow. Tighten all four straps evenly so the canvas runs straight. Make the straps just tight enough so the tensioned canvas can carry grain without slipping. Start the canvas around one of the rollers, ensuring it will run in the proper direction. Pull the canvas to the other roller and feed it around that roller, then pull the ends together and buckle the four straps.

Before using the machine, reengage the tensioning devices. Most binders are equipped with a hand crank that, in addition to raising and lowering the bull wheel, and in some cases tensioning the platform canvas, may be placed into a socket in one of the rear elevator drive gears and used to turn the rollers, helping with the canvas

installation. After the canvases are installed, use the hand crank to turn over the entire mechanism several times to make sure nothing catches or binds.

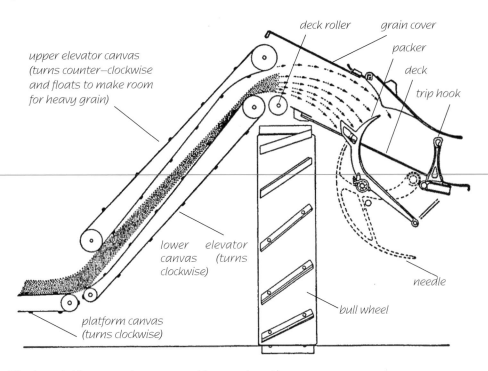

upper elevator canvas (turns counter–clockwise and floats to make room for heavy grain)

deck roller   grain cover   packer   deck   trip hook

lower elevator canvas (turns clockwise)

needle

bull wheel

platform canvas (turns clockwise)

Binder platform and upper and lower elevating canvases.   *Deere & Co.*

• Add twine and thread the binding mechanism. The twine cans on most binders hold two balls of binder twine, one on top of the other. Always unwind twine from the center of the ball. Place the first ball into the can and pull out a few inches of the center loose end. Tie this loose end to the outside loose end of the second ball, using a tight square knot.

Place the second ball into the can on top of the first, and then thread the loose end from the center of the top ball through the tensioner—which may be located on the top or side of the twine can, or beneath the binder deck—and through any twine guides on the binder frame. Feed the twine through the hollow needle point and out over the needle roller. Although not all binders are threaded exactly the same way, they are similar enough that a careful examination of your machine should reveal how it is to be threaded.

Finish threading the knotter by pulling the twine end across the binder deck and holding it firmly with one hand. With the other hand, trip the trip hook, grasp the discharge arms, and turn them once around. The needle will advance and place the twine into the twine holder or disc, where it is held fast. Pull the knot off the bill hook, and your binder is threaded and ready to tie bundles.

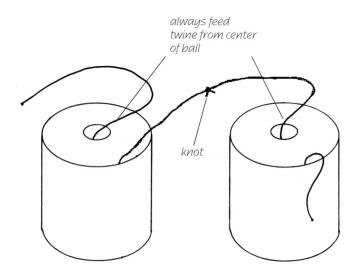

always feed twine from center of ball

knot

Correct way to splice two twine balls.

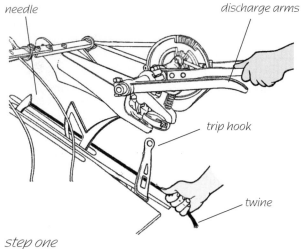

needle

discharge arms

trip hook

twine

step one

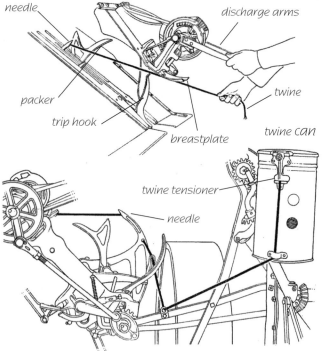

needle

discharge arms

packer

twine

trip hook

breastplate

twine can

twine tensioner

needle

Threading a type D binder.   *International Harvester*

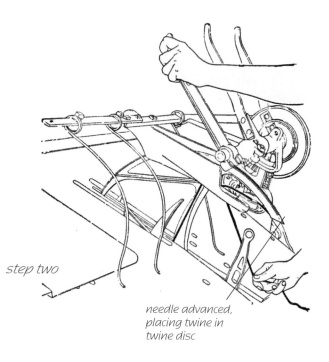

step two

needle advanced, placing twine in twine disc

twine tensioner

needle

twine can

Threading a type M binder.   *International Harvester*

Field Operation

After reaching the field, change the binder from transport to field mode: Unhitch your team and raise the tongue and platform end of the binder, tilting it on the transport trucks. Unlatch the tongue from the outside platform sill, and unhook the end of the tongue from the center sill. If your binder is equipped with a tongue truck, adjust it to operating mode.

After removing the tongue, crank down the grain wheel and lower the platform to the ground, where it is supported by the grain wheel. Move the outside grain divider from its folded position forward into its operating position and lock it in place.

Use the hand crank to lower the bull wheel and raise the binder to its highest position. While tipping the binder rearward onto the rear transport wheel, pull the front transport wheel from its socket in the binder main frame, and set it aside.

Attach the tongue and tongue brace to the front of the binder. Attach the tilting arm to the tongue. Lower the tongue to the ground, and remove the rear transport wheel. On some binders the inside grain divider folds back out of the way for transport, and must be moved

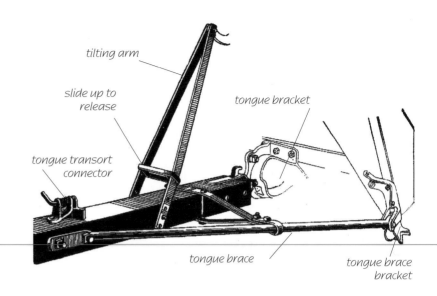

Tongue attached to the front of the binder. *International Harvester*

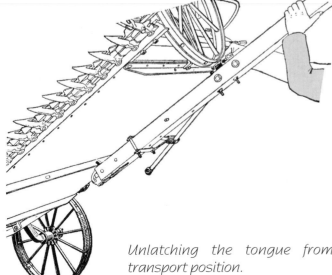

Transport wheels in position. The axles are locked in place by the binder's weight, and slide out of their sockets when the weight is removed. Some binders use a spring clip to secure the transport wheel axles.

International Harvester Co

to its forward position before use. Rehitch your team to the binder. Set the desired cutting height by raising or lowering the bull and grain wheels. Make sure the platform is level from side to side.

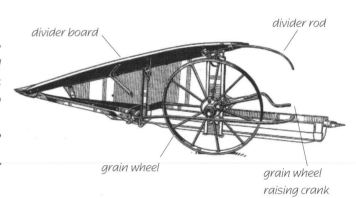

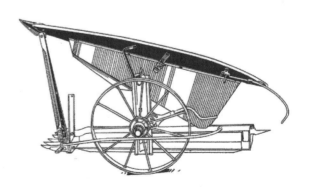

Unlatching the tongue from transport position.
International Harvester

Outside grain divider in operating position (top) and transport position.
International Harvester

Grain Binders

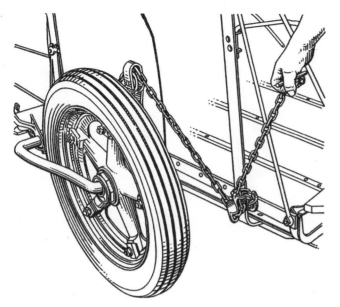

Grain wheel that is raised and lowered by sliding the chain through a lock.

Deere & Co.

clutch in gear and, to prevent clogging, make sure the knife is moving before the cutter bar enters the grain. When making the first round, a team and binder usually must be driven through standing grain. After a couple of rounds you can cut the grain left standing on the opening round by driving around the field in a clockwise direction. Some operators prefer to make the clockwise round first, although any obstructions at the edges of the field are more difficult to see. Be careful to keep the reel from striking any overhanging tree branches, as the wooden arms and bats are easily broken.

To turn square corners without missing any standing grain, run the binder to the corner until the cutter bar just leaves the standing grain. Stop the binder, and turn and back the team so the full width of the cutter bar is ready to enter the grain in the new direction before driving forward.

If you have to stop the binder while cutting, back the machine a foot or two before resuming forward motion. This action allows the cutter bar and the rest of the mechanism to get up to speed before entering the standing grain.

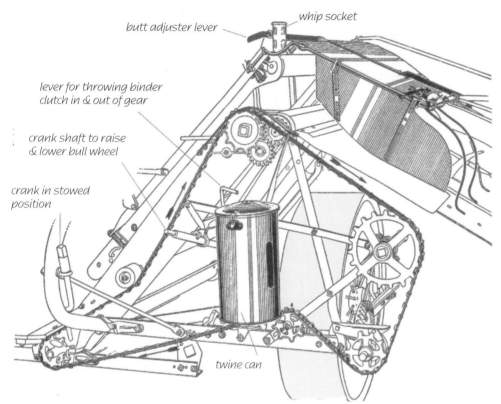

butt adjuster lever

whip socket

lever for throwing binder clutch in & out of gear

crank shaft to raise & lower bull wheel

crank in stowed position

twine can

Rear view of a binder.

International Harvester

Adjustments

A good binder operator continually monitors the varying condition of the standing grain, and makes frequent adjustments to ensure that all the grain is cut, and that well–shaped, tightly tied bundles are produced. Several control levers are provided for making various adjustments.

Set the height of the platform above ground by raising and lowering the bull and grain wheels. These adjustments, along with the binder tilting lever and the tongue tilting arm, allow a wide range of adjustments for cutting the stubble high or low, or for picking up tangled and lodged grain. In normal conditions, run the platform nearly level and tilted slightly forward. When you encounter a patch of short grain, tilt the platform farther forward to cut more of the stalks. When cutting lodged or tangled grain, raise the machine slightly more than halfway on the wheels, and tilt

Starting to Cut

When cutting with a left–hand cut binder, drive around the field in a counter–clockwise direction. Put the binder

Harvesting Machinery

the platform forward until the guard fingers are running close to the ground.

To make neat bundles, set the reel so the cut grain is laid onto the platform canvas evenly, and perpendicular to the direction in which the canvases are moving. Two levers adjust the reel—one moves it up and down, the other moves it forward and back. Under normal conditions, the reel bats should hit the grain just below the heads, and should not leave the grain until after it has been cut. If stalks of cut grain are catching on the bats and being carried around with them, raise the reel a little. If a strong wind is blowing, experiment to find the best reel position to place the grain evenly on the canvas. If the grain is leaning away from the direction of travel, or is lodged, set the reel low and forward to pick up the grain and lay it on the platform.

The binding mechanism shifting lever moves the binding attachment forward and backward on the binding deck and changes the position of the twine band on the bundle. No matter the height of the grain, the twine band should always be placed at the center of the bundle. When making a round in a field containing grain of uneven height, you may need to shift the binding mechanism several times.

The notched butt adjusting lever crosses the binding deck at an angle, and controls the position of the butter, a vertical board at the front of the binding deck. Don't use the butter to regulate the twine band placement. The butter should normally be set as far forward as possible and left in that position. Only in short grain should the butter be shifted backward to allow the twine band to be placed near the bundle center.

The binding deck cover may be adjusted up or down. In heavy or tangled grain, raise the cover to give more room. With light, fluffy grain, lower the deck cover to prevent the straw from piling up as it comes onto the deck.

The canvas windshield at the rear of the platform, and the windboard at the rear of the binding deck may be adjusted for long or short straw. Proper adjustment will help prevent the scattering of straw, and will make better bundles.

Operating a binder requires you to not only drive your team and keep an eye on all the variables during cutting, but also monitor the bundles to make sure they are tied properly, and trip the bundle carrier so the bundles are dumped in a convenient location for the shockers and out of the way of your team and binder on the next round. Check the twine box at intervals to assure a sufficient supply of twine. Throughout the binding operation, you must stay attuned to the mechanical performance of the

entire machine, and stop and check any unusual sound or vibration that might signal a problem.

If you leave the binder in the field overnight, or if rain interrupts cutting, release the tension on the canvases, or better still, cover the machine with a tarpaulin. Moisture from dew or rain causes the canvas to shrink. If you leave tension on the canvases, they may be so tight when you resume cutting that draft will be increased and bearing failure may result. Before beginning to cut, reset tension on the canvases so they run square on the rollers and are just tight enough to carry grain without slipping.

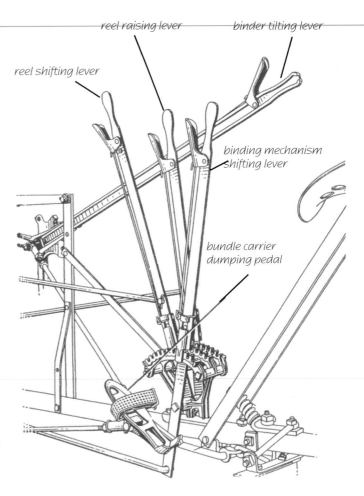

Control levers on a typical grain binder. *Deere & Co.*

Lubrication

Because of its large number of light, fast moving parts, a grain binder requires frequent, thorough lubrication. On older machines, most lubrication points are little more than open holes, although some have caps to protect them from dirt. To make sure an oil hole isn't clogged with dirt, use a short piece of wire to clean out the hole before oiling. Thoroughly oil the bearings of every moving part often during he work day, and before starting each morning.

Later binders are equipped with grease fittings, which make lubricating with a pressure grease gun an easy job. The main drive gears on these machines usually run in a bath of oil in an enclosed case. Check the oil level in these cases daily. Keep the knotter parts, small rollers, pinion faces, and cams well oiled. Keep the knotter bill hook and twine disc free of grain, straw, and bits of twine.

After Cutting

When cutting is finished, a partial bundle of grain usually remains in the binding mechanism. Operate the trip hook by hand and rotate the discharge arms to tie and eject this last bundle.

Drive the binder back to where you left the transport wheels and unhitch your team. Release the tension on the canvases. Using the bull wheel crank, raise the binder to its highest position and slip the rear transport wheel into position. Disconnect the tilting arm from the tongue and tilt the binder back onto the rear wheel. Disconnect the tongue and brace, and slide the front transport wheel into position. Raise the bull wheel to its highest position, then raise the grain wheel.

Unlatch and fold back the outside grain divider, as well as the inside divider if appropriate. Lift the end of the platform and connect the tongue to the middle and outside platform sills. Lower the tongue and rehitch your team. When transporting the binder, move the reel into its lowest and rearmost position.

Storing a Binder

At the end of each season remove the canvases and clean them of any dirt and bits of straw. Carefully roll the canvases and store them in a dry place. To prevent damage from mice, hang each canvas over a round stick or pipe, with the ends free and even. Labeling each canvas will help prevent confusion when you reinstall them the following season.

Clean all the dirt, straw, chaff, and old grease from the entire machine. Check all the nuts and bolts for tightness, and examine the binder for any missing, broken, or worn parts. Thoroughly lubricate the machine, and coat the cutting parts and knotter with oil. Coat the needle point and bill hook with grease to prevent rust. Store the binder under cover.

Common Grain Binder Troubles

Because a grain binder is so complicated, many things can go wrong. Foremost among these problems is a missed knot that allows the grain to string out behind the machine in loose clumps. When a binder fails to tie, each missed bundle has to be gathered up and hand tied by the following shockers, who usually consider untied bundles a good reason to roundly cuss the binder operator. Following are some nuggets of advice on operating your machine properly to avoid the dreaded untied bundle.

Chain and Gear Problems

Excessive wear of the chains or sprockets may be caused by the chains being installed either backwards or too tight. Make sure chains are installed to run with the hooks leading and the hook openings facing outward. Running a chain with the bar of the link forward will cause the sprocket teeth to wear into a hook shape, resulting in broken chains. Run chains just tight enough to stay on the sprockets. Running chains too tight causes binding, as well as excessive wear of the chain links, sprocket teeth, and shaft bearings. Make sure the sprockets line up with each other.

Gears must be properly meshed to prevent wear and the possibility of slipping. The large bevel gears at the rear of the binder are driven from the bull wheel, and deliver all the power needed to run the binder. When these gears are properly adjusted, the teeth fit into each other as far as possible without bottoming out in the opposite gear.

Rapid wear of the large main bevel gear on the countershaft and the pinion on the crankshaft (pitman shaft) is caused by improper mesh between the two, or by using oil on the gears in sandy or dusty conditions. The bearing at the inside end of the countershaft is adjustable, allowing proper adjustment of the mesh between these two gears. Older machines often have a plug screwed into the housing that supports the end of the countershaft opposite the large bevel gear. Screwing this plug in forces the shaft endwise, taking up any slack between the main bevel gear and the pinion.

If you use your binder in a sandy field or in dry conditions where sand or dust will be picked up by the bull wheel and thrown into the main gears, don't use oil or grease on the gears or chains. Lubricant holds the sand and grit, causing rapid wear.

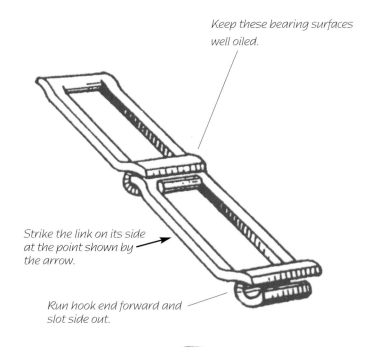

Keep these bearing surfaces well oiled.

Strike the link on its side at the point shown by the arrow.

Run hook end forward and slot side out.

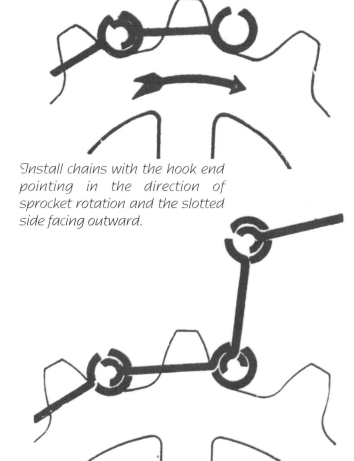

Install chains with the hook end pointing in the direction of sprocket rotation and the slotted side facing outward.

To detach the chain, bend a link outward and, using a sprocket tooth as a brace. Strike the link on its side at the point shown by the arrow (see above).

Correct way to install chains.   *Deere & Co.*

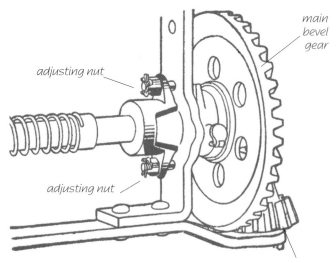

main bevel gear

adjusting nut

adjusting nut

main bevel pinion

One style of main bevel gear and pinion adjustment—tighten the two nuts to take up slack in the mesh between the two gears.   *International Harvester*

Canvas Problems

Broken slats and creeping or slipping canvases are caused by the elevators not being square, or by the canvas straps being too loose or unevenly tightened. Check the elevators for squareness by using a carpenter's square, or by measuring the diagonals and making the measurements equal by means of the squaring adjustments.

Buckle the canvas straps so the canvases are just tight enough to do their work. Running them tighter than

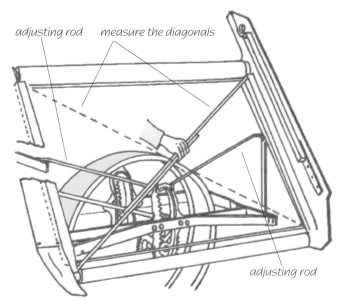

adjusting rod   measure the diagonals

adjusting rod

Squaring elevators by equalizing diagonal measurements.   *U. of Illinois, Circular 309*

necessary increases wear and draft. Make sure the front and rear edges of the canvases are at the same tension. To test for equal tension, lift first the front edge, then the rear edge with one finger. If the tension feels unequal, adjust it by loosening or tightening the canvas straps.

Roller Problems

If a roller binds at one end, make sure the bearing is properly fitted and lubricated. If binding occurs at both ends, the frame is probably being pulled together too tightly by the tie rods, which should be loosened. Sometimes short pieces of straw or weeds wrap around, or get between, the canvas and the front end of the inside platform roller, causing the canvas to jam. If the roller wraps with green weeds, raise the machine on the wheels, or tilt up the cutter bar a little, so weeds aren't cut.

If the jam is due to short pieces of straw, the outside end of the platform is probably set higher than the inside end, causing straw at the outer end to be cut higher. On the next round, the inside end of the cutter bar recuts this longer straw, creating a lot of short straws that jam the roller. Adjust the grain and bull wheels so the platform runs level.

Draft Problems

Heavy draft usually results from either poor lubrication or too–tight chains. Otherwise, check the bull wheel and make sure it's mounted squarely in the quadrants.

Excessive side draft is usually caused by the grain wheel being set incorrectly, allowing the outer end of the platform to drag or cut too low. Side draft may also result from a bad bearing or bent grain wheel.

Poorly Shaped Bundles

If bundles are poorly shaped when you're cutting good grain, chances are you are improperly manipulating the control levers. The levers must be continually adjusted to meet varying grain conditions in a field. Proper manipulation of the reel is essential to making good bundles. The reel slats should hit the grain just below the heads and, to lay the straw back evenly on the platform, must be raised and lowered to suit the grain's changing height. A reel that's too low throws straw too far back, and the slats carry the straw up and over, losing it on the ground in front of the machine.

In passing from short to tall grain, or vice versa, raise or lower the reel and shift the binder head forward or backward to keep the twine band in the center of the bundle. Don't use the butt board to move the twine band.

Keep the butt board at right angles to the elevator rollers and as far forward as possible, moving it to the rear only in short grain. Adjust the header board on the binder deck to suit the length of the straw; in long straw it may be laid down flat. Keep the grain checks just tight enough to prevent straw from working under and past them.

The head ends of the cut grain stalks tend to travel faster than the butt ends, going up the elevators and onto the binding deck first. This problem is especially common when cutting short straw and results in poorly formed bundles. A remedy is to fasten a light steel strip to the platform's outer framework, allowing it to ride on top of the canvas where the heads will fall. The steel strip slightly retards movement of the heads, allowing the straw to hit the elevators parallel to the slats. In a more severe case, crimp the last half of the strip to offer more resistance. In an extreme case, tie a piece of rope to the platform end and allow it to ride on the canvas. Tying knots in the rope every few inches will further retard the heads.

To pick up down grain leaning forward or away from the platform, tilt the front of the platform down and move the reel forward and down. To get down grain leaning toward the cutter bar, tilt the front of the machine down, and run the reel as low as possible and back on the platform to carry the straw away from the sickle.

Making good bundles in short grain is difficult. Lower the binder on the wheels and run the platform level or, if possible, tilted up at the front. Lower the reel enough to throw the straw well back on the platform canvas, and take one of the measures for retarding the grain heads. Move the binder head as far forward as possible. To tie the bundle in the center, you may also need to move the butt board back.

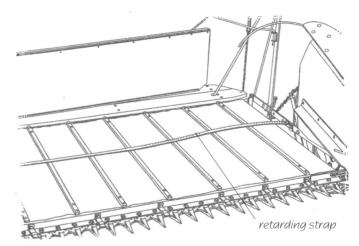

retarding strap

Grain head retarding strap placed over the platform canvas.   *Deere & Co.*

Badly shaped bundles in long, tangled grain may be improved by loosening the grain checks over the binder deck, and by adjusting the head to tie smaller, looser bundles.

Choking Down

In heavy, tangled grain the binding head sometimes can't discharge a bundle, and the whole machine is stopped by choking down. This problem occurs more frequently when the ground is soft, causing the bull wheel to slide when the head tries to discharge a bundle. To remedy these situations, adjust the head to tie a smaller, looser bundle and loosen tension on the compressor spring.

Binding Attachment Problems

The binding attachment is made up of the *binder head* and the *knotter,* both of which may cause tying troubles. Every working part of the binding attachment, with the exception of the packers, must operate at a certain time and in a definite relationship to each of the other parts. This synchronization is referred to as the timing of the binding attachment, and requires the dog, stop arm, needle, twine holder, bill hook, and discharge arms to all do their job at the correct time for the bundle to be properly tied.

Once in the field, don't fret because a loose bundle is occasionally cast—looking for trouble is impractical until you're sure you have a problem. A few drops of oil will often correct what appears to be a serious difficulty. Something as simple as a loose nut can cause major trouble. Experienced binder operators look for small troubles before attempting complicated adjustments.

Binder Head Problems

The binder head can cause many tying troubles because of either worn parts or being out of time. All makes of binder head are similar and the functions of the various parts are the same, although the parts themselves may vary in shape or location. You can diagnose most troubles in the binder head by observing the action of the discharge arms.

Discharge arms revolve continuously, resulting in small bundles.
This problem may be caused by one of two things:

1. The trip dog is out of time. The relationship between the trip dog and the trip stop arm is maintained by the position of the dog bevel gear and the pinion on the binder head countershaft. A dog that has been removed and reinstalled incorrectly will be out of time and the discharge arms will revolve constantly.

Time the mechanism as follows: Remove the trip dog driver and move the discharge arms to the rest position.

Slide out the bevel gear that carries the dog far enough for the teeth to be out of mesh with the driven pinion. Hold the dog back against its fully compressed spring, and rotate the dog bevel gear until the face of the dog touches the face of the stop arm. Slide the dog bevel gear into mesh with its mate and replace the dog driver. Adjust the stop arm by means of the binder lock adjusting bolt until you have $1/16$– to $1/8$–inch clearance between the dog and stop arm.

2. The dog slips past the trip stop arm. Badly worn striking faces of the dog and stop arm sometimes slip past each other, often intermittently, resulting in a small bundle followed by a large one. Replace the worn parts or build them up with weld.

Discharge arms either fail to start or stop during the cycle. This problem is usually caused by the dog. When the binder head is at rest, the stop arm holds the dog out of engagement with the dog driver. When the pressure of a full bundle against the compressor arm or trip hook arm raises the stop arm out of the way, the dog spring forces the dog into engagement with the dog driver. If the dog spring is weak, broken, or missing, this trouble will occur. The remedy is to replace the dog spring.

Discharge arms move jerkily, or stop during the cycle. The striking faces between the dog and the dog driver are worn to the point that the parts slip past each other. Replace the parts, or build them up with weld.

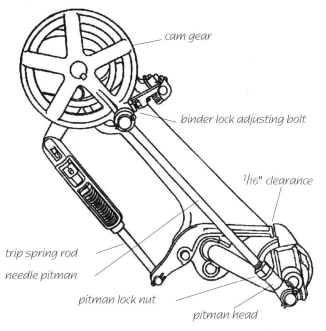

Adjustments for one style of binder head. To shorten the needle pitman, disconnect the pitman from the cam gear, loosen the lock nut, and screw the pitman into the pitman head.   *International Harvester*

Knotter Head Problems

Don't mutilate the knotter by attacking it with cold chisels, files, punches, or hammers. To make repairs you need only a wrench, a little oil, and reasonably good sense. Keep knotter parts, knife roller, and faces of cam and pinions well lubricated, but free of greasy dirt and straw buildup. Keep the twine holder or disc clean of bits of straw and twine. The bill hook should be rust free, smooth, and bright to allow the knot to be easily stripped from it. If the binder fails to tie properly, first check the twine in the box to make sure it is unwinding freely, then follow its path through the roller tension, twine guides, needle, and disc looking for anything that may cause slack or too much tension. Uneven, weak, wet, dried–out, or poor twine may cause missed bundles. Test the twine tension, trip hook tension, and the twine holder or disc tension as explained below.

Before making any adjustments to the knotter, get all the information possible about the trouble and then carefully examine your machine. If you try a certain adjustment that doesn't fix the trouble, put it back exactly the same as it was. Make all twine disc spring and bill hook spring adjustments gradually, by giving the adjusting screws no more than one–quarter of a turn per adjustment. A careful examination of the twine bands of untied bundles will help you diagnose the cause of the problem.

Bundle Size and Tightness

The size of the bundle is controlled by the amount of space between the packers and the trip hook. The packers compress the grain against the trip hook, which stands vertically in the center of the binding deck. To make smaller bundles, move the trip hook inward along the trip hook arm and slightly loosen the trip stop spring. For larger bundles move the trip hook outward farther away from the packers, and slightly tighten the trip stop spring.

Tightness of the twine around the bundle is adjusted by means of the trip stop spring. To test the force required to trip the binder and start the tying process, hook a spring scale into the eye of the trip hook and pull in a line parallel to the discharge arms when they are in their home position. The tension should be 20 to 24 pounds. The more tension, the more tightly tied the bundle will be. Don't try to regulate the size or tightness of bundles with the twine tension or by adjusting the knotter spring.

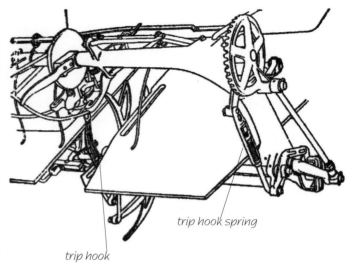

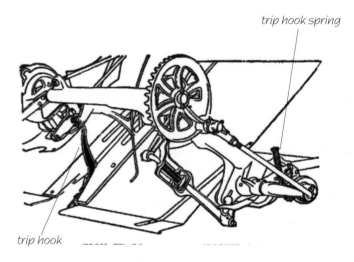

Adjusting a binding attachment for size and tightness of bundles. Move trip hook in to make smaller bundles. Loosen trip hook spring (for type M attachment, top) or trip stop spring (for type D attachment, bottom) to make looser bundles. International Harvester

Twine Tension Troubles

Twine leaving the twine can passes through a tensioning device before reaching the needle. This device is intended to keep the twine from becoming slack and tangling between the twine can and needle eye. Keep the twine tension tight, but not too tight. Incorrect twine tension is one of the most common causes of missed bundles.

To determine twine tension, thread the machine with the exception of bringing the needle over to get the twine in the disc. Tie a loop in the twine under the breastplate and hook the loop to a spring scale. Pull the twine through the needle

Harvesting Machinery

eye. Tie a loop in the twine under the breastplate and hook the loop to a spring scale. Pull the twine through the needle eye on a line parallel with the binder deck. Correct tension should be between 8 and 12 pounds. To adjust the tension, loosen or tighten the tension spring on the twine tensioner.

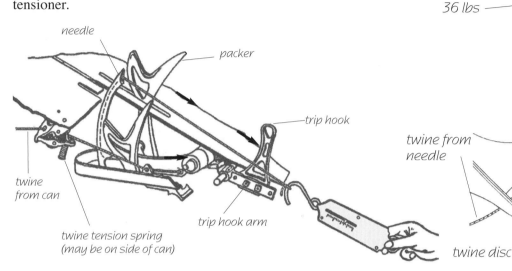

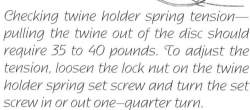

Checking twine tension from the can—moving the twine should require 8 to 12 pounds of pull. Adjust tension by tightening or loosening the twine tension spring. Check trip tension by hooking the scale to the trip hook and pulling in a direction parallel to the discharge arms in home position. Adjust the trip stop spring until the tension is 20 to 24 pounds.

U. of Saskatchewan, Bulletin 67

Checking twine holder spring tension— pulling the twine out of the disc should require 35 to 40 pounds. To adjust the tension, loosen the lock nut on the twine holder spring set screw and turn the set screw in or out one–quarter turn.

U. of Saskatchewan, Bulletin 67

Twine Disc Problems

The twine holder and disc must be set at the proper tension to hold the twine until the knotter hook makes its revolution and the knife cuts the twine. To test the tension, thread the machine ready for tying, trip the trip hook, and turn the discharge arms one complete revolution. Take off the band and knot just completed, so the twine is securely in the disc or holder. Tie a loop in the twine directly above the knotter and hook it in a spring scale. Pulling straight up on the twine should require 35 to 40 pounds to pull the twine out of the disc.

To adjust the tension, loosen the lock nut on the twine holder spring set screw and turn the set screw in or out as needed.

Never turn the set screw more than one–quarter turn at a time.

Be sure to tighten the lock nut after each adjustment

Bill Hook Problems

The knotter bill hook cam presses against the knotter cam roller and holds the bill hook jaw, or tongue, closed on

the two twine ends while the knot is being completed. The jaws must be tight enough to hold the twine ends until the knot is formed and pulled tight. Pressure of the cam against the knotter cam roller is controlled by a coil spring that is often tightened too much. The knotter hook cam spring should be just tight enough to hold the knotter tongue closed until the tying process is completed. A pull of about 12 pounds should be needed to pull the twine from the bill hook jaws. Adjust spring tension by tightening or loosening the knotter hook cam spring.

Never turn the set screw more than one–quarter turn at a time.

Knotter Frame Problems

The face of the knotter hook pinion should set up close to the face of the tier wheel. On some binders wear on these parts is taken up by adjusting eccentrics to make the knotter and worm shaft pinions mesh properly with the tier wheel, without crowding them too tightly into mesh. The knotter frame should be set just close enough to the tier

Type M Knotter

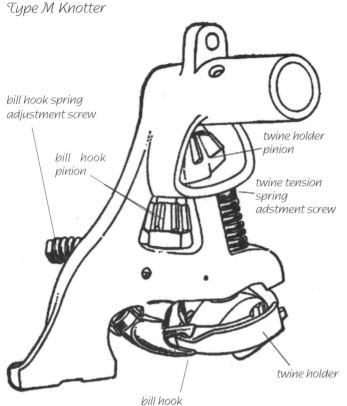

bill hook spring adjustment screw

bill hook pinion

twine holder pinion

twine tension spring adstment screw

bill hook

twine holder

Parts of a type D knotter.

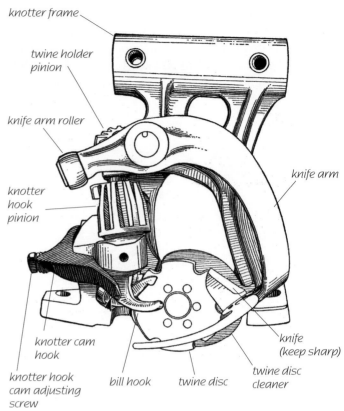

knotter frame

twine holder pinion

knife arm roller

knotter hook pinion

knife arm

knotter cam hook

knotter hook cam adjusting screw

bill hook

twine disc

knife (keep sharp)

twine disc cleaner

Deere & Co.

Type D Knotter

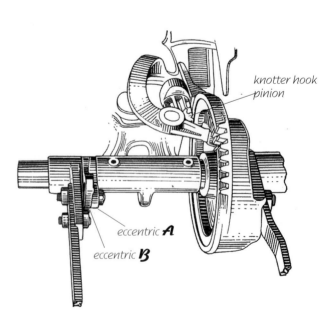

tier wheel

knotter worm pinion

twine holder spring

knotter worm gear

knotter worm

wine tension adjustment screw

knotter hook pinion

eccentric *A*

eccentric *B*

To take up wear and keep knotter pinions in proper mesh, loosen locking bolt and adjust eccentrics A and B.

Deere & Co.

Adjustments for the two knotter types.

International Harvester

wheel to allow the flat face of the knotter hook pinion to rub against the face of the tier wheel without binding.

Dull Knife

For reliable knots, keep the twine knife sharp. If the binder misses bundles, check the knife for sharpness before making any adjustments. Frequently sharpen the knife by removing it from the knotter and using a whetstone to give it a keen edge that cuts easily. *Do not use a file, and be careful to maintain the blade's original bevel.*

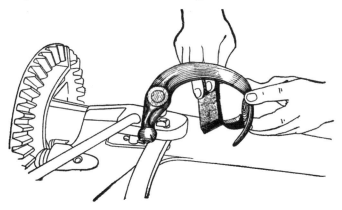

Using a whetstone to sharpen the knotter knife, taking care to maintain the blade's original bevel.   Deere & Co.

Needle Problems

The needle point should be sharp, smooth, and bright, and the needle surface smooth from point to hub. Use fine sandpaper or steel wool to polish the surface.

The needle's purpose is to place the twine in the twine holder or disc notches. To do so, the needle must press hard against the knife arm or the breastplate when the binder is tripped and turned over empty. The bottom of the needle point, at the roller, should clear the twine holder disc by 1/4 inch when the needle passes through the knotter frame on a type D knotter. In addition, the needle point should pass close to the knotter pinion when it moves through the knotter frame. If the needle doesn't advance far enough to place the twine in the disc, shorten the needle pitman by one or more threads.

A bent needle will cause problems. To check for a bent needle, sight along the rim and check the position of the needle tip as it passes through the frame. On a type M knotter, the bottom side of the needle should clear the top of the knotter disc post by 5/16 to 3/8 inch. A bent needle may be straightened by slipping a piece of pipe over the point and bending with care, and being careful not to twist the needle.

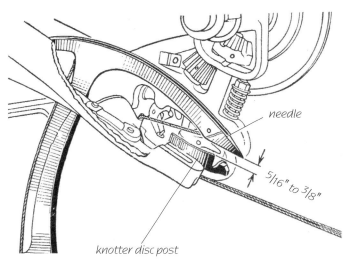

needle

5/16" to 3/8"

knotter disc post

Correct distance between needle and knotter disc post on a type M knotter.   *International Harvester*

Rust

A rusty bill hook, needle point, or twine disc will most certainly cause tying troubles. Use fine sandpaper or steel wool to remove any rust and polish the surface. Don't use coarse sandpaper or a file, which would scratch the surfaces.

Failed Twine Bands

In diagnosing binder knotter troubles, the appearance of the band and where you find it will point to the cause of its failure. When a binder misses enough bundles to indicate that the knotter is out of adjustment, stop the machine as soon as the next missed bundle is cast. Locate and study the failed band, and compare it to one of the following examples:

Band clings to the bill hook with a simple loose knot tied in one end, and the other end cut off square. This condition is caused by the twine holder spring being too loose, or the twine tension to the twine can being too tight. When the needle advances, the twine is being pulled out of the twine holder instead of out of the can, and a single knot is tied at the needle end of the band. The remedy is to loosen twine tension from the can. If the trouble persists, slightly tighten the twine disc spring.

Band resembles the previous one, but is with the bundle, rather than on the bill hook. The single knot is pulled fairly tight, and the free end is cut square. This problem is common and may not be evident until you pick up the bundle and the free end pulls out of the slip knot. Of the numerous potential causes, many relate to wear. The twine holder tension may be too loose, in which case tighten it slightly. The twine disc may be badly worn, preventing it from grasping the twine. If this band occurs at regular intervals, such as every fifth bundle, look for wear in one notch of the twine disc. In both cases, replace the worn disc. The knotter hook cam or roller may be worn to the point that the jaw isn't opening far enough to catch both strands of twine, in which case the worn parts must be replaced. The bill hook may have dropped down too low as a result of excessive wear under the pinion. Check for excessive vertical play in the shaft, which you may be able to correct by placing a thin shim washer on the shaft under the pinion. If the twine holder pinion, worm, or gear is badly worn, the twine disc may be out of time. Replace the worn parts. A loose or broken twine tension may result in the twine not being stretched tightly across the bill hook. Adjust tension; repair or replace defective parts.

Band is on the bill hook, with the free end crushed and torn. The only difference between this and the first described band is the condition of the free end. The crushing is caused by the twine tension and twine holder spring both being too tight. The twine disc crushes and weakens the twine, while the twine from the can is so tight that when the needle advanced the twine breaks at the disc before being pulled from the can. The remedy is to loosen the twine tension. If the trouble persists, loosen the twine holder spring a little.

Band resembles the previous one, but is with the bundle and the knot is tighter. This condition is caused by the twine disc being so tight it seriously damages the twine, which breaks at the disk when the bill hook rotates. Loosen the twine holder spring slightly.

Band is with the bundle and both ends are torn and ragged. This situation is caused by the twine disc being so tight it will not yield any twine to the rotating bill hook, which then breaks both strands at the disk. Loosen the twine holder spring slightly.

Band is with the bundle and both ends are bent. The bent ends indicate that the knot was formed around the bill hook, but not completed by pulling the twine ends through the loop. This situation is usually caused by a too–loose knotter hook cam spring, which should be tightened slightly. It may also be caused by bits of straw or other debris lodged between the bill hook jaws, preventing the jaws from closing tightly enough to grip the twine. Keep the bill hook, along with the entire knotter, free of straw, dirt, and twine clippings. The knife arm may be bent and cutting too close to the bill hook. Bend it back into position to cut the twine midway between the twine disc and the bill hook. The jaws of the bill hook may be worn badly enough to prevent them from gripping the twine. A little judicious filing may provide a temporary fix until you can replace the worn parts.

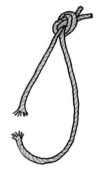

Band is broken and hanging on the bill hook. This situation sometimes happens when the binder is making loose bundles and the knotter hook cam spring is tight. The stripper pulls the band up from beneath the breastplate instead of stripping the knot from the bill hook. When the discharge arms strike the bundle, the bill hook holds the band, which then breaks. Loosen the knotter hook cam spring slightly. If the trouble persists, set the machine to tie a tighter bundle. This trouble may result from a badly worn cam roller on the knife arm, which also functions to strip the knot from the bill hook, preventing the arm from advancing far enough to strip the knot. In this case, replace the knife arm cam roller.

Band is found with a slip noose tied around the bundle, and the twine extending back to the eye of the needle. The needle has failed to place the needle end of the band in the twine holder for one of the following reasons:

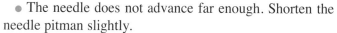

- The needle brings up straw or, in weedy conditions, green matter that blocks the disc and prevents the twine from being placed firmly into the notch. Cut the straw higher to eliminate as much weedy matter as possible.

- The needle does not advance far enough. Shorten the needle pitman slightly.

- The needle is bent or the needle eye is worn badly enough that the twine cannot be placed into the disc notch. Straighten or replace the needle.

- The disc notches may be badly worn. Replace them.

Cutter problems

The cutter bar on a grain binder works exactly like that of a mowing machine. If you experience cutting troubles, consult the chapter on mowers to determine the cause.

Operating a grain binder requires keeping an eye on all the field variables while monitoring the bundles to make sure they tie properly and dump in a convenient location.

Courtesy of Robert Mouw

15 *Grain Threshers*

Threshing machines, or separators, as they are often called, don't strictly qualify as horse–drawn equipment, but are related. Any farmer who cuts grain with a binder will likely thresh it with a threshing machine. Although a good many separators have survived, few threshermen remain except in Amish communities.

According to Isaiah, writing in the Old Testament, threshing instruments have been around since Biblical times. Archeologists uncovered a clay tablet in Iraq that has been dated to about 3,000 BC and is purported to show a threshing sledge in use. The Romans threshed grain with a device called a tribulum, according to Marcus Varro, who wrote in the first century BC: "The grain should be threshed on the floor. This is done in some districts by means of a yoke of oxen and a threshing sledge (tribulum). The latter is constructed... of a board roughened with stones or pieces of iron imbedded in it, which separates the grain from the ear when it is dragged [over the grain]."

From these ancient times until well into the 19th century, separating grain from the straw was done by hand with a flail, or by animals either treading on the grain or pulling a heavy toothed roller over it. The flail consisted of a straight wooden handle and a short wooden club tied together by a leather thong. The thresherman could stand erect and deliver sharp, heavy blows to a pile of grain lying on the floor.

After the grain was thoroughly beaten, which knocked the kernels

A jointed flail made up of a longer handle, called the staff or helve, and a shorter piece, called the whipple or swiple.

loose from the heads, the straw was removed with a fork. The grain was then cleaned of the chaff and other debris by a process called winnowing, for which the grain and chaff mixture was shoveled into a container and then slowly poured from a height. Wind blew the lighter chaff and dirt to one side, while the heavier grain fell into another container. Sometimes the grain and chaff were instead placed in a large shallow basket, tossed into the air (where wind blew away the chaff), and the grain caught again in the basket. Most barns built during the 1800s had a large door on the opposite side of the barn floor from the main door to create a draft of air across the barn floor, which doubled as a threshing floor.

Winnowing was repeated as many times as necessary to get the grain clean. As you can imagine, threshing with animals resulted in a lot more dirt that had to be removed before the grain could be used. One mid–19th century source estimated that one man could thresh 7 bushels of wheat, 8 of rye, 18 of oats, or 15 of barley per day. An equal amount of time was then needed to clean the grain.

Machines for separating grain from the heads were developed in England and Scotland starting in 1750. Some of these threshers were imported into this country, while others were made here. They were nicknamed groundhog threshers because, as the story goes, someone thought the squat, rounded shape of those early threshers—which were staked to the ground and driven by treadmills—resembled that of a groundhog digging into the ground.

Several patents for threshers were issued to American inventors during the early 19th century, but the 1837 patent given to Hiram and John Pitts of Maine for a horse–operated apron–type thresher is generally considered the beginning of the modern thresher. Improvements to the machine by the Pitts brothers, Jerome I. Case, and others were continued during the rest of the 1900s, with the addition of greater capacity, self feeders, grain weighers, and windstackers. By the beginning of the 20th century the all–steel thresher with which we're familiar today was in use throughout the country.

Features of a Grain Thresher

The modern threshing machine has a self feeder attachment that cuts the twine bands and conveys the

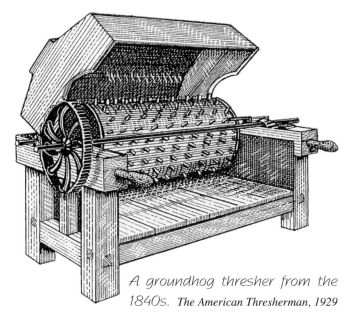

A groundhog thresher from the 1840s. *The American Thresherman, 1929*

sheaves of grain into the cylinder. The cylinder knocks the kernels of grain from the heads, and then the threshed grain is cleaned of all chaff, straw, and other debris, such as dirt or weed seeds. The clean grain is automatically weighed and delivered to a wagon or a sacking attachment, while the straw and chaff is blown onto a stack.

The size, or capacity, of a thresher is expressed in numbers representing inches, such as: 18x22, 20x35, 28x46, and so forth. The first number indicates the width of the cylinder, the second is the width of the separating chamber, or straw racks. Cylinder width nominally indicates the machine's threshing capacity, while the width of the separating chamber indicates the separating capacity. The true capacity of any thresher, however, depends on the machine's design, adjustment, and feeding, along with the condition of the grain.

Right side (top) and left side view of a modern all–steel thresher. *Dion Freres, Inc.*

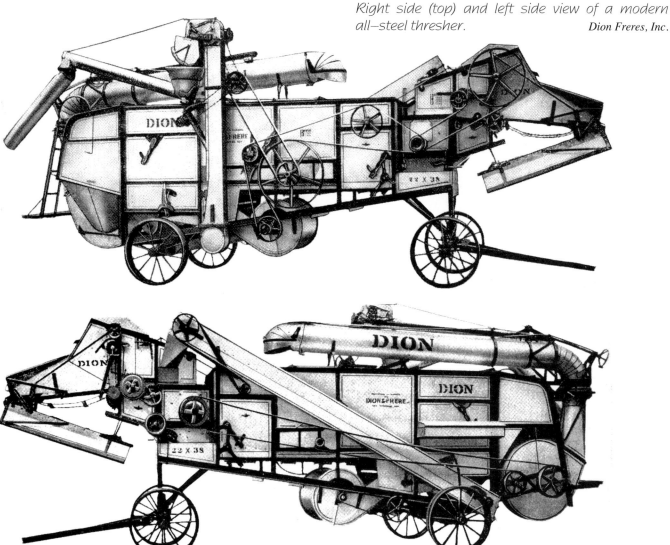

Self Feeder

The *self feeder* carries the unthreshed sheaves into the cylinder, cutting the twine bands along the way and sending through to the cylinder an even stream of grain without solid bunches. The self feeder includes a sheet metal trough extending to the front of the thresher, which may be folded when the machine is transported between jobs.

A conveyor chain, regulated by a speed controlled clutch, runs on the flat bottom of the trough. The speed governor prevents the conveyor from starting to feed until the cylinder is turning at a satisfactory threshing speed. Bundles of grain are pitched onto the moving conveyor, which carries them into the band cutters, a series of revolving or reciprocating knives.

The chopping action of the knives cuts the twine bands around the bundles, and loosens and spreads the grain before delivering it to the feed fingers or rakes in the throat, which then feed the cylinder. Most self feeders have a straw governor, in addition to the speed governor. The straw governor clutch slips if a bundle, or clump of bundles, too large to pass under the knives hits the band cutters. This slight delay gives the band cutters and feed fingers time to even out the stream before it hits the cylinder, and thereby prevents slugging of the cylinder. Slugging can slow down the cylinder to the point where the machine may clog and have to be stopped and cleaned out. Even if a slug doesn't actually clog the machine, the slowing of the cylinder causes the rest of the machine to slow as well, resulting in uncleaned grain in the sacks. To keep grain from being fed into the cylinder too rapidly, the feed fingers or rakes work opposite a set of retarder fingers that tend to hold back the straw.

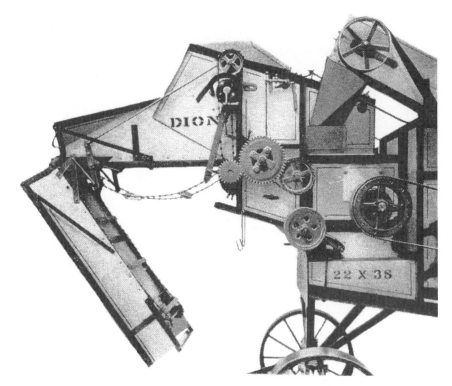

Partially folded self feeder.   *Dion Freres, Inc.*

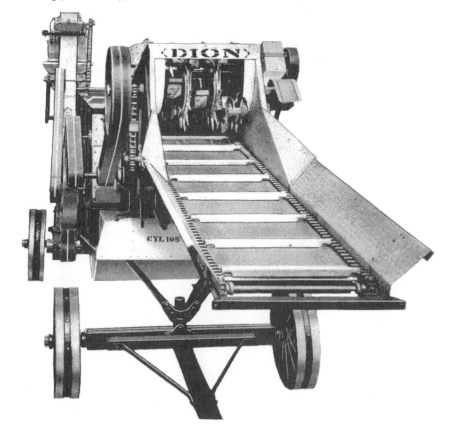

Front view of a self feeder showing the conveyor chain, sometimes called a raddle, and the band cutters.   *Dion Freres, Inc.*

Harvesting Machinery

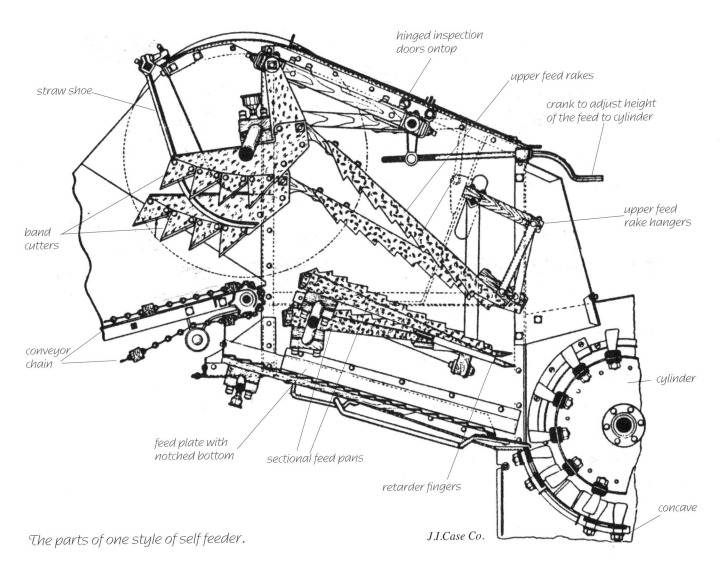

The parts of one style of self feeder.

Labels on figure:
- hinged inspection doors ontop
- upper feed rakes
- crank to adjust height of the feed to cylinder
- straw shoe
- upper feed rake hangers
- band cutters
- conveyor chain
- feed plate with notched bottom
- sectional feed pans
- retarder fingers
- cylinder
- concave

J.I.Case Co.

Threshing Mechanism

In the threshing mechanism the beating action of the revolving *cylinder* teeth against the fixed *concave* teeth threshes or shells the grain kernels from the ears or heads. The first step in the process of threshing is to loosen and separate the grain kernels from the heads, which is accomplished by the rotating cylinder teeth striking the grain and knocking it against the stationary concave teeth with great force.

A threshing cylinder consists of discs or spiders mounted on the cylinder shaft. Around the outer edges of these discs are bolted a number of heavy parallel bars— usually 9, 12, or 20—each of which has a series of heavy steel teeth bolted at regular intervals along its length. The threshing cylinder is heavy and turns at high speed, giving it a flywheel effect to help the machine maintain its momentum when a tough bunch of grain enters the cylinder.

The other part of the threshing mechanism consists of the concaves, so called because of their shape. Located beneath the front part of the cylinder, the concaves are narrow bars, usually made of gray cast iron, each with two rows of teeth like those on the cylinder, as well as holes through which some of the threshed grain falls. The number of teeth may be varied by removing a toothed section and replacing it with a blank one.

The concave sections may be moved closer to, or farther from, the cylinder, usually by means of a lever on the outside of the machine. The closer to the cylinder the concaves are set, the more aggressive their action becomes.

Separating Mechanism

The grain and chaff are carried by the *grain pan*, or *grain conveyor*, to the *cleaning shoe*, which contains the *sieves*.

Cylinder or concave teeth in two sizes; modern teeth are drop forged of high-grade steel and have a hardened threshing edge that resists wear.

Dion Freres, Inc.

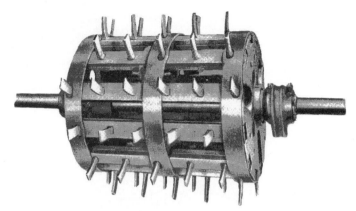

A 12-bar threshing cylinder.

Dion Freres, Inc.

A toothed concave section. The steel strip under the nuts reinforces the cast iron and helps keep the nuts tight.

Dion Freres, Inc.

The grain passes through the shoe while being blasted with air from the *fan*, which blows away the chaff and dirt. Any unthreshed heads pass over the grain pan *chaffer* to the *tailings auger*, and then to the *tailings elevator*, which returns them to the cylinder for rethreshing.

The separating mechanism combines the *concave* under the front part of the cylinder, the *grate* under the rear of the cylinder, the *beater* behind the cylinder, and the *straw racks* to separate the grain and chaff from the straw. Some of the threshed grain falls through the concave, while the majority is thrown through the grate, which consists of parallel steel bars, or tines, set about 1/2 inch apart. The straw is carried across the grate to the straw rack, while the threshed grain, chaff, and small bits of refuse pass through the openings. The straw is prevented from wrapping around the cylinder and is formed into a stream and fed onto the straw rack by the revolving *beater*. The beater also deflects any grain thrown back by the cylinder, while a hanging *check board*, usually supplemented by a *canvas apron*, performs the same function for any grain thrown back by the beater.

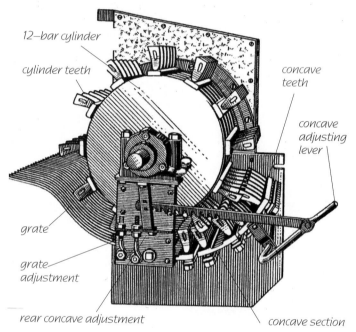

Parts of a 12-bar threshing cylinder.

J.I. Case Co.

The function of the straw rack is to carry the straw to the rear of the machine, while at the same time shaking or agitating it so any loose grain still mixed with the straw is shaken out and falls through the rack to the grain pan below. The straw rack may be of the endless apron or raddle type, or of the vibrating or oscillating type. Most modern threshers employ the oscillating type, with the rack divided into sections attached to a *crankshaft* that not only provides the agitation needed to shake out the grain, but imparts the walking action that keeps the straw moving to the rear. Straw movement is aided by sawtooth *fishbacks* attached to the top of the racks.

Harvesting Machinery

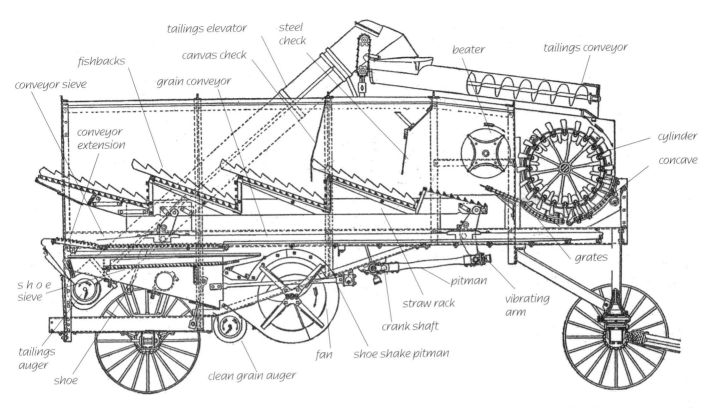

Parts of a separator.

J.I.Case Threshing Machine Co.

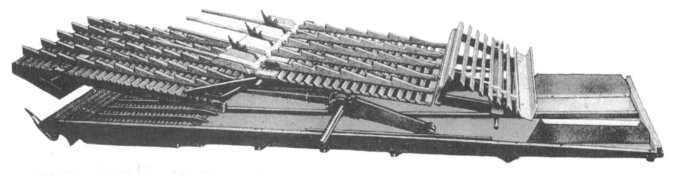

Side view of a two—section straw rack, with the grain pan and chaffer beneath.

Dion Freres, Inc.

Cleaning Mechanism

Grain that has been separated from the straw is still mixed with a large amount of chaff, unthreshed heads, and other refuse that passed through the grates and the straw rack along with the kernels. To separate the kernels from this refuse is the purpose of the cleaning mechanism.

Although technically not a part of the cleaning apparatus, the grain conveyor, or grain pan, is essential to the operation of a thresher. Extending from under the cylinder, almost to the rear of the straw rack, the grain conveyor catches all the kernels that fall through the concave, the grate, and the straw rack, and convey them to the cleaning shoe. At the rear end of the grain pan is

attached a sieve called the chaffer or conveyor sieve, which allows the grain to fall onto the shoe sieve. Larger refuse and unthreshed grain heads pass over the chaffer—which receives part of the air blast from the fan, blowing away much of the chaff—and end up on the *extension chaffer*. The extension chaffer is coarser than the chaffer sieve and allows the unthreshed heads to fall into the the tailings auger trough, from which they are carried back to the cylinder for rethreshing.

The sieves and screens are mounted in a cleaning shoe, consisting of a box with a tight sloping bottom. Sieves are distinguished from screens in that grain passes through a sieve, but over a screen. Most threshers have adjustable sieves with opening sizes that may be changed to suit the kind of grain or seed being threshed. Screens are sometimes used in the bottom of the shoe to let particles smaller than the grain, such as weed seeds or sand, fall through while the grain passes over the screen.

The shoe is agitated to shake the kernels through the sieves and to keep the chaff loose so it can be blown away by a fan located in front of the shoe. The fan consists of a series of blades on a shaft, and is mounted inside a housing with an outlet into the shoe. Each end of the fan housing may be closed off with adjustable *fan blinds* to help regulate the amount of air blast given to the shoe.

A conveyor sieve with the extension chaffer at the left.
Dion Freres, Inc.

Grain and Straw Handling

The cleaned grain falls from the cleaning shoe into the *clean grain auger*, which carries it across the bottom of the thresher to the *clean grain elevator*. The elevator lifts the grain to a *grain weigher* at the top of the thresher. The weigher consists of a small hopper balanced against an adjustable weight on a beam. As the hopper fills with grain, the weight eventually overcomes the balance weight, at which time the hopper bottom is swung out of the way and the grain is dumped into the grain chute. Each dump is counted by a mechanical counter that records the number of bushels of grain. Some machines have a reversible conveyor auger across the top of the deck so the chute can be set up to discharge on either side of the separator. The chute may dump into a wagon or truck, or into a bagging attachment, or *sacker,* with twin spouts so you can put on an empty sack before removing the full one.

A modern thresher is equipped with a *windstacker* that blows the straw into a stack. Windstackers eliminate the dirty, backbreaking work once involved in bucking straw away from a separator and building it into a stack. Straw and chaff coming off the rear end of the straw rack and extension chaffer enters a slanting enclosed hopper made of sheet metal. To the side of this hopper is a vertical fan that provides a powerful blast of air to force the straw up and out through a pipe. Some machines have knives attached to the fan blades to chop the straw as it is blown away.

The windstacker is quite flexible, allowing the straw to be placed in almost any position around the thresher. Not only may the pipe be swung in a 360–degree circle, but it also telescopes to permit straw to be placed nearer to or farther from the machine. A folding hood at the outer end of the pipe may be opened or closed, or turned from one side to the other, to aim the straw stream. Some windstackers have a provision for a power drive to allow the pipe to oscillate back and forth in a predetermined arc while the thresher is operating.

shoe sieve adjustment lever

chaffer/conveyor sieve adjustment
(turn clockwise to open)

loosen wing nut to
adjust fan blinds

inspection
hole cover

fan blinds

fan
housing

clean grain auger

Cleaning shoe and fan.

J.I. Case Co.

Harvesting Machinery

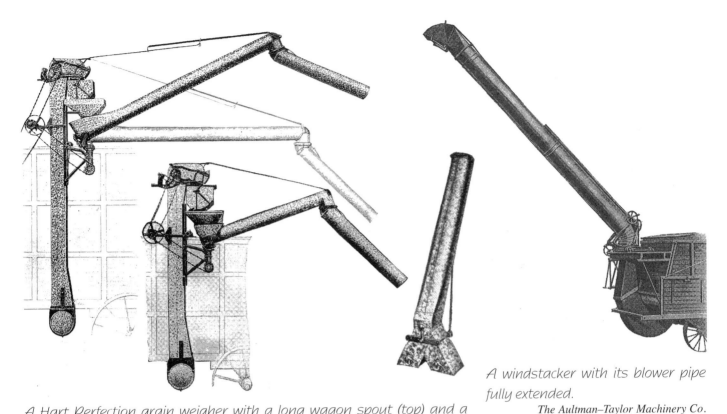

A Hart Perfection grain weigher with a long wagon spout (top) and a shorter elevator and spout (below). Adding a bagging spout (right) allows one sack to be filled while a full sack is taken off, tied, and replaced with an empty. Hart weighers are used on most modern threshers. Dion Freres, Inc.

A windstacker with its blower pipe fully extended.
The Aultman–Taylor Machinery Co.

Pre-Operation Check

New threshers haven't been built for years, and many existing machines haven't been run recently. Before putting a separator into use, clean out the entire machine. You won't believe the amount of pine cones, nut shells, nest material, and other debris rats, mice, and squirrels can drag into an unused separator. Be sure to clear the elevators, grain chutes, and blower pipes throughout their whole lengths.

Feeder

Examine the framework and tinwork to be sure all bolts and rivets are tight and no holes are in the bottom tin that will allow shelled grain to fall through. Check the conveyor's slats and chains, and repair any broken or badly worn parts. Sometimes you can save chain links that are worn enough for the chain to come apart by bending down the lip or hook a little.

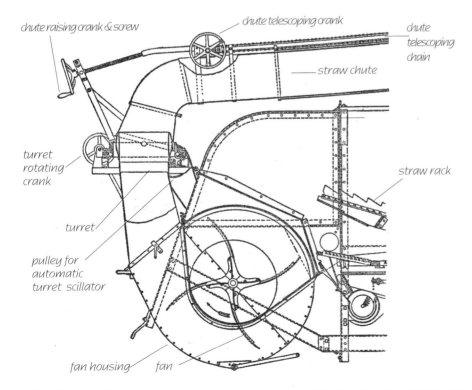

chute raising crank & screw

chute telescoping crank

chute telescoping chain

straw chute

turret rotating crank

straw rack

turret

pulley for automatic turret scillator

fan housing   fan

A typical windstacker.

J.I. Case Threshing Machine Co.

Grain Threshers

Be sure the blades on the band cutters are sharp and not bent or broken. The crank boxings, or bearings, are usually made of wood. If they are loose, take them up to fit the shaft by planing off a little or by removing shims. If necessary make new wooden boxings from hardwood, or have them made by a competent woodworker.

Check to see that the feed and retarder fingers aren't loose, bent, or broken. Check any wood boxings and adjust them in the same way as those of the band cutters.

Check the vibrating feed plate for loose parts, or holes that allow grain to fall through. Inspect the feed and straw governors to see they are free from dust, dirt, or caked grease and they stop the conveyor when they should.

Cylinder

Check the teeth and replace any that are badly worn. Tap each tooth lightly on its side with a hammer to determine by the sound if it is tight. Drive any loose tooth firmly into place with a heavy hammer and draw the nut up tight with a long wrench. Do not remove broken or badly worn teeth without replacing them, or you will have an unbalanced cylinder, causing severe vibration and worn bearings. A mixture of worn and new teeth can also cause an unbalanced condition. If you suspect the cylinder is out of balance, remove it and take it to a machine shop for balancing.

Inspect the keys that hold the cylinder to the shaft and see that they are firmly in place. Examine the cylinder shaft bearings, and remove shims or replace the bearings if they are loose. Most modern machines use ball or roller bearings, but if the machine has babbitt bearings that are badly worn or scored, rebabbitt them. See that lubrication fittings are in good shape and the bearings are getting grease or oil. Check cylinder shaft end play, which should be no more than $1/64$ inch.

Concave

Inspect the concave teeth the same way as the cylinder teeth, and replace or tighten them as needed. If the concave bars are of cast iron, which most are, be careful not to break them while driving in the teeth for tightening. The concave sections are held in place by screws that bear against each end. These screws let you obtain the correct lateral spacing between the cylinder and the concave teeth, which is about $1/8$ inch.

If the concaves appear to be too far to one side, move them over by loosening the screws on one side and tightening the ones on the other. After you have moved the concaves sideways until the majority of teeth are centered, any remaining teeth that do not center are probably bent.

Whether a bent tooth is on the cylinder or the concave, straighten it by removing the tooth, placing it on an anvil, and striking it with a heavy hammer. Be sure to bend not just the tip of the tooth—straighten the entire tooth so all parts of it are at equal distances from the other teeth. If the space between the teeth is less than $1/8$ inch, cracking of the grain will result.

Inspect the mechanism for raising and lowering the concave. Make sure it is in good condition and working freely.

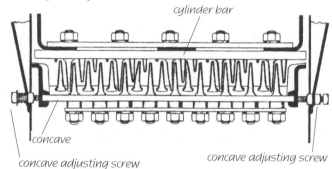

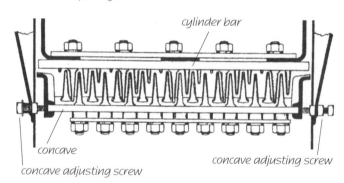

The correct lateral setting of concaves (bottom) compared to concaves set too far to the left (top), allowing them to be struck by the cylinder teeth.

J.I. Case Co.

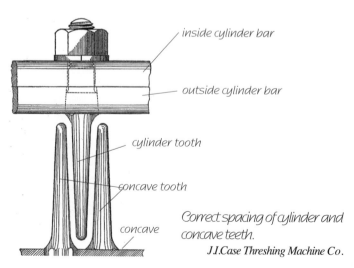

Correct spacing of cylinder and concave teeth.

J.I.Case Threshing Machine Co.

Grate

Inspect the grate, making sure the bolts holding the sections together and in place are tight. Straighten any bent bars. If the grate is adjustable, be sure the adjusting mechanism works as it should.

Beater

Inspect the beater bearings to see they are in good condition and the beater is centered in the machine. Check for loose keys or set screws. If your thresher has twin beaters, be sure they are properly timed. Check for bent or broken fingers, or broken wooden blades if used.

Check Boards or Aprons

Make sure the check boards or aprons are properly fastened to the roof of the machine and that any hinges work freely. If canvas curtains are badly torn or rotted, replace them. If the board is adjustable for height, see that it raises and lowers as it should.

Straw Racks

Inspect for broken slats, fingers, or fishbacks and replace them as needed. If the fishbacks are reinforced with metal strips, make sure the nails are driven in securely and no metal ends stick up to catch the straw. Replace any of the wooden framework that is broken, split, or rotted. Check the cranks and crank bearings, and adjust them if necessary. Inspect any hangers or links. Check the pitmans and pitman bearings, and adjust them if needed. Be sure the two pitmans are of equal length.

Grain Pan

Make sure the frame and bottom of the grain pan are in good condition, and the pan works freely in the separator. Drive in any loose nails, patch any holes, and replace any broken, split, or rotted wood. See that any canvas or wooden shields that prevent the grain from falling between the pan and the separator sides are in place and in good condition. Tighten or replace them if needed. Check to see that the bearings on the grain pan hangers or links are in good shape, and the pan is level crosswise with respect to the separator.

Chaffer

Inspect the chaffer frame to see it isn't broken or bent, and is attached firmly to the grain pan. If the chaffer or extension has wooden slats, replace any that are broken.

If your machine uses an adjustable metal sieve, see that the blades are in good condition and respond to the adjusting mechanism.

Cleaning Shoe

Examine the shoe carefully. See that the framework and the slides that hold the sieves are in good condition. Check the shoe bottom for holes that could allow grain to fall through. See that the hangers and bearings are in good condition, and the pitmans are of the same length. Inspect all sieves and screens. See that the frames are in good shape and not warped. Check adjustable sieves for bent or badly rusted blades and make sure the adjusting mechanism works freely.

Fan

Examine the fan housing to see that it isn't badly dented or rusted out. Make sure the fan blinds are in good shape, work freely in their guides, and are held in any desired position by the locking mechanism. Check the fan bearings and adjust or replace them as needed. Replace any split or broken fan blades, and see that blades don't hit the housing. If your thresher uses a wind board or tail board for controlling the blast, see that it isn't broken and can be adjusted properly.

Augers and Elevators

Check the auger troughs to be sure they aren't rusted out or badly dented, and straighten or repair them as appropriate. Some machines have removable trough bottoms that easily can be replaced. Check the auger bearings and replace them as needed.

Examine the elevator housings and make sure they are firmly attached to the thresher's frame. See that there are no dents that might interfere with the elevator chains, or holes that allow grain loss, especially in the clean–out doors at the bottom of the elevators where rust damage often occurs.

See that the elevator chains run smoothly and don't bind or jump off the sprockets. Check the chain tightening mechanism, which is usually at the top of the elevator. The mechanism should take up equally on each side so the chain runs true. Check the chains for worn or broken links. Make sure the drag blocks or plates are not broken or bent, and are fastened securely to the chain. Check any slip clutches on the chain drives by locking the chain and turning the belt pulley by hand.

Straw Stacker

Inspect the fan housing for dents or rust out. Pound out any dents and repair rusted out spots, or rivet a plate over them. Check the fan bearings and adjust or replace them as necessary. Check the fan blades and see that all bolts, set screws, and keys are tight. Make sure the fan is balanced, as it turns at a high rate of speed.

Examine the turret mechanism to make sure it has no broken parts and all bolts are tight. Make sure the screw for elevating the stacker tube works freely throughout its length of travel. Inspect the telescoping mechanism to be sure it works freely. A rusty chain, or rusty rack and pinion, may cause difficulty in telescoping the tube, and may be overcome by turning the handwheel while pulling on the chain or rack. See that the sections of the hood aren't bent and telescope freely. If the hood doesn't turn freely around the main tube, a liberal application of oil and working by hand will often loosen it. If the ropes used for turning and telescoping the hood are rotted or missing, replace them.

Weigher and Bagger

Examine the weighing mechanism and see that the hopper bottom swings freely, and that none of the moving parts rub or interfere with the framework or other parts. The hopper must move up and down freely. The trip pin at the end of the trip bracket may require a little judicious filing so it disengages readily from the trip dog. Replace badly worn parts, or build them up with weld.

Trucks and Frame

See that all rivets, bolts, and braces holding the framework of the separator are tight. Check the wheel bearings and make sure they're greased and adjusted properly. If your machine is equipped with rubber tires, make sure they are properly inflated. If the thresher has a wooden tongue, inspect it closely to make sure it is sound and not dry rotted.

Belts

Just about every component of a threshing machine is driven by a flat belt. Every manufacturer used a different number and arrangement of belts, and even the various models and sizes from the same manufacturer were often different. It is therefore impossible to give accurate directions for installing the belts on every thresher. Since all threshers are made up of the same components, the belting will be similar, and a careful examination of your machine should indicate how to install the belts.

Be sure to note the direction in which the drive pulley normally turns, as well as the direction the driven pulley must turn to operate the equipment. Some belts may have to be twisted for the driven pulley to turn in the proper direction. The pulleys must be in line so the belt runs on them its full width. When the shafts are parallel, a belt will always run to the tightest place, or where the pulleys are largest. A thresher's pulleys are therefore crowned, or enlarged in the middle, so the belts will run in the center

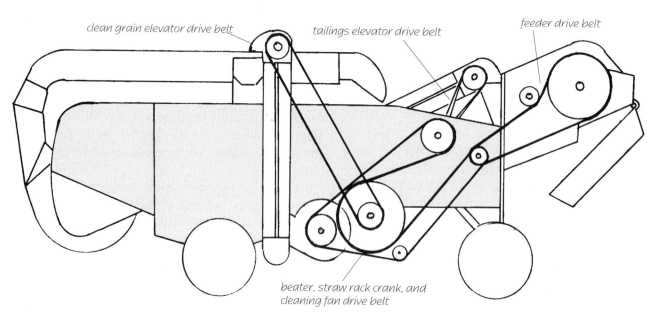

clean grain elevator drive belt   tailings elevator drive belt   feeder drive belt

beater, straw rack crank, and cleaning fan drive belt

Right side (bottom left page) and left side belting (top right page) diagram for a Case 12–bar thresher; note the twist in the power turret and tailings elevator belts.

Harvesting Machinery

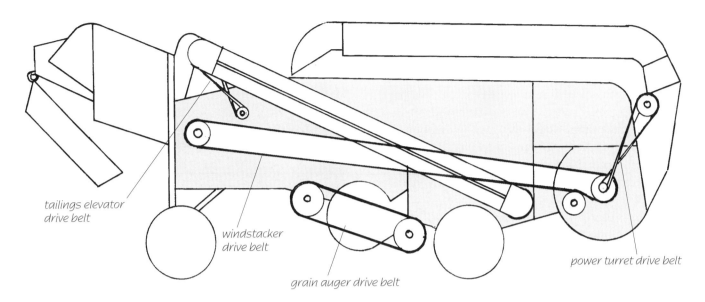

tailings elevator drive belt

windstacker drive belt

grain auger drive belt

power turret drive belt

of the pulleys. Most belts have an adjustable idler pulley to take up any slack in the belt.

Lubrication

The life and good work of a threshing machine relies to a great extent on frequent and thorough lubrication. Older machines have grease cups that must be kept filled with grease and turned down at intervals to force the grease into the bearings. Later machines are equipped with grease fittings for use with a pressure grease gun. Many lubrication points have oil holes, rather than grease fittings. Always use a good grade of oil and grease, and keep it clean. A bearing may be quickly ruined if dirt and grit are allowed to get in.

Some of the oil holes may be partially filled with wool or cotton waste to help keep out dirt and retain the oil longer. Renew the plug periodically, or if it becomes gritty or sandy. Before oiling, clean any dirt out of the oil holes with a bit of wire. Fill oil holes every morning and mid–day, or every two hours when the thresher is in heavy use.

Before filling grease cups, always clean the edge of the cup and the threads inside. Fill the cup full, thread it onto the bottom, and turn it down until you see clean grease at the sides of the bearing. Wipe off the excess grease. At least twice a day turn the cups down enough turns to again force clean grease out of the bearing. For a thresher in heavy use, turn the cups down every two hours.

Observe the same lubrication intervals if you use a pressure grease gun. Wipe off each fitting before pumping in grease, until clean grease is forced out the sides of the bearing. Wipe off any excess. Grease the wheels before moving the thresher on the road.

Gathering bundled oats to haul to the thresher.

Photo by Ted Rose

Operating a Grain Thresher

The modern separator is a complex machine made up of many components, all of which must work together to assure that clean grain, in good condition, flows from the grain spout. Many manufacturers built threshers, each model differing in its details of construction and the adjustments necessary to do good work. Although the method of making adjustments may differ, the same principles apply to separators of any make.

Setting the Thresher

Try to find a position where the wind is blowing in the same general direction as the straw will be blown. Set the separator level, both crosswise and lengthwise. If you

Grain Threshers

cannot find a level place to set the machine, use a carpenter's level on the rear axle and the sills on each side and the front, and dig a hole in front of each high wheel. Then pull the machine into the holes. If it is still not level, pull the machine out, fill in or dig out a hole, and back the machine in again. The low side may be blocked up a little, but with great care, since the rocking motion of the separator in operation may cause it to slip off the blocks. If the left rear wheel is not in a hole, place a block in front of it to prevent the machine from being pulled forward by the drive belt.

In the days of steam traction engines, main drive belts of 150 feet or more in length were common. The long belts kept the engine away from the straw that could be easily set afire by sparks from the engine's stack. The internal combustion engine has largely eliminated the risk of fire from stray sparks, and belts of 50 or 60 feet are commonly used. Even shorter belts will work, but a short belt is difficult to line up and keep tight. The weight of a long belt sagging between the pulleys helps maintain belt tension. Side–mounted belt pulleys usually turn in a clockwise direction so the belt must be given a half–twist to make the threshing cylinder turn in the correct counter–clockwise direction. Which way the belt is twisted makes no difference, except in a cross wind. In that case, the belt should be twisted into the wind, so the slack side of the belt is held in position against the wind by the taut, or power, side of the belt.

Power

Early separators were commonly powered by treadmills. As the machines became larger, rotary horse powers were developed. Modern threshers, with their windstackers, grain weighers, self feeders, and large capacities, require far more power than can be provided by a treadmill or a horse power. When even 16 horses on a horse power couldn't provide enough power, steam and then gas engines came into widespread use. At first, these engines weren't self–propelled and had to be pulled into position and between jobs by horses. Eventually they became self–propelled tractors and could not only move themselves, but pull the thresher as well.

Line up the tractor with its front end facing the front, or feeder end, of the threshing machine, at a distance approximating the length of the drive belt being used. Place one end of the belt around the drive pulley on the left side of the thresher. Unroll and stretch out the belt toward the tractor, give the belt a half–twist, and place the belt around the drive pulley on the right side of the tractor.

A threshing machine properly belted to a tractor, with both machines parallel and the two pulleys exactly aligned. A half–twist in the belt reverses the clockwise direction of the tractor pulley to match the required counter–clockwise direction of the threshing machine pulley.   J.I. Case Co.

Back the tractor until the belt is fairly tight. Take care to not get the belt too tight, which would cause unnecessary wear on the bearings in both machines and would require more power to operate the outfit.

The belt must be sufficiently tight so it doesn't drag on the ground or on any part of either machine. It should be just tight enough to transmit power from the tractor to the thresher without the belt slipping. A short belt must be

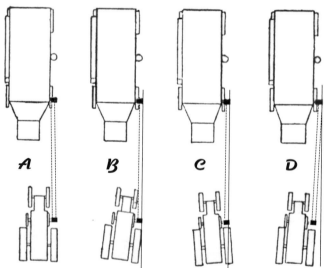

*The tractor and thresher must be parallel and the pulleys aligned **A**. If the pulleys are in alignment, but the machines aren't parallel **B** and **C**, the belt will either run off the outside of one of the pulleys, or will rub against the machine on the inside of the pulleys. Pulleys far out of line **D** will cause the belt to run off.*

Farm Equipment for Mechanical Power

Harvesting Machinery

tighter than a long one. After the tractor is in position and the belt is tensioned properly, either firmly set the tractor brakes or block the right rear tractor wheel so it can't move forward. The tractor must be level and accurately lined up to keep the drive belt from running off the outside of the pulleys under a load, or from crowding the flange on the inside of the main drive pulley.

These instructions apply to setting any belt–driven implement, although a half–twist may not be required, depending on the direction in which the belt–driven machine must be run. A little caution and good judgement, along with a lot of practice, are required to quickly and properly line up and set a tractor and belt–driven machine combination. Take the time necessary to get the alignment so the belt runs in the center of both pulleys without slipping or rubbing on anything.

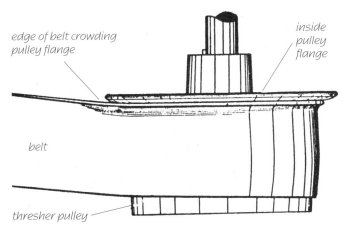

edge of belt crowding pulley flange

inside pulley flange

belt

thresher pulley

If the tractor is out of alignment to the inside, the edge of the belt will crowd the pulley flange as shown here, and the belt will be quickly ruined. If the tractor is misaligned to the outside, the belt will be thrown off one of the pulleys.   J.I. Case Co.

> **Safety First!**
>
> ☞ *Always* keep spectators away from the belt while lining up the machines, when initially starting the thresher, and any time the rig is in operation. *Never* duck under or step over a moving belt.

Test Run

Unhook the front section of the folding self–feeder chute and swing it up into position, making sure it is locked into place. Unstrap the straw blower pipe from its bracket on top of the separator and, using the hand–wheel cranks at the windstacker turret, position the pipe above the desired location for the straw stack.

When operating a thresher for the first time, start it slowly and run it awhile at about half speed. Check to see that all the belts stay on and that all pulleys, fans, elevator chains, and augers not only turn, but in the right direction. Make sure the straw rack, grain pan, and cleaning shoe are oscillating as they should. The feeder conveyor should not operate at the slow speed. Trip the grain weigher and see that the hopper bottom properly dumps and resets. Listen for any unusual knocking or pounding noises, and locate and correct any you hear.

If everything is okay, bring the separator up to normal operating speed, at which time the feeder conveyor should start. Repeat all the same checks to determine that all parts of the machine are operating correctly.

Running the Self Feeder

The person feeding the thresher should take care to pitch the bundles onto the conveyor so the grain heads enter the cylinder first. To maintain a steady stream of grain, the head of each subsequent bundle should overlap the butt of the previous one. Even, steady feeding is essential for the good operation of a thresher.

By turning the screw crank above the cylinder, you can set the feeder to feed either high or low into the cylinder, depending on the condition of the grain. The cylinder has the most suction when fed low, and more of a combing action when fed high. A center position is normally best. The upper feed rakes are adjustable up and down by means of a hand lever. When threshing tough, damp grain, set the rakes fairly close to the feed pans. In dry straw, raise the rakes.

Set the speed governor so the feeder conveyor doesn't start before the cylinder attains threshing speed. Make this adjustment by turning the wing nut on the weight spring behind the large feeder drive pulley. Keep the inside discs, inclined cam surfaces, pulley hub, and straw governor clutch discs well oiled.

Running the Threshing Apparatus

A speed of a little more than 6,200 feet per minute at the tips of the cylinder teeth give the best results in threshing small grains such as wheat, oats, and barley. Therefore, a thresher with a 20 bar cylinder that is $31^5/8$ inches in diameter must be run at about 750 to 800 revolutions per minute. Smaller cylinders, such as those on 9 ($21^3/4$ inches) and 12 ($22^1/4$ inches) bar machines must be run about 1100 to 1150, and 1075 to 1,100 rpm, respectively. The proper cylinder speed must be maintained if you expect to do a good job of threshing.

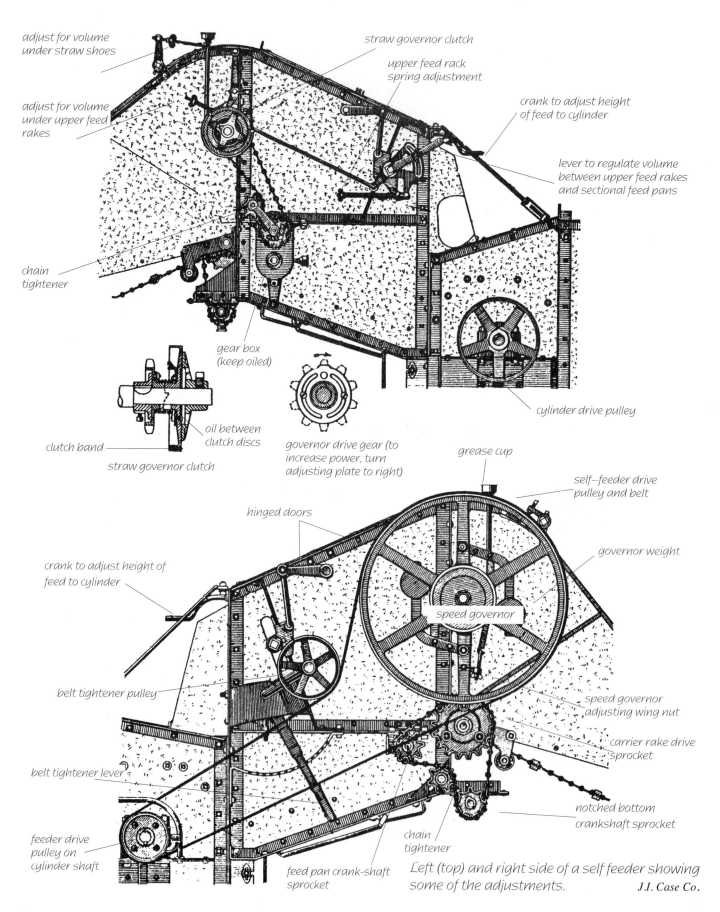

adjust for volume under straw shoes

straw governor clutch

upper feed rack spring adjustment

adjust for volume under upper feed rakes

crank to adjust height of feed to cylinder

lever to regulate volume between upper feed rakes and sectional feed pans

chain tightener

gear box (keep oiled)

oil between clutch discs

cylinder drive pulley

clutch band

straw governor clutch

governor drive gear (to increase power, turn adjusting plate to right)

grease cup

self–feeder drive pulley and belt

hinged doors

governor weight

crank to adjust height of feed to cylinder

speed governor

belt tightener pulley

speed governor adjusting wing nut

carrier rake drive sprocket

belt tightener lever

feeder drive pulley on cylinder shaft

feed pan crank-shaft sprocket

chain tightener

notched bottom crankshaft sprocket

Left (top) and right side of a self feeder showing some of the adjustments.

J.I. Case Co.

If the speed is too slow, all the grain will not be threshed from the heads, and the other parts of the machine will be operating at too slow a speed to function properly. If the speed is too high, the grain kernels will be cracked, while the straw will be so cut up it will interfere with the work of the straw rack and cleaning shoe, resulting in dirty and lost grain. The speed should not be allowed to vary as a result of insufficient power on the belt, or too heavy or uneven feeding.

Cracked grain is almost always caused by improper spacing of the teeth, although too high a speed, too many concave teeth, or the concave set too high can cause cracking as well. If cracked grain is a problem, first determine the cause. Carefully examine the tooth spacing and look for any teeth that may be bent. Check the cylinder shaft for excessive end play, which causes the tooth spacing to vary. If none of these conditions could be causing the cracking, chances are your culprit is either too fast a speed or too many concave teeth.

The concaves are adjusted up and down by a lever on the outside of the machine. To remove the concave sections, first loosen the set screws holding them in, on one side only so you don't disturb the teeth's lateral adjustment. Using the lever, raise the concaves up and drop them a few times to knock out the dust and dirt and help jar the sections loose. With the concaves in their lowest position, place a stick of wood between the concave and cylinder teeth and raise the concaves until the cylinder teeth can't pass the block. Then roll the cylinder backward, striking the block against the concave teeth with the momentum of the cylinder, until the concave sections are jarred loose and forced out the front of the concave holding frame.

The number of concave teeth to be used, and their adjustment, will depend on the kind of grain you are threshing, and its condition. Using fewer rows of teeth and setting the concaves higher is usually better than using more teeth with the concaves low. When you use too many teeth, the straw will be cut up too much, making separation and cleaning more difficult, and the grain may be cracked.

Two to four rows of concave teeth are usually needed for wheat or barley, although six may be required for damp grain. Rye can be best threshed with two rows, but the cylinder speed should be faster than for wheat. Dry oats can generally be threshed with two rows of teeth and a slower speed than wheat. Always use as few teeth as possible and still thresh clean. Examine several bunches of straw from the rear of the straw rack to see if any unthreshed heads are getting by the cylinder, and take steps to keep them to a minimum.

No definite rules cover the concave setting or number of teeth to be used under all the varying conditions you may encounter, because you can obtain the same results from different settings. You will get good results if you understand the principles involved and gain a little experience as a thesherman.

Running the Separating Mechanism

The grate, beater, straw rack, and check board combine to separate the threshed kernels of grain that are still mixed with the straw after passing through the cylinder. The layer of straw and grain must flow evenly across the rack at a steady speed, and must be thoroughly agitated in order to dislodge all the kernels, which then fall through the rack and onto the grain conveyor, also known as the grain pan.

The grate is where the bulk of separation takes place. The grate is placed under the rear part of the cylinder in a position to catch most of the grain knocked loose and thrown back by the cylinder. The grain pan extends forward under the cylinder and catches grain that falls through the grate.

While the height of the grate may be adjusted, usually by adjusting the grate hanger bolts inside the machine, it should normally be carried as high as possible to assure maximum separation. Long and tough straw may require slight lowering of the grate to prevent the straw from bunching behind the cylinder, or wrapping around the cylinder or beater.

The beater prevents the straw from wrapping around the cylinder, and moves it onto the straw rack in a uniform layer. It also deflects any flying grain downward through the grate. Usually the beater is not adjustable, although some machines provide a way to move it up and back. Raising the beater may help when threshing heavy or tough grain, if the straw tends to wrap around the beater.

The straw rack and grain pan are usually both carried on the same rocker arms so they counterbalance each other. The rocker arms are arranged to give the rack more leverage and movement than the grain pan, and are usually not adjustable. The proper speed of the straw rack is essential for good separation and grain cleaning. If the speed is too fast, the grain will go over the sieve with the chaff, and if too slow, the sieve will be overloaded and the grain pan may clog. Maintaining the correct cylinder speed will assure the correct straw rack speed.

The fishbacks on the straw rack are necessary for sufficient agitation of the straw. Replace any that become broken or worn down.

The check board, made of wood or metal, hangs over the straw rack. This board deflects any grain thrown back by the beater, and under normal conditions should be kept low. Damp grain, especially rye or oats, may necessitate raising of the board so it doesn't impede the flow of straw through the machine. Farther back is a canvas apron that performs the same function as the check board. The apron has no adjustment, but should be replaced if torn or worn out.

continuation of the pan, are the chaffer and extension chaffer. The chaffer is usually adjustable. Its purpose is to let all the grain being carried to the rear by the grain pan drop through onto the shoe sieve. On most machines, part of the fan blast is allowed to blow through the chaffer to aid in removing the chaff. Too much air, however, can cause grain to be blown over as well. Any unthreshed grain heads and most of the large refuse passes over the chaffer onto the extension chaffer. The extension chaffer sieve may

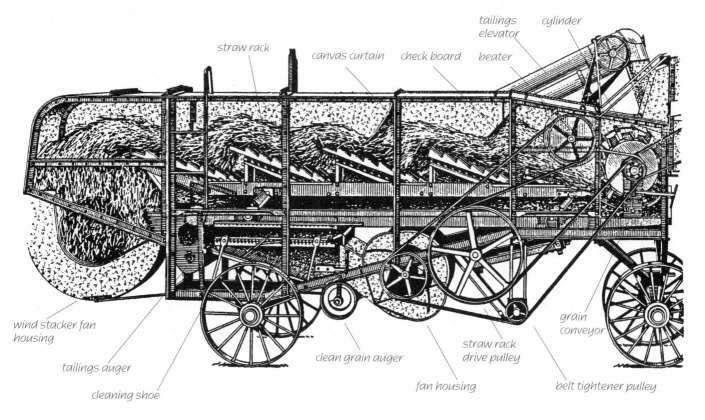

Separating grain.   *J.I. Case Co.*

Running the Cleaning Apparatus

Cleaning the grain consists of separating the kernels from any chaff and refuse that passes through the concaves, grate, and straw rack. Partial cleaning takes place on the chaffer at the rear of the grain pan. Final cleaning is accomplished in the cleaning shoe, where the grain is passed over one or more sieves, while being exposed to an air blast from the fan. Clean grain is the whole reason for the exercise of threshing, so this phase of the operation deserves special attention.

Good work of the cleaning shoe relies on three aspects—the sieve or sieves, the air blast, and the shoe's motion. At the rear of the grain pan, and forming a

or may not be adjustable, is coarser than the chaffer, and serves to let unthreshed grain heads fall through into the tailings auger trough. The tailings auger and the tailings elevator carry these unthreshed heads, along with some debris and any grain that may have gotten this far, back to the cylinder for rethreshing.

The chaffer sieve may be adjusted by either a lever or a handwheel on the outside of the machine, and may be changed while the thresher is running. The sieve should be set so all the grain, but as little trash as possible, drops through. Any grain that passes over the chaffer sieve is blown over with the chaff and lost, or returned to the cylinder with the tailings, where it may be cracked.

The extension chaffer, if adjustable, should be set to allow all the unthreshed heads to fall through. Any heads that pass over are lost.

Older machines require a different sieve for each kind of grain or seed. On a modern thresher, the cleaning shoe has an adjustable sieve that may be used for wheat, rye, barley, oats, and all the common cereal grains. The size of the openings in the adjustable shoe may be changed by moving a lever on the side of the shoe. The adjustment may be made while the machine is running.

For ordinary threshing, place the adjustable sieve in the shoe with the front end next to the fan high, or about the second notch or hole from the top. The rear end should be somewhat lower, or about the fourth hole from the top.

Adjust the sieve with $3/8-$ to $1/2-$inch openings for oats and $1/4-$ to $7/16-$inch openings for wheat, rye, or barley. Under certain conditions you will obtain better results with different settings. Make the adjustment so the openings are large enough to freely pass the clean kernels without retarding the air blast. If the openings are too small, grain and refuse will accumulate on the sieve, pass over it, and enter the tailings. Openings that are too large will allow bits of straw and other refuse to pass through with the grain.

A screen is sometimes placed in the bottom of the shoe. The screen removes particles smaller than the grain being threshed, such as weed seeds and sand. A screen is mounted in the shoe by means of hooks and thumb nuts, and should be fastened securely. If you use a screen, take out the removable strip in the shoe bottom so the screenings can fall out. Screens are difficult to keep clean and can easily clog the shoe, so don't use one unless you feel it is necessary.

The air blast is an extremely important part of the cleaning process and should be carefully monitored. The blast should be strong enough to lift the chaff and light material and keep it from falling through the sieves, but not so strong as to blow over any of the grain. The blast should be spread evenly over the entire width of the shoe, and should not be stronger on one side than on the other.

The strength of the blast is regulated by the fan blinds. Open both blinds on each side when you want more blast. The blinds on one side of the fan housing affect the blast from the opposite side of the

fan. If the blast is too strong on one side, close the opposite blind a little. In windy weather you may need to close the blinds on the windward side of the machine more than on the leeward side. The blast is retarded by the volume of material it is moving. A fan blind adjustment that is correct for heavy feeding may therefore blow over grain when the feeding is light.

Under normal conditions use as much of an air blast as possible without blowing over any grain. A correct blast will blow away the chaff as soon as it enters the chaffer sieve. The rear end of both the chaffer sieve and the shoe sieve should be virtually free of grain and chaff, while the grain coming from the chute is clean.

Unthreshed heads and any trash that is too coarse to fall through the chaffer sieve, and too heavy to be blown away by the air blast, drops through the chaffer extension. This material is called tailings, and is returned to the cylinder to be rethreshed. A careful examination of the tailings will tell you how well the threshing and separating are being accomplished. If the tailings include a large number of unthreshed heads, the threshing isn't adequate—use more concave teeth or raise the concaves. If the tailings have a lot of chopped straw and chaff, the concaves are probably too high or you are using too many teeth. Excessive chaff and chopped straw on the chaffer sieve indicate that the blast isn't strong enough.

The tailings should be small in amount and contain little threshed grain. If the tailings have too much good grain, determine if it's coming from the chaffer extension or is passing over the shoe sieve. If the grain is passing over the shoe sieve, the sieve is probably overloaded with chaff. To fix this, close up the chaffer sieve a little to let less straw through. A little more air may be required to keep the

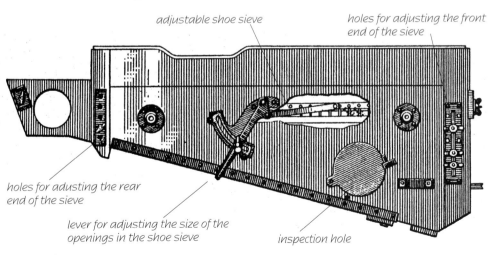

adjustable shoe sieve

holes for adjusting the front end of the sieve

holes for adjusting the rear end of the sieve

lever for adjusting the size of the openings in the shoe sieve

inspection hole

Side view of the cleaning shoe.

J.I. Case Co.

screen free of chaff. Too much air through the shoe can also blow grain over the end of the sieve. If the good grain is passing over the chaffer sieve and falling through the chaffer extension, open the chaffer sieve a little to let the grain fall through. Grain in the tailings has a good chance of being cracked as it goes through the cylinder for the second time, so take care to keep the quantity of tailings as small and as free of threshed grain as possible. Most separators have an inspection hole in the pipe that carries the tailings from the elevator into the cylinder. Inspect a handful of tailings from this hole.

The tail board behind the shoe helps direct the air blast, along with keeping any grain from being blown out the back of the separator. The board should normally be carried in the high position to better block the grain and to force the blast up through the shoe sieve. Some machines have an additional tail board behind the rear of the chaffer extension. Incline this board outward at the top at an angle of about 75 degrees, and keep it near its top position.

Running the Grain Handler

Most modern threshers are equipped with a Hart weigher. This weigher has a mechanical counter to record the number of bushels of grain threshed. The counter may be reset to zero by opening the face through which the three numerals are read. The face is hinged at the bottom and has a catch at the top. Once the face is open, you can set each of the three numeral discs to zero by pulling out on the disc and turning it until zero is in the top position.

Set the weigher for the weight of the grain being threshed by sliding the cast iron weight along the curved beam. Since the hopper holds a half–bushel of grain, set the weigher for half the weight of a bushel of the grain being threshed. For the most common cereal grains the standard weight is:

wheat—60 pounds per bushel
rye—56 pounds per bushel
barley—48 pounds per bushel
oats—32 pounds per bushel
buckwheat—48 pounds per bushel

If the hopper doesn't dump when full of grain, make sure:

- The hopper moves up and down freely and doesn't catch on anything.
- The trip pin disengages readily from the trip dog, and laps about 1/8 inch on the dog.
- The weight and scale beam move freely without catching or rubbing on any stationary part, and the end of the beam rests on its stop when down.
- The trip crank is past dead center when the trip pin rests against the dog, so the weight of the cut off, which is connected to the upper trip crank by a chain, revolves the shaft and engages the worm as soon as the trip dog is released by the downward movement of the hopper bottom.
- The vertical shaft turns freely, except when stopped by the trip pin.
- The chain length allows the cut off to fully close when the trip crank is at its extreme throw.
- The weigher gears and bearings are well oiled.
- The grain elevator sprocket chain is adjusted tight enough not to come off the sprockets or come apart, but loose enough to run freely.

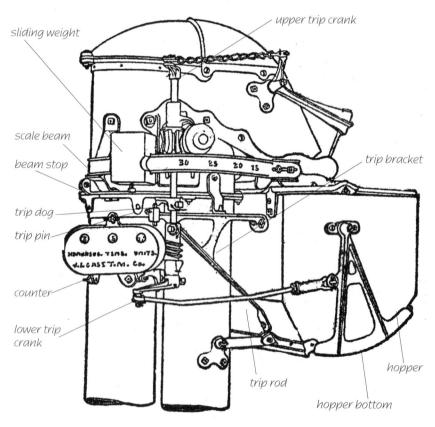

The grain weigher will count up to 999 half–bushels as each is dumped.

J.I. Case Threshing Machine Co.

Harvesting Machinery

Running the Windstacker

A handwheel or crank at the back of the windstacker pipe operates a long screw or cable that raises and lowers the discharge pipe. Another wheel at the side of the turret swings the pipe around in a circle. A handwheel on top rear of the pipe operates a telescoping device, which may be a chain or a rack and pinion, that moves the outer pipe outward on the inner pipe and extends the length of the discharge pipe. The telescoping hood at the end of the pipe may be adjusted by means of ropes. The hood may be pulled back to shoot the straw straight out, or closed to blow it down. It may also be turned so the straw blows to the right or left. When transporting the separator, telescope the stacker discharge pipe to its shortest length, swing it around, lower it into the saddle on top of the thresher deck, and secure it with a canvas strap.

The stacker may be manipulated to build a straw stack with little hand forking. In starting the stack, set the pipe about level with the ground and fully extended. Raise the hood slightly and build the back of the stack first, traversing the turret as necessary. Always keep the farthest side of the stack the highest, as it provides a back wall to stop the force of the blown straw. Build the bottom by traversing the turret and telescoping the pipe as required. The size of the bottom depends entirely on how much straw you will be stacking, but don't make it too large. If necessary, you can always build an additional stack beside the first. Always blow the straw onto the stack, rather than over it. In topping off a stack, allow the straw to strike just at the top and glance over it, so the far side of the stack will be filled out, but the straw won't be blown too far over. When the pipe is at the corner of the stack, raise and lower the hood quickly to distribute the straw and bind the corner. To fill in the corners you may have to turn the hood a little to the right or left.

Threshing Various Grains

Before the days of combines, seeds such as peas, beans, rice, and most grasses were threshed with a separator, although doing so required special sieves and screens and, in some cases, special cylinders and concaves. Since the advent of combines, the following cereal grains are more likely to be threshed with a separator:

Wheat is usually easy to thresh with a machine in good condition. The ordinary varieties of wheat are usually threshed with two to four rows of concave teeth. Run the cylinder at normal speed: 750 rpm for a 20–bar machine, 1,075 rpm for a 12–bar, and 1,100 rpm for a 9–bar

machine. The concaves should be carried quite high. The position of the concaves, as well as the number of rows of teeth, will depend on the condition of the grain. If, for example, the wheat is being thoroughly knocked out of the heads, but an excessive amount of chaff and chopped straw gets through, replace one toothed concave with a blank, or else slightly lower the speed. Separation and cleaning are improved by reducing the amount of chopped straw.

The adjustable chaffer, chaffer extension, and shoe sieve can best be adjusted while the machine is running by noting how much chaff each is handling, how the wheat is being cleaned, and the amount of tailings being returned. Place the adjustable shoe sieve at or near the top at the front or fan end of the shoe; the back end of the sieve should be in the fourth hole from the top. Adjust the conveyor sieve so the openings are about $3/8$ to $1/2$ inch and the shoe sieve $1/4$ to $7/16$ inch.

Buckwheat is easily knocked from the straw, and only one row of teeth will do the job. Keep the cylinder speed low to prevent cracked grain. Set the sieves the same as for wheat.

Rye is quite easy to knock out of the heads, and two rows of concave teeth are usually enough. Damp straw is tough and, as rye straw is long, tends to wrap on the cylinder and beater. To prevent problems, run the cylinder a little above normal speed. Tough rye straw tends to wrap more if it is bruised by the cylinder, so use no more than two rows of concave teeth, and set them quite low. Use the same sieves for rye as for wheat.

Oats that are dry are best threshed with two rows of concave teeth and with a somewhat slower cylinder speed. Dry oats thresh easily, but damp oats are tough and matted. Threshing tough oats requires a slightly higher cylinder speed. Open the conveyor sieve to $1/2$ to $5/8$ inch, and set the shoe sieve at $3/8$ to $1/2$ inch. Since oats weigh much less than wheat or rye, use less of an air blast in cleaning. Keep the tail board as high as possible.

Barley is the easiest grain to thresh, and two rows of concave teeth are usually sufficient to assure clean grain. If you find, however, that the beards are tough and the kernels are difficult to knock loose, you may need to use as many as six rows of concave teeth and keep the cylinder speed fully up to normal. Open the sieves a trifle more than for wheat, but not as much as for oats. Be sure to have the front of the shoe sieve high and the rear low to give the air blast a better chance to blow away the increased amount of chaff.

Storing a Grain Thresher

Before storing your thresher, run it at full speed for ten or fifteen minutes to blow out as much dirt as possible. First open the bottoms of the tailings and grain elevators and, if possible, remove the bottoms of the tailings and grain augers. Clean the entire machine inside and out and remove all chaff, dirt, grain, and straw. A high pressure air gun is a big help in cleaning out all the nooks and crannies inside a separator.

Remove the concaves, clean them, and coat them with oil. Spray all metal parts with a coat of diesel fuel or light oil. Coat all wood parts with linseed oil. Remove all the belts, and clean and inspect them for damage before storing them in a clean, dry place. Clean all the lubrication points and oil or grease them thoroughly. House the machine in a building with a good roof, where it's not exposed to sun or rain.

Cleaned oats blow through the horizontal grain spout into the grain wagon parked on the far side, while straw and chaff are sent through the windstacker onto the stack at the rear.

Photo by Ted Rose

Harvesting Machinery

16

Combines

The first patent for a "traveling thresher" was issued in 1828 to Maine resident Samuel Lane. In Michigan in 1836, after lots of experimentation, Hiram Moore built a machine that both cut and threshed grain. Although his machine did the job, it kept breaking down. Moore persisted and made many improvements, adding both a winnowing device to clean the grain and a bagger, but the Midwest wasn't ready for the combine. Moore became discouraged and returned to farming in 1852.

Meanwhile A.Y. Moore, who was not related to Hiram, bought one of Hiram's harvesters and sent it to California by boat. In the dry climate the machine performed well, until someone forgot to lubricate the bearings. A bearing overheated, caught fire, and burned the harvester, along with the wheat in the field where it was working. The practicality of a combined harvester–thresher had,

Hiram Moore's early harvester–thresher had no provision for cleaning the grain. The Growth of Industrial Art

however, caught the imagination of several California farmers and inventors. Soon combined harvester–threshers were being built by the Holts, Daniel Best, L.U. Shippee, Daniel Houser, and others.

An early Holt combine.

Implement & Tractor

These early combines were heavy and had a tremendous draft. One ground wheel usually drove the cutting apparatus, while the second ran the threshing machinery. More than thirty horses or mules were normally needed to pull a huge wooden combine through the fields. Eventually steam and gas engines replaced the ground drives, reducing the required number of animals to twenty or so. Finally steam traction engines and gas tractors replaced all the horses and mules.

Labor shortages during World War I caused the large-scale use of tractor-drawn combines across the wheat belt. Eastern farmers, and small farmers everywhere were slow to adopt combines, but by the end of the 1930's most full-line implement manufacturers were selling small 5- or 6-foot cut combines that could be run by one or two men, and that could be used profitably on all but the smallest farms.

Features of a Combine

Most modern small combines will harvest a wide range of crops, including barley, edible beans and peas, soybeans, buckwheat, clover and alfalfa, flax, all kinds of grass seeds, oats, rye, sorghums, timothy hay, and wheat. Successfully threshing and cleaning some of these crops requires special screens and other attachments.

A small pull–type power take off driven combine is suitable for use behind a motorized forecart. A combine fitted with an engine of its own may be pulled by a basic forecart. Although the cutting, threshing, separating, and grain handling components are similar for all models, combines are complicated machines and each make varies in its method of adjustment, so try to obtain an operator's manual for your particular machine.

Pull–type combines suitable for use with horses range in size from 4– to 6–foot cut and are usually of the straight–through design. In a straight–through machine, the grain is carried in a straight line from the cutter bar back through the cylinder and separating mechanism. One popular model deviates from the norm by having the straw rack, grain conveyor, and cleaning shoe at right angles to the cylinder and cutter bar.

The primary functions of a combine are to:
- cut standing grain;
- feed the cut grain into the cylinder;
- thresh or beat the grain from the head;
- separate the kernels of grain from the straw;
- clean the grain by removing the chaff and dirt;
- move the cleaned grain into a grain tank or sacks;
- move the grain from the tank (if used) into a wagon or truck.

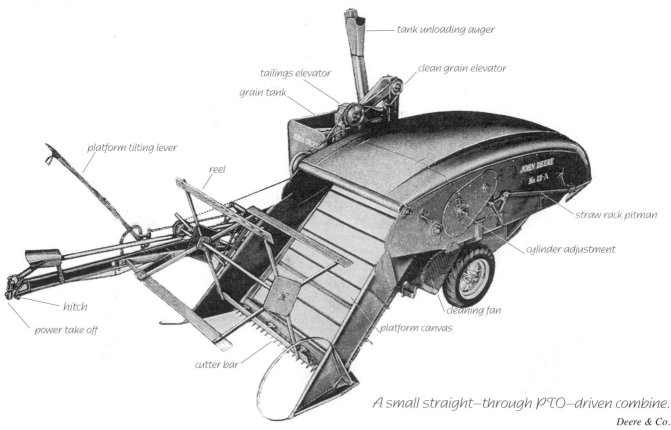

A small straight–through PTO–driven combine.

Deere & Co.

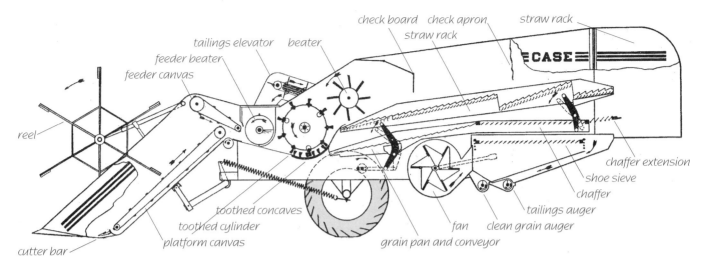

The interior of a combine with a toothed cylinder, toothed concaves, and a feeder beater.

J.I. Case Co.

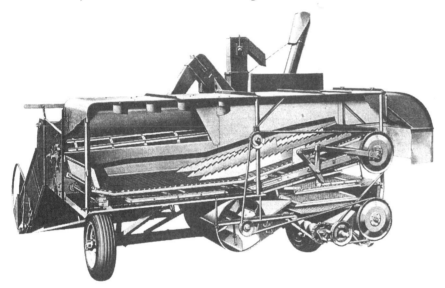

A rear interior view of a combine with the separating and cleaning mechanisms at right angles to the cylinder.

Allis–Chalmers Mfg. Co.

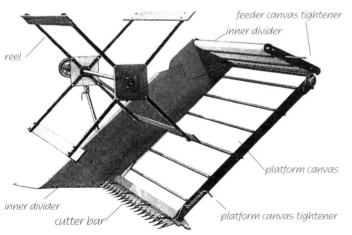

Parts of a typical straight–through combine.

Deere & Co.

Cutting Mechanism

A combine's cutting mechanism is virtually identical to the equivalent parts of a grain binder. The knife operates between guards and is given its back and forth motion by a rocker arm pitman. Serrated knife sections shear the ripe straw, which is held in place by the guards. A hand lever or hydraulic cylinder allows adjustment to cut the grain at any height desired, from as low as 1½ inches to a height of about 30 inches. A reel of four or six bats above the cutter bar sweeps standing grain into the sickle or knife, and then back onto the platform. The reel may be ground– or power–driven and is adjustable in height above the cutter bar, as well as forward or backward.

Feeding Mechanism

Different combines use different combinations of canvases or drapers, augers and/or conveyor chains to carry cut grain away from the cutter bar and to assure a thin, even stream of grain to the threshing cylinder. On a typical machine the cut grain is carried up a sloping platform by the platform canvas and compressed by the feeder canvas, before being delivered to the cylinder. Some combines have a beater in front of the cylinder to assist feeding.

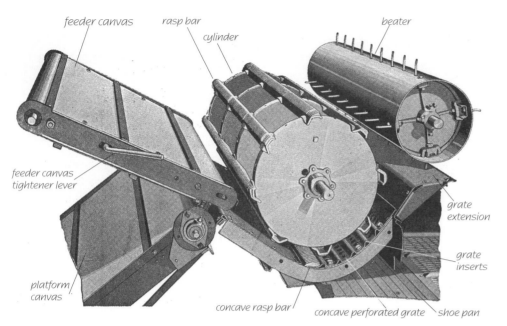

feeder canvas
rasp bar
cylinder
beater
feeder canvas tightener lever
grate extension
grate inserts
platform canvas
concave rasp bar
concave perforated grate
shoe pan

Side view of the threshing mechanism; on later machines the grate extension is perforated.   *Deere & Co.*

Threshing Mechanism

The threshing mechanism consists of the revolving cylinder and the concave, assisted by the beater behind the cylinder. While some older combines used teeth on the cylinders and concaves, the same as on a threshing machine, most modern small combines use rasp bar cylinders and concaves. The rubbing action between the cylinder rasp bars, and the rasp bar and inserts on the concave, removes grain from the heads rather than knocking it out. The threshing and most of the separation take place here, when grain falls through the perforations in the concave grate and grate extension.

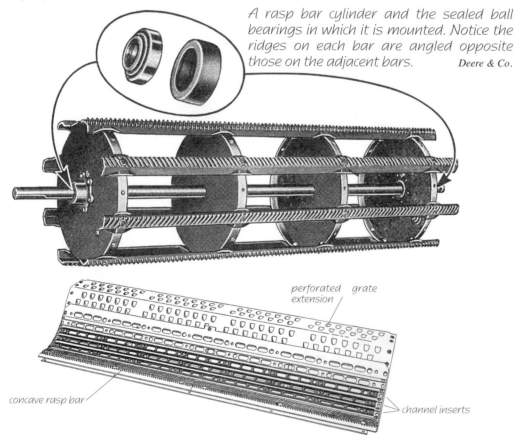

A rasp bar cylinder and the sealed ball bearings in which it is mounted. Notice the ridges on each bar are angled opposite those on the adjacent bars.   *Deere & Co.*

perforated grate extension
concave rasp bar
channel inserts

Concave grate and perforated grate extension. Notice the herringbone pattern of the rasp bar. One, two, or three of the steel channel inserts may be removed if grain cracking is a problem. The channel inserts have slotted holes that conform to those in the grate and allow threshed grain to fall through onto the grain pan.   *Deere & Co.*

Separating Apparatus

The beater behind the cylinder slows down the material being thrown back by the cylinder and passes the straw across the chaffer at the front of the straw rack. The oscillating motion of the straw rack shakes loose any remaining grain, which falls through the rack and onto a grain conveyor. The chain and slat raddle on the grain conveyor carries the grain that is shaken from the straw forward and drops it on the grain pan. The hanging canvas curtains help prevent the straw from being thrown too far back, and deflect any thrown grain down through the straw rack. Fishbacks provide maximum agitation of the straw as it travels over the rack.

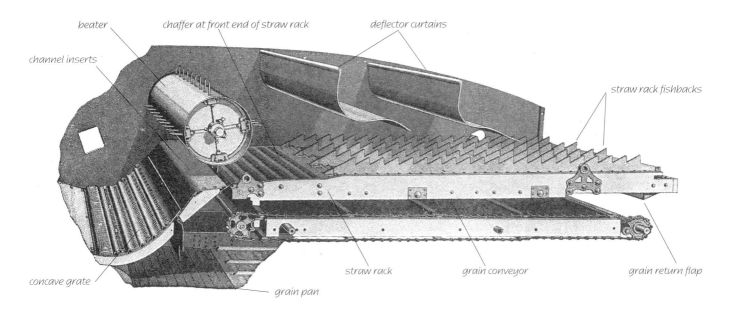

beater • chaffer at front end of straw rack • deflector curtains • channel inserts • straw rack fishbacks • concave grate • grain pan • straw rack • grain conveyor • grain return flap

Separating mechanism.

Deere & Co.

Cleaning Apparatus

The grain pan, chaffer, and sieve all work together as a unit called the cleaning shoe. An undershot cleaning fan supplies a blast of air, controlled by the windboard, up through the front part of the cleaning shoe. The air blast, along with the shaking action of the chaffer and sieve, keeps the chaff and dirt lifted off the sieves and moving to the rear and out of the machine. The heavier clean grain drops through the sieve into the bottom of the combine, where it is picked up by the clean grain auger. Chunks of unthreshed heads are moved by the chaffer and sieve to the rear, where they drop through the tailings fingers into the tailings auger. The auger carries them to the tailings elevator, which lifts the material to the cylinder for rethreshing.

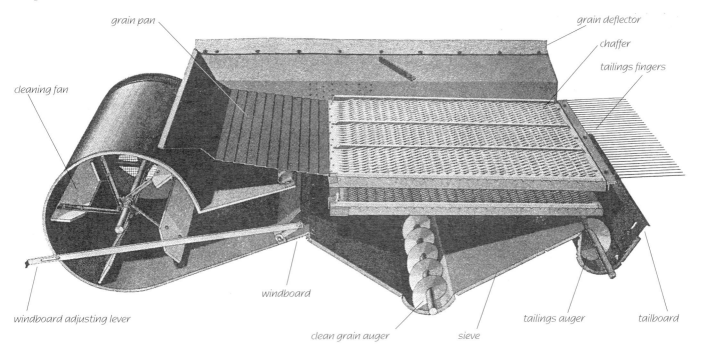

grain pan • grain deflector • chaffer • tailings fingers • cleaning fan • windboard adjusting lever • windboard • clean grain auger • sieve • tailings auger • tailboard

Grain cleaning apparatus.

Deere & Co.

Combines

Grain Delivery System

The clean grain auger in the bottom of the combine carries the grain to the bottom of the clean grain elevator, where it is carried up and dumped into a grain tank. When the grain tank is full, a power–driven auger empties the grain into a wagon or truck.

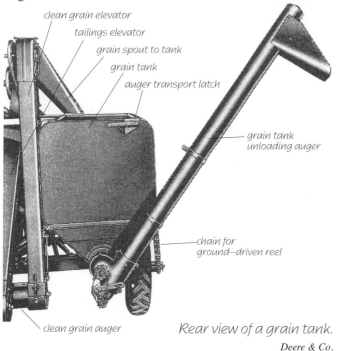

Rear view of a grain tank.
Deere & Co.

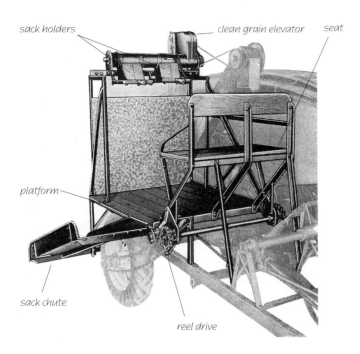

A bagging attachment used in place of a grain tank.
Deere & Co.

In areas where grain is usually sacked, a bagging attachment is used instead of a grain tank. The attachment has holders for two sacks, and a valve to switch the grain from one sack to the other. A seat and platform are provided for the sacker. A chute carries filled sacks to the ground.

Transport Features

In the field position, the cutter bar must extend to the side, so the team and forecart do not trample the uncut grain. Since the entire rig is too wide to easily pass through gates or travel narrow roads, most small pull–type combines have a provision for swinging the tongue or hitch so the machine is centered behind the forecart, making it easier to transport.

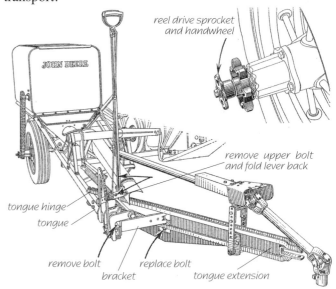

For transport remove the long bolt holding the tongue extension to the tongue. Swing the tongue extension to the left and secure it to the end of the bracket with the long bolt. Raise the header to its highest point and remove the top bolt in the two–section hand lever, allowing the lever to fold back. Loosen the handwheel on the reel drive sprocket so the reel won't turn during transport.   Deere & Co.

Hitching and Draft

For proper operation of the combine, the forecart drawbar should be 15 inches from the ground. The draft of a combine is not much affected by the crop condition, since the machinery is run either by power take off from an engine forecart, or by an engine mounted on the combine. The weight of a small combine is approximately 2,500 to 4,000 pounds, depending on whether or not it has an

Four horses abreast, working on flat land, easily handle a John Deere No. 30 combine behind a power cart.

engine. In determining how many horses to use, take into consideration not only this weight, but also the nature of the terrain and the weight of grain in a full grain tank. Be especially careful when turning on hillsides, as the heavy combine can easily push a light forecart sideways.

Operating a Combine

If your combine is equipped with an engine, check the engine oil and coolant level, and fill the fuel tank. Check over the machine and make sure all nuts and bolts are tight. Thoroughly lubricate the entire combine. Check the V–belts and see that all belts are tight enough to prevent slippage. Install canvases, if your machine uses them. Open the clean–out doors at the lower end of the tailings and clean grain elevators. Start the power source and run the combine at idle speed for a few minutes.

While the machine is running, make sure no belts are slipping and all parts are moving properly with no binding or loud noises. If all is okay, gradually bring the machine up to operating speed and continue observing for proper operation. After running the engine for a few minutes, stop it and check carefully for loose belts or bolts, heated bearings, and binding parts. Correct any problems before attempting to use the machine in the field.

Cutting Mechanism

The first rule for successful combining is to make sure your crop is dead ripe and dry. Green or damp grain interferes with the threshing and cleaning operations, and is subject to spoilage when stored. Tough straw winds on the cylinder and beaters, especially if they are driven below normal speed. Small bits of tough straw are hard to remove from threshed grain, because they are heavy and easily fall through the chaffer and sieve without being blown away by the fan. Before starting to combine, make certain the grain is ready. If the straw feels damp, or is still green, don't combine. Thresh a head or two in your hands, and don't combine if the kernels feel damp or are easily dented with a thumbnail. Cutting grain that is damp or not quite ripe is the leading cause of combine troubles.

Travel at a speed that will not overload your combine, particularly on the first round of the field. Overloading results in lost grain, as you'll take in more straw than the machine can handle, and grain will be carried through the combine and out the back.

Constantly monitor crop conditions and adjust the height of the platform so just enough straw is taken to get all the heads and to deliver the heads and straw to the cylinder. Cutting excess straw may overload the threshing and separating units, resulting in lost grain. In weedy conditions, cut the grain as high as possible, or avoid cutting patches of heavy weeds and undergrowth. Be sure the platform canvas runs square, and the canvas edges and slats do not rub or catch. Neither the drive belt nor the canvas itself must slip. Promptly clean out any straw or weeds that wrap around the platform's lower roller.

The position of the reel depends on the height of the grain, the amount of straw being cut, and the condition of the straw. Under normal conditions the reel bats should hit the standing grain 6 to 10 inches above, and slightly ahead of, the cutter bar. If the grain is lodged or badly tangled, set the reel low and right over the cutter bar, making sure the reel bats clear the knife and auger or canvas. If the cut grain falls back over the front of the cutter bar, the reel is probably set too high and/or too far forward to allow the bats to sweep the grain onto the platform. If excessive grain is carried around by the reel bats, add more reel bats or increase the reel speed.

Combining

Combines of different makes vary in their details. To offer complete instructions for every model is therefore impossible. Try to procure an operator's manual for your specific machine. The components and layout are all similar, however, and so is the operation. In general, grain is cut, threshed, separated, cleaned, and put into the bin of a typical small straight–through combine as follows.

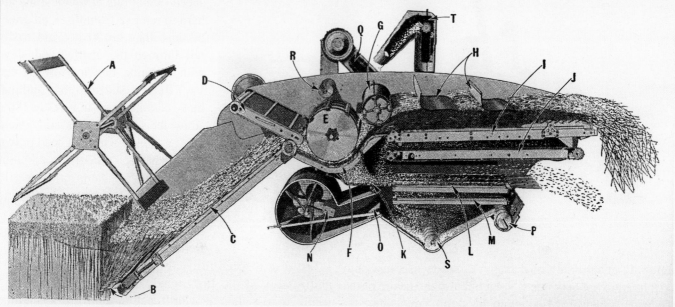

 The reel **A** forces standing grain into the cutter bar **B** and then onto the platform. The platform canvas **C** carries the cut grain up the sloping platform, where it is compressed by the feeder canvas **D** and delivered to the threshing cylinder **E**. The grain travels between the cylinder **E** and the concave and grate **F,** and then against the beater **G,** where most of the separation takes place.

 Threshed grain falls through the perforated grate at **F** onto the grain pan **K.** The beater **G** deflects any grain thrown back by the cylinder down through the chaffer section at the front of the straw rack **I,** and moves the straw rearward onto the rack. The hanging canvas curtains **H** help prevent the straw from being thrown too far back, while deflecting any grain down through the straw rack.

 As the straw moves to the rear, straw rack agitation shakes loose any remaining grain from the straw, where it falls through holes in the rack and onto the grain conveyor **J.** This grain is carried forward by the conveyor to the grain pan **K,** while the straw is dumped out the back of the combine, where it falls to the ground. A blast of air from the fan **N** is directed by the adjustable windboard **O** through the front part of the cleaning shoe—which consists of the chaffer **L** and the sieve **M.** This air blast, along with the agitation of the shoe, blows away the chaff and dirt, and moves the tailings to the tailing auger **P.** The auger carries them to the tailings elevator **Q,** where they are elevated to the distributing auger **R,** which dumps the tailings into the center of the cylinder for rethreshing.

 Clean grain drops through the chaffer **L** and sieve **M,** and is carried by the clean grain auger **S** to the clean grain elevator **T.** The clean grain elevator lifts the grain to the grain tank or the sacking attachment.

Feeding Mechanism

A combine using canvases has an adjustable throat opening. On a machine equipped with an auger, the auger clearance may be varied. When combining a heavy crop, or one with coarse straw, raise the auger or widen the throat clearance. In a light crop, do the reverse. In all cases keep the clearances as narrow as possible to handle the crop without jamming. In light crop conditions maintain enough clearance to prevent the auger flights or canvas slats from hitting.

Threshing Unit

Correct cylinder speed and a proper cylinder–to–concave clearance are essential to good threshing. Keep the cylinder speed as low as possible and concave clearance as high as possible, while still assuring thorough threshing with a minimum of cracked grain. Beater speed should be high enough to prevent straw from wrapping on the beater. The correct cylinder speed and concave clearance vary from crop to crop. The operator's manual for most combines includes recommendations for the cleaning fan speed and shutter settings, the windboard setting, and the beater and straw rack speed settings, along with the cylinder speed and concave clearance settings. If the shoe chaffer and sieve are adjustable, these settings are given as well.

For a typical combine working under normal conditions, the cylinder speed for most small grains might be 1,300 rpm. Higher speeds may be necessary when threshing fine grains or small seeds, while lower speeds are required for coarse seeds. If the grain is tough and hard to thresh, a slightly higher cylinder speed may be required. If too much speed causes cracking of the grain, reduce the speed; if that doesn't cure the cracking, increase the concave clearance.

Cylinder speed is the most important component of good threshing, so don't guess at it. Measure the speed with a good tachometer or speed indicator on the end of the cylinder shaft. Most combines have a method of varying cylinder speed independently of the rest of the machinery.

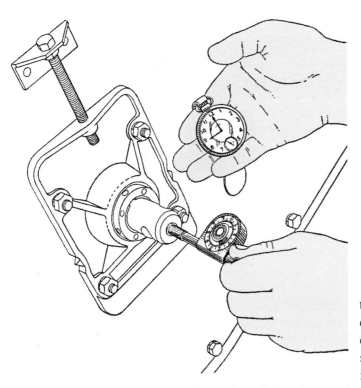

Checking cylinder speed with a hand-held speed indicator and a watch.   Deere & Co.

Adjusting Cylinder Speed

On some combines the cylinder shaft pulley wheel, or sheave, and drive sheave on the gear box are both made in two parts, one of which is threaded onto the hub of the other and may be moved in or out on the hub. The distance between the two halves affects the position of the belt on that pulley, in effect changing the pulley's diameter, which in turn varies the cylinder speed. A big driving pulley turning at a given rpm causes its smaller driven pulley to turn at a much faster rpm. (The reverse is also true—a large driven pulley turns slower than its smaller driving pulley.)

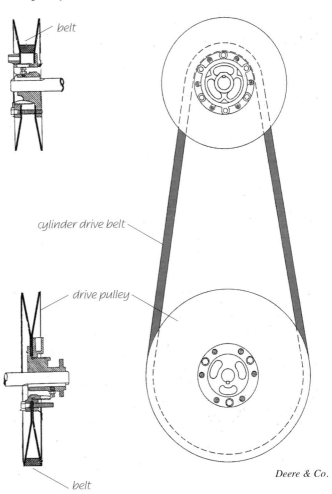

Deere & Co.

To increase cylinder speed, *increase* the distance between the plates of the cylinder shaft sheave and *decrease* the distance between the plates of the drive sheave. To decrease cylinder speed, do the reverse. Moving the outer plate of the shaft sheave and the inner plate of the drive sheave one turn in opposite directions changes the cylinder speed by about 100 rpm. Most small combines use similar split sheave pulleys to regulate cylinder speed.

Combines

The average cylinder–to–concave setting on the illustrated machine is ¼ inch, which will satisfactorily thresh most small grains. Final adjustment of the spacing must be done in the field to meet the actual conditions. If all the grain is not being threshed out, decrease the spacing, but watch out for excessive cracking. If the grain is getting cracked, and lowering the cylinder speed doesn't help, increase the spacing. As you can see, good threshing with a minimum of cracked grain depends on a delicate balance between concave spacing and cylinder speed. You will need to do some experimentation in the field to obtain the proper balance.

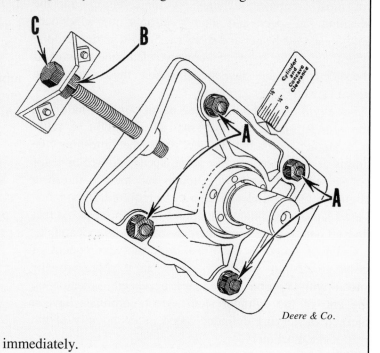

Deere & Co.

This combine has, on the cylinder shaft bearing bracket on each side, an indicator pointing to a scale on the combine side that is marked in gradients of 0 to ½ by sixteenths. When the pointer is on 0, the cylinder rasp bars will touch those of the concave. When it points to the ¼–inch marking, the clearance is ¼ inch. To adjust the clearance, loosen the take–up bolt on the cylinder drive belt tightener arm and release the belt tension. Loosen the four nuts at **A** and the lock nut **B**. Turn bolt **C** into the bearing bracket casting to raise the cylinder, and out to lower it. Be sure to evenly adjust both ends of the cylinder. Retighten the lock nuts and retension the drive belt.

Frequently check the nuts holding the rasp bars to make sure they are tight. If a cylinder bar becomes bent due to a rock or some other object, straighten it immediately.

Separating Apparatus

The beater behind the cylinder tears apart the straw coming from the cylinder and spreads it over the straw rack. It also deflects any thrown grain down through the holes in the grate extension. On a typical combine the beater speed is set at about 650 rpm, although it may be varied by shifting shims between the two halves of the sheave on the beater shaft.

The straw rack has a perforated bottom and is oscillated at about 270 rpm. This oscillation not only moves the straw to the rear, but shakes any remaining grain loose from the straw. The grain falls through the perforated straw rack onto the grain conveyor, while the straw drops out the back of the combine. The saw–tooth shaped fishbacks on the straw rack make the rack more aggressive in shaking the straw, as well as keeping the straw from moving sideways and bunching up on rolling land. The curtains hanging over the straw rack help deflect thrown grain downward and prevent the straw from moving too quickly to the rear.

The grain conveyor beneath the straw rack is a chain and wooden slat conveyor, or raddle, operating over a solid bottom. It carries the grain that has fallen through the straw

rack forward to the grain pan at the front end of the cleaning shoe.

Cleaning Apparatus

The final major function of a combine is to clean the grain of all dirt, bits of straw, and chaff. This important function is performed by the cleaning fan, shoe chaffer, tailings fingers, and shoe sieve. The threshed grain, plus a lot of chaff, small pieces of straw, and parts of unthreshed grain heads fall through the grate, grate extension, and straw rack before ending up on the grain pan at the front end of the chaffer. The grain pan, chaffer, and sieve are constantly oscillating and this motion carries the mixture from the pan onto the chaffer, where rough cleaning is done. The larger bits of straw and unthreshed heads pass over the chaffer and the tailings fingers, where the unthreshed heads and small bits of straw fall through into the tailings auger and are returned to the cylinder for rethreshing. The longer pieces of straw pass over the fingers and out of the machine.

Meanwhile the grain and some chaff fall through the chaffer onto the sieve where final cleaning takes place. A strong blast of air from the fan is directed by the adjustable windboard up through the sieve and chaffer. This blast must be strong enough to keep the lighter material, such as the chaff and straw bits, alive and dancing on the chaffer and sieve. The air blast, combined with the shaking action of the sieves, moves the debris to the rear and out of the combine, while the heavier grain falls through.

The fan blast is controlled by a butterfly–style sheet metal cover, or shutter, at each end of the fan housing. These shutters may be opened or closed to allow more or less air into the fan. Use as strong an air blast as possible without blowing the grain over the straw rack. Usually you'll lose more grain by using too little blast than not enough. Some crops, of course, require a stronger blast than others. The amount of air necessary to clean wheat for example, would blow timothy seed out the back of the combine.

The adjustable windboard allows the air blast to be directed to the front or rear of the sieves, as desired. The blast should normally be directed to the front part of the sieves.

Most combines have adjustable screens on the chaffer and sieve. Set the openings in the chaffer screen so the grain works its way through to the sieve before it passes over two–thirds the length of the chaffer. Start out with the adjustable chaffer lips about halfway open. If too much coarse material falls through, close the screen a little. If too much threshed grain goes into the tailings, open the screen a little.

The adjustable sieve under the chaffer does the final job of cleaning. The openings in the sieve screen are smaller than those of the chaffer and should be set so all the grain, but none of the debris, falls through before it reaches the rear of the sieve. The sieve is regulated by a lever that should be set so the openings are about one–third open. If grain goes into the tailings, open the screen slightly; if the grain is full of small bits of debris, close up the sieve slightly.

Right under the tailings fingers at the rear of the chaffer is a sliding tailboard. When a lot of chaff is present, lower the tailboard so the chaff is blown out the back of the combine. If the seed is light and tends to blow out with the chaff, raise the tailboard. Careful adjustment of the tailboard improves cleaning and saves grain, especially in crops with a light seed.

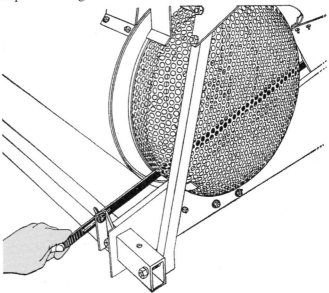

The windboard adjustment lever on this machine is located on the left side in front of the fan housing. Slide the lever to the rear to throw the blast to the rear of the shoe. The blast should normally be directed through the front one–third of the cleaning shoe. Deere & Co

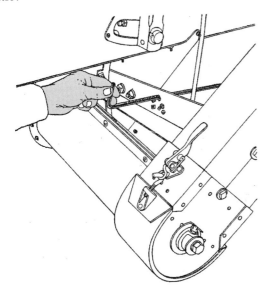

The adjusting lever for the fan valves, or blinds, is located on this combine between the bottom of the tailings elevator and the right–hand side of the combine. Push the lever forward to open the blinds; pull it to the rear to close them. Deere & Co.

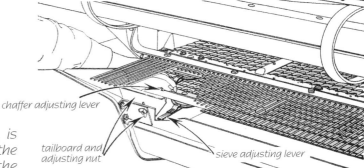

chaffer adjusting lever

tailboard and adjusting nut

sieve adjusting lever

Chaffer and sieve adjusting levers, and tailboard adjusting points. Deere & Co.

Elevators

Run the conveyor chains in the tailings and clean grain elevators just tight enough that the chains don't climb off the sprockets. Each elevator has chain adjustments at the top for this purpose.

Keep the elevator drive belts tight enough to prevent slippage. A slipping drive belt will cause the elevator to clog.

Each elevator has a clean–out door at the bottom so you can inspect the chains and clean the elevator of clogs and debris. The tailings elevator usually has an inspection door at the top so you can inspect the tailings before they go into the cylinder.

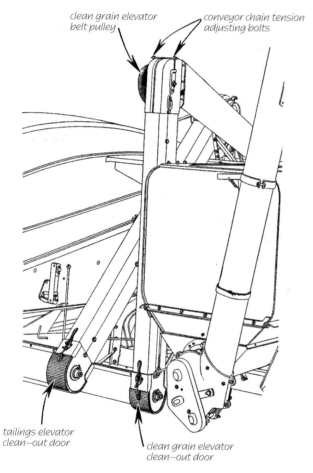

Clean grain and tailings elevators.   Deere & Co.

Grain Tank

Monitor the amount of grain in the tank and empty the tank when it becomes full. When the tank is full, stop the combine next to the wagon and disengage the power take off or the engine clutch. Release the unloading auger from the transport latch and swing the auger head over the wagon box.

Put the unloading auger into gear, which on most machines also disengages the drive to the rest of the combine. Re–engage the PTO or the engine clutch with the engine at about half–throttle and run it until the grain bin is empty. Disengage the PTO and shift the gearbox back to the combine run position.

A clean–out door is usually at the bottom of the auger, and sometimes also in the tank, for removing any accumulation in the tank. Many tanks have a drain plug for draining any accumulation of water.

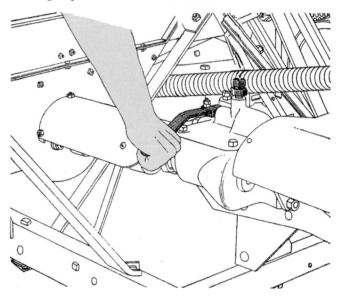

Shifter lever for unloading the grain tank.

Maintaining a Combine

Thorough and timely lubrication and maintenance are essential to keeping a combine working efficiently, and for many years. Neglect results in excessive wear, breakdowns, and expensive repairs, as well as the loss of crops. Grease and oil aren't nearly as expensive as burned out bearings. Take care to closely follow the lubrication recommendations for your model; keep the belts correctly adjusted and the bolts tight; clean the machine after use and store it properly, and you should get your grain into the bin on time and in good condition.

Lubrication

A combine has many lubrication points, and none should be neglected. Lubricate the combine thoroughly and regularly. If you are lucky enough to have an operator's manual, it should contain charts showing the location of all lube points, as well as how often each should be lubricated. Keep the grease gun nozzle clean, and wipe every grease fitting clean before greasing.

To make sure each bearing is full of grease and any dirt is flushed out, pump grease into each fitting until clean grease oozes out. Wipe off the excess grease. Fill gear cases to the proper level, and oil the chains, sprockets, and knife, except when you are working in sandy or dusty conditions. Don't forget to clean out and repack the wheel bearings with fresh grease before each season.

V-Belts

The proper operation of a combine depends to a great extent on a large number of V–belts. Since each model has a different arrangement of belts, try to obtain an operator's manual for your particular machine. You may find a decal with a belting diagram on the side of your combine. Following several rules will help you properly maintain your V–belts:

- Before installing or removing a belt, loosen the tightener. Prying a belt over the edge of a sheave with a bar may rupture some of the cords, weakening the belt and causing premature failure.

- Make sure the drive and driven sheave are aligned, to prevent excessive wear on the sides of the belt or the possibility of the belt being thrown off under load.

- New belts stretch with use, so check and adjust the tension during the first few days of use.

- Keep the tension of all belts properly adjusted, otherwise slipping and burning of the belt will occur.

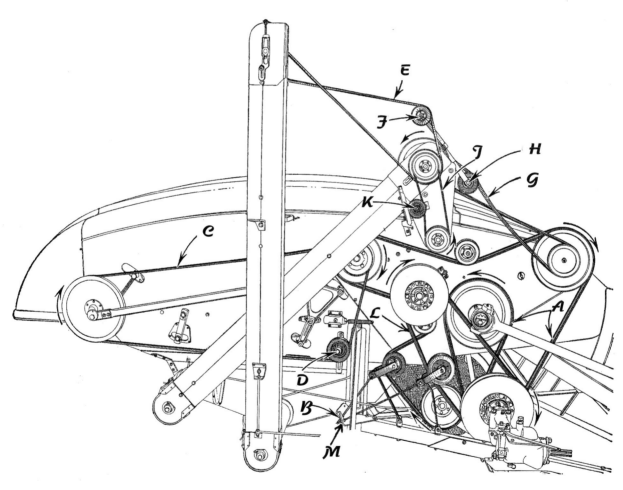

*Typical drive belts on a combine. **A** is the feeder, fan, platform, and beater drive belt with the tightener adjustment at **B**. **C** is the straw rack drive belt with tightener at **D**. **E** is the clean grain elevator drive belt with tightener at **F**; this belt is twisted to make the elevator run in the proper direction. **G** is the tailings elevator drive belt, and is twisted with a spring–loaded tightener at **H**. **J** is the tailings distributer auger drive belt with a tightener at **K**. **L** is the cylinder drive belt with a tension adjustment at **M**. Tension all belts to be just tight enough to run without slipping.*

Deere & Co.

Slipping belts often cause clogs inside the combine or elevators.

- Keep all slip clutches functioning properly. If clogging occurs, and the slip clutches don't work as they should, the shock to the belts can cause them to break.
- Avoid getting grease or oil on the belts. Grease may be removed with a rag moistened with a solvent, but don't dip the belt into solvent.
- At the end of the season, remove all belts and store them in a cool, dry place.

Slip Clutches

The slip clutches require periodic attention if they are to function properly. Slip clutches are mechanical spring–loaded devices that protect a drive line from damage if a clog occurs from excess straw or grain, or from a foreign object getting into the mechanism. They are usually found in the main drive shaft, the reel drive shaft, the clean grain and tailings auger drive shafts, and the grain tank unloading auger shaft, although some machines may have more or fewer.

A slip clutch consists of two mated wavy–toothed iron or steel cogs held tightly in mesh by a heavy adjustable spring. If a clog occurs, the driven cog stops and the driving cog forces the spring back enough to slip against the now stationary driven cog. Besides making a loud racket to warn you a clog has occurred, the slippage protects the machinery from damage.

When a clutch slips, stop immediately, determine the cause, and correct it. Slip clutches should be set tight enough for ordinary work without slipping, but loose

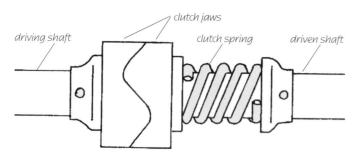

A slip clutch is designed to protect moving parts on a machine by slipping in case of a blockage. In normal operation, spring pressure holds the two jaws together. If the driven shaft is stopped by a blockage, the spring pressure is overcome, allowing the two jaws to separate enough to slip past each other. Not all slip clutches look exactly like this one, but they all operate on the same principle.

enough to slip should clogging occur. Don't over lubricate slip clutches, or you may have unwanted slipping. Before using your combine for the first time, slip all clutches to see that they operate.

To test a slip clutch for proper operation, first throw the machine out of gear with the main PTO or engine clutch. Insert a sturdy block of wood into the driven mechanism in such a way that it will block the operation. *Slowly* engage the PTO or engine clutch, and the slip clutch protecting the drive line to the mechanism you have blocked should operate. If not, clean and lubricate it, repair it, or adjust it. Be careful to engage the PTO or engine clutch slowly and disengage it immediately. An improperly inserted block could possibly be thrown from the machine, so keep everyone away during this test.

Engine

If your combine is equipped with an auxiliary engine, check the oil and coolant level each day before starting, and top up as necessary. Fill the fuel tank as well. Keep the radiator and its screens clear of accumulated chaff and dirt. Clean the air filter daily. Keep the engine clean and free of a buildup of grease and oil. Change the engine oil and filter regularly. Before storing your combine for the season, take the following measures:

- Clean the outside of the engine with solvent and a stiff brush.
- Change the engine oil and filter, and run the engine for a few minutes afterward.
- If the engine is water cooled, check the coolant level and strength of the antifreeze, or drain the radiator and engine block.
- Drain fuel from the tank.
- Clean the air cleaner.
- If your combine is equipped with a battery, remove and recharge it, and store it in a clean, dry place where it won't freeze.

Storing a Combine

At the end of the season open the clean–out doors at the bottom of the tailings and clean grain elevators. Lower the grain tank unloading auger to the ground and open the clean–out door in the auger housing, as well as any drain plugs at the bottom of the tank. Operate the combine to clean out the augers. Leave the doors open and the plugs out.

Remove and clean all belts, wrap them in plastic or other protective material to keep them clean, and store them in a cool, dry place.

Remove and clean all belts, wrap them in plastic or other protective material to keep them clean, and store them in a cool, dry place.

Thoroughly clean the combine inside and out, paying close attention to the cleaning shoe and straw rack—trash and dirt hold moisture that causes metal to rust and wood to rot. Make sure the augers and elevators are thoroughly cleaned and leave the doors at the lower ends of the elevators open. Clean out the bottom of the grain tank and unloading auger and remove any drain plugs. Clean out the lower end of the platform behind the cutter bar and remove the platform drain plug, if one is provided.

Thoroughly grease the entire machine and oil the slip clutches, chains, sprockets, and cutter bar to prevent rust. Repaint or coat shiny surfaces with oil to prevent rust. Block up the platform to take the weight off lifting springs or hydraulic cylinders. Note any necessary repairs and order the parts.

Store your combine under a roof in a clean, dry place. If the machine must be left outside, remove all belts, canvas, and wooden reel parts, and store them inside. Cover the combine with a good tarp and tie it down so it will neither blow away nor collect pockets of water

Safety First!

☞ *Never* clean, lubricate, or adjust a combine while it is running.

☞ *Never* operate a combine while wearing loose clothing or long, hanging hair.

☞ *Always* make sure safety shields and guards are in place and in good condition.

☞ *Always* keep everyone away from the combine, forecart, and team before starting.

☞ *Never* try to clear a slugged cylinder or an obstruction of the cutter bar without first stopping the combine and shutting off the engine.

☞ *Aways* replace frayed or worn belts before they break.

☞ *Always* shut off the combine engine before refueling.

☞ *Always* disengage the forecart PTO clutch, or the combine engine clutch, before dismounting from the forecart.

Combining Various Crops

Settings for different crops are similar for all rasp bar combines.

Wheat should be combined with a cylinder speed of about 1,300 rpm, although some hard–to–thresh bearded varieties may require a speed as high as 1,500 rpm. Cylinder–to–concave spacing should be about $1/4$ inch. Beater speed should be the normal 650 rpm, although you may increase it slightly if damp straw has a tendency to wind. The straw rack should run at the normal 270 rpm. Fan shutters should be from two–thirds to three–fourths open and the blast should be well to the front of the sieve. Set the adjustable chaffer two–thirds to three–fourths open, and the sieve one–third to one–half open.

Barley should be combined at a cylinder speed of 1,200 to 1,300 rpm and a concave spacing of $1/4$ to $3/8$ inch. Beater and rack speeds should be the same as for wheat. Set the chaffer from one–half to two–thirds open and the sieve from one–third to one–half open. Fan shutters should be from two–thirds to wide open, as long as grain is not being blown over. Set the air blast well to the front of the shoe and sufficient to keep the beards from forming a mat on the sieve, which prevents grain from falling through.

Rye settings should be about the same as for wheat, although rye kernels are somewhat smaller and lighter than those of wheat, necessitating a slightly closer sieve setting and a little less blast. Rye straw is quite long and should be cut high to prevent excess straw from overloading the machine.

Oats should be combined with a cylinder speed slightly below 1,300 rpm to prevent the grain from being hulled. Concave spacing is $1/4$ inch, and beater and rack speeds are the same as for wheat. Open the chaffer and sieve slightly more than for wheat.

Buckwheat threshes easily and requires a cylinder speed of from 750 to 900 rpm. Concave spacing should be from $3/8$ to $1/2$ inch. Buckwheat cracks easily, requiring carefully adjusted speed and spacing. Set the chaffer about two–thirds open and the sieve one–fourth to one–third open. Open the fan blinds about halfway.

Soybeans are easy to thresh, but crack easily and should not be combined until the pods are fully matured and the beans are hard, usually after the first frost. Cylinder speed should be about 650 rpm and concave spacing should be set at $7/16$ to $1/2$ inch. To obtain a speed of 650 rpm, you may need to interchange the cylinder and drive sheaves. If the beans are not being threshed, decrease the spacing slightly. If cracking occurs, reduce the cylinder speed a little. Set the chaffer about two–thirds open and the sieve about one–half open. Keep the amount of tailings as low as possible to prevent cracking. Keep the fan shutters wide open and place the air blast on the front half of the sieves.

Fundamentals of Combine Harvesting

By carefully observing the fundamentals of combine harvesting, you should consistently obtain good results.

● Make sure the crop is in a condition to thresh. The straw should not be green or damp, and the grain should be dead ripe and dry.

● Cut the crop as high as possible while still getting all the low grain heads. In badly lodged crops, where more straw must be taken, drive at a slower speed or take less than a full swath to avoid overloading the machine with straw.

● Adjust the reel for even feeding.

● Set the cylinder speed as low as possible and concave clearance as high as possible while still threshing thoroughly without excessive cracking.

● Maintain sufficient rack speed to ensure the steady movement of straw through the machine. If clogging is a problem, and the rack is operating at the proper speed, raise or remove the front check board or curtain, or remove the fishbacks from the rack.

● Set the chaffer openings so the grain falls through before it has passed over two–thirds the length of the chaffer.

● Close the adjustable shoe sieve as much as possible without any grain going over the back into the tailings.

● Use as much air as possible without blowing over grain.

● If material loads up on the front of the chaffer, move the air blast more to the front.

● Keep the amount of tailings as low as possible.

Common Combine Troubles

Many combine troubles are directly caused by a careless or inattentive operator. To avoid such problems, observe the following precautions:

● At all times, keep the engine driving the combine at full throttle, or at the setting that gives 540 rpm on the PTO. On a typical combine you can check this speed by measuring the speed at the left–hand end of the feeder canvas drive roller shaft, which should be 540 rpm.

● When stopping the combine in standing grain for any reason, let the combine clean itself out before turning off the power. Before starting again, back up a few feet and bring the machine up to speed before re–entering the standing grain.

● Round off the corners of the standing grain, so you can maintain a uniform speed while turning.

● Carefully monitor the condition of the standing grain and adjust the platform to cut just enough straw to get all the grain heads. If the crop is extremely heavy, or badly lodged, avoid overloading the combine by taking less than a full swath.

● If you hear the sound of a slipping safety clutch, immediately stop forward travel, and determine and clear the cause.

● The sound of the engine slowing and lugging down usually occurs when the cylinder starts to slug. Immediately stop the combine's forward motion before the machine becomes completely plugged.

A properly adjusted combine throws out a minimal amount of tailings.

Cutting Problems

Missed or uncut grain.
　　cutter bar set too high to get all the short grain
　　dull, missing, or broken knife sections or guard ledger plates
　　no shear cut due to loose sickle
Reel carries straw around.
　　reel speed too fast
　　reel set too low
Cut grain falls back over front of cutter bar.
　　reel too far forward or too high

Feeding Problems

Uneven or bunched feeding to the cylinder.
- canvases not operating properly
- auger not operating properly
- drive belts slipping

Threshing Problems

Cylinder slugging.
- feeder canvas not working properly
- auger not working properly
- cylinder speed too slow
- combine overloaded
- cylinder drive belt slipping
- cylinder set too close to concaves

Grain not threshed from heads.
- crop not ripe enough to thresh
- uneven feeding to cylinder
- slugging of cylinder
- cylinder speed too low
- rasp bars bent
- cylinder–to–concave spacing too wide

Cracked grain.
- slugging of cylinder
- uneven feeding to cylinder
- cylinder speed too high
- cylinder too close to concave
- tailings too heavy
- dented clean grain auger sides

Straw wraps around beater.
- crop too green or damp
- beater speed too slow
- beater drive belt slipping
- straw rack not not moving straw to the rear

Straw bunches up on straw rack.
- beater speed too slow
- beater belt slipping
- straw rack drive belt slipping
- straw rack not oscillating

- crop cut too low, resulting in too much straw
- front check apron interfering with straw flow
- fishbacks impeding straw flow

Loss of grain over straw rack.
- combine speed too fast or too slow
- holes in rack are clogged
- rack speed too fast
- combine overloaded

Cleaning Problems

Chaff, straw, and other debris in cleaned grain.
- crop too tough and damp to combine
- insufficient air blast
- air blast not directed properly
- chaffer and/or sieve screen openings too large
- cleaning shoe overloaded

Cleaning shoe overloaded.
- cylinder speed too high, breaking up straw too much
- concave spacing too close, breaking up straw too much
- insufficient air blast
- air blast directed too far to the rear of shoe
- combine overloaded
- point of hitch too low

Grain going over back of cleaning shoe.
- chaffer and sieve overloaded
- too much blast blowing grain over the shoe
- sieve clogged with beards, causing grain to ride over with chaff
- point of hitch too high
- tailings too heavy

Excessive tailings.
- adjustable chaffer and sieve screens closed too much
- insufficient fan blast
- windboard throws blast too far to front of shoe
- tailboard too high
- point of hitch too low

International combine equipped with a pickup attachment combines wheat that was windrowed using a grain binder with a disabled binding mechanism.

Harvesting Machinery

17 Corn Harvesting Machines

"Heap high the farmer's wintry hoard!
Heap high the golden corn!
No richer gift has Autumn poured
From out her lavish horn!"
from John Greenleaf Whittier's "The Corn Song," 1847

For centuries corn was harvested by pulling the ears from the stalks, then stripping the husks from the ears, all by hand. If the fodder was to be used for animal feed, the stalks were first cut with a hand knife and then bound together into bundles. The bundles were stacked together into shocks, where they dried. As time permitted, usually during the winter after other field work was done, the shocks were taken apart and the corn ears husked out by hand. The fodder was then hauled to the barn for feed, or the shocks were reassembled and left in the field for later use. The husked ears were hauled to the farm and stored in a crib. The extensive hand labor required to harvest the crop seriously limited the amount of corn that could be raised and put into the crib and, as you might expect, was an impetus for inventive people to come up with a way to mechanize the drudgery of harvesting corn.

The earliest such machines appeared during the 1820s and were based on the reciprocating knife blades of mowers and reapers. Unfortunately, these lighter duty knives couldn't stand up to the shock involved in suddenly striking a hill of two, three, or four thick and tough stalks, and none of the machines was successful. A corn cutter patented in 1844 set the pattern for the successful sled–type corn harvester that was state of the art until the 1890s.

The corn sled has many variations, but each is basically a wooden or iron platform mounted on wheels or wooden runners, with one or more fixed, angled blades attached. The sled is pulled close enough alongside a row of corn stalks that the angled blade slices through the stalks a few inches above ground level. The operator rides on the sled and, sometimes with the help of a curved gathering arm, catches the cut stalks in his arms. When he can hold no more stalks, he throws them to the side for someone else to tie

and shock. Some sleds have larger platforms and railings so stalks may be accumulated on the platform. Periodically the sled is stopped and the shock set up and tied.

In 1892 A.S. Peck of Geneva, Illinois, patented the first successful corn binder. This machine cut the stalks evenly and tied them into neat, compact bundles that could be set up into shocks or, if the corn was to be chopped for silage, hauled directly to the chopper. In 1850 Edmund Quincy of Peoria, Illinois, invented a mechanical corn picker that used two spiked cylinders to tear off the ears. Corn pickers with rolls for snapping off the ears appeared about 1874, but shelled a lot of corn and therefore were unpopular. Until World War I, emphasis was on developing the corn binder rather than a mechanical picker, but that changed due to labor shortages caused by farmers leaving for the armed services or high paying defense jobs. Early corn pickers were ground driven, had a heavy draft, and weren't efficient. A power take off driven picker was introduced about 1930, and corn pickers finally came into their own.

An age–old method of hand picking corn involves a wagon and a team trained to move forward along the corn row when given a voice command. The farmer walks along the row, stripping ears of corn from the standing stalks, removing the husks, and tossing the ears over his shoulder into the wagon. The higher bang board along the top of one side of the wagon intercepts high thrown ears and drops them into the bed. Photo by Michael J. Lacivita

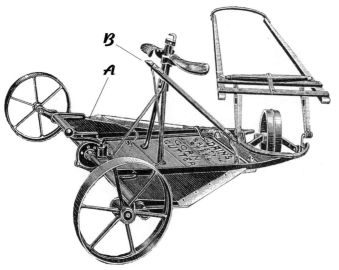

An early ground driven corn picker.

Farm Equipment, Frank N.G. Kranich, 1923

*John Deere two–row wheeled corn sled, designed to be pulled between two rows by a single horse. The angled blade at each side cuts the corn stalks, which are gathered by two men riding on the two saddle–type seats. Safety guards cover the blades when the sled is not in use; **A** shows a guard in place, **B** shows the guard raised.* *Deere & Co.*

Corn Binders

New corn binders haven't been built since the mid 1950s, but good used machines may still be found. They are available in single row ground driven, as well as one– and two–row PTO, models. Except for the source of power, operation of a PTO binder is virtually the same as for a ground driven model.

As it passes along the corn row, the binder's pointed wooden divider boards and gathering chains gather corn stalks and guide them into a heavy–duty reciprocating knife. After the knife cuts the stalks, the elevating chains carry the upright stalks to a binding unit, where they accumulate and are tied into a bundle. After being tied, a bundle is ejected onto the ground, onto a bundle carrier, or into an elevator that conveys it up to a trailing wagon.

The binder consists of three main components—the units for cutting, elevating, and binding. The proper operation and correct adjustment of each component is critical to the binder's efficient operation.

The first patented corn binder, designed by A.S. Peck.

A Popular History of American Invention, 1924

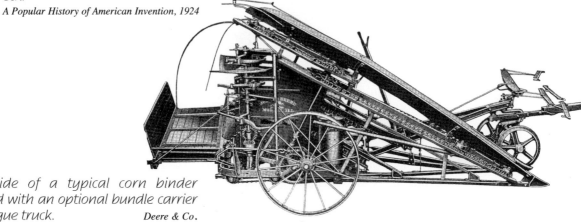

Right side of a typical corn binder equipped with an optional bundle carrier and tongue truck. *Deere & Co.*

Harvesting Machinery

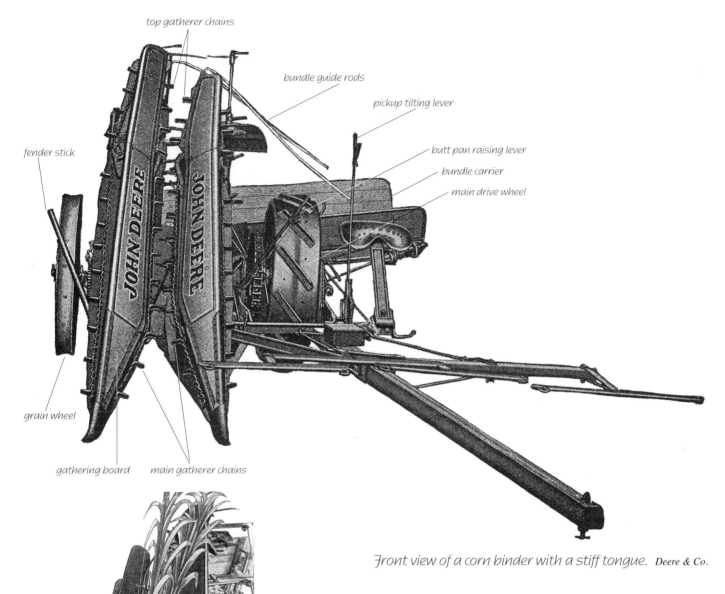

top gatherer chains

bundle guide rods

pickup tilting lever

fender stick

butt pan raising lever

bundle carrier

main drive wheel

grain wheel

gathering board   main gatherer chains

Front view of a corn binder with a stiff tongue. **Deere & Co.**

Front of a corn binder showing how the points and chains gather in the corn stalks.

The Massey–Harris Co.

Cutting Unit

The cutting unit consists of two wooden boards that angle downward and taper to iron points at the front. The machine is run so one of these *gathering boards* is on each side of the row of corn stalks. Inside the gathering board on each side, is a *gatherer chain* on which are spaced horizontal lugs that catch the corn stalks and carry them to the rear.

The knife of a corn binder must withstand the intermittent shock of hitting a thick, tough corn stalk every few inches. The reciprocating knife has one triangular *section* that operates between a *fixed knife* on each side. The knives must be kept sharp and in proper adjustment so the sickle knife section and the two fixed side knives make a shear cut—the key to light draft and good work with the corn binder.

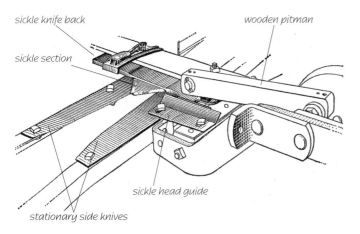

- sickle knife back
- wooden pitman
- sickle section
- sickle head guide
- stationary side knives

The corn binder cutting mechanism.   *Deere & Co.*

Elevating Unit

The elevating unit consists of several pairs of lugged chains stacked one above the other on the gathering boards on each side of the machine's throat. The lugs act as fingers to catch and move the corn stalks, and the flat side of the lugs should run next to the corn. The chains are called the main gatherer chains, the top gatherer chains, and the butt chains.

Each pair of chains run opposite to each other, and turn in opposite directions. As they turn, the lugs on opposite chains should alternate, rather than match. An idler sprocket on each of the chains is adjustable to maintain chain tension, and the chains should be run just tight enough to prevent them from climbing off the sprockets.

In addition to the tightness adjustment, the top gatherer chains on some machines may be moved in or out to give more or less throat capacity. A long, flat adjustable *throat spring* is usually provided to hold the cut stalks into the chains.

Binding Unit

The binding unit of a corn binder is virtually the same as that of a grain binder, complete with similar adjustment and tying difficulties, except the stalks are accumulated and tied while in a vertical, rather than horizontal, position. Some corn binders tie the stalks in a leaning or a horizontal position, but few of these have survived. If you use one of these corn binders, the same general principles apply as for a vertical machine.

Operating a Corn Binder

Each make of corn binder varies in some of its details, but the operation of all of them is similar. Knotters, especially, are virtually identical, since most manufacturers used one

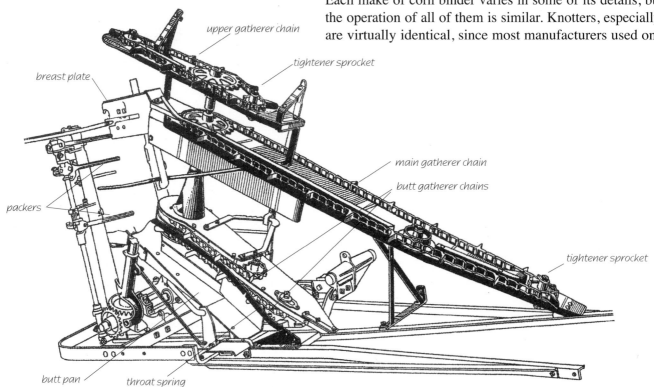

- upper gatherer chain
- tightener sprocket
- breast plate
- main gatherer chain
- butt gatherer chains
- packers
- tightener sprocket
- butt pan
- throat spring

The throat and left gatherer of a typical corn binder.

International Harvester

Harvesting Machinery

of two types. Before taking any corn binder to the field, take the following steps:

- Check the entire machine for loose or missing nuts and bolts, and badly worn or broken parts, all of which should be tightened, repaired, or replaced.

- Thoroughly lubricate the corn binder. Older models have oil cups and oil holes, while newer models are equipped with high pressure grease fittings. Look for these lubrication points anywhere one mechanical component moves against another. Oil the sickle knife and the chains and sprockets, unless you'll be operating the binder in dusty or sandy conditions.

- Add twine, and thread the binding mechanism. The twine cans on most corn binders are identical to those of a grain binder, and loading twine is the same. Although not all corn binders are threaded exactly the same way, a careful examination of your model should reveal how it is to be threaded.

- Finish threading the knotter by pulling the twine end across the breast plate and holding it firmly with one hand. With the other hand, trip the trip hook, grasp the discharge arms, and turn them once around. The needle will advance and place the twine into the twine disc, where it is held fast. Pull the knot off the bill hook, and your corn binder is ready to tie bundles.

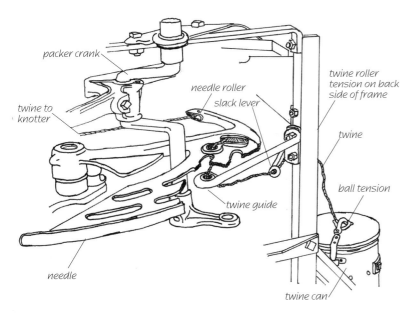

packer crank

needle roller

slack lever

twine to knotter

twine guide

needle

twine roller tension on back side of frame

twine

ball tension

twine can

To thread a corn binder, pull the twine end out of the can and up through the ball tension in the can lid, through the roller tensioner, slack lever, and twine guide, then up through the hole in the flat of the needle, through the needle point, and out over the needle roller before going to the twine disc in the knotter.

Deere & Co.

Field Operation

Before starting to cut corn stalks, set the height at which you want them cut. The initial height setting is controlled by cranks on both the bull wheel and the grain wheel, which should normally be at the same height. When you need additional traction on the bull wheel due to muddy conditions, run it a little lower to throw more of the machine's weight onto that wheel. On a typical corn binder, the grain wheel is mounted on a crank axle that allows the binder's weight to be shifted from the front to the rear, as well as up and down. If you use either a tongue truck or a bundle carrier, move the wheel to the rear to shift the machine's weight toward the front, placing more weight on the tongue truck or preventing the tongue from whipping from the extra weight of a bundle carrier. If you use neither a tongue truck nor a bundle carrier, move the wheel to the front to take weight off the horses' necks.

After setting the initial height of the binder, control the height of the gathering points above the ground by the tilting lever. In standing corn, run the points fairly high and level, and adjust the fender stick to run just outside the grain wheel. If the corn is lodged and tangled, adjust the fender stick farther outside the grain wheel, and run the gatherer points close to the ground. Drive your team so the corn row is exactly centered between the gathering points, and maintain a steady speed.

The butts of the corn stalks slide from the cutting knife to the binding unit on a butt pan that may be adjusted up or down with the butt pan lever at the side of the seat. Keep the butt pan as low as possible, raising it only when you want to place the twine tie closer to the butt, such as in short corn.

In heavy or weedy corn, the binding unit may not be able to eject the completed bundle, causing the bull wheel to slide. To remedy this situation, adjust the trip fingers to make smaller bundles. Making the bundles a little looser may also help.

If you are cutting tall top–heavy corn, move the top gatherer chains closer together (if your machine has this adjustment), causing the tops to move to the rear a little faster. In short corn, set the top chains farther apart.

The knotter on a corn binder is virtually identical to the knotter on a grain binder. Knotting troubles are therefore caused and resolved similarly, as described in the chapter on grain binders.

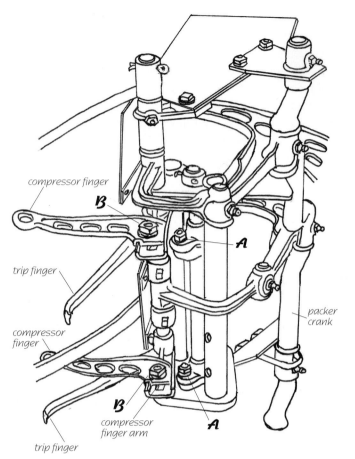

compressor finger

B

A

trip finger

compressor
finger

packer
crank

B

A

compressor
finger arm

trip finger

To make smaller bundles, loosen the nuts at A and move the trip fingers toward the breastplate. To make looser bundles, remove the bolts at B and move the compressor fingers outward on the arms. *Deere & Co.*

Bundle Carriers and Elevators

A bundle carrier isn't necessary for the proper operation of a corn binder, but using one has advantages. By carrying bundles and dumping them off to the side of the binder, a bundle carrier puts the bundles out of the way of the horses as they make the next round. Since the bundle carrier is under your control, you may dump bundles in a windrow to make the job of picking them up easier for shocking or loading.

Some corn binders have a finger style carrier that is manually dumped by operating a foot pedal. Although

its operation is spring assisted, a finger carrier requires more physical effort to dump than a power carrier. Additionally, the finger carrier may not dump all the bundles out of the way of the next round.

Many machines have a power bundle carrier, consisting of a wooden platform with a chain and crossbar conveyor. When you want to dump the bundles, you operate a foot pedal that engages a slip clutch, causing the conveyer on the bottom of the bundle carrier to turn and dump the bundles. The power carrier is driven from the same bull wheel as the rest of the machine, so the corn binder must be moving for it to work.

The optional bundle elevator is useful when cutting corn for filling silos. It saves the labor of lifting the heavy bundles onto a wagon for hauling to the ensilage cutter. The elevator attaches to the rear of a corn binder and consists of an angled wooden platform with a chain and crossbar conveyor. As the bundles are ejected from the binding unit, they fall onto the elevator's conveyor chain, which carries them up to a height where they may be easily loaded onto a wagon pulled alongside the binder. The elevator is driven from the machine's bull wheel, and significantly increases draft.

Draft of a Corn Binder

The draft of a corn binder is influenced by many factors, chief among them being the yield of the corn and the height at which it is cut. The average draft of a corn binder cutting drilled green silage corn, yielding 50 or 60 bushels to the acre, is 480 pounds on dry land. Cutting dry check–rowed

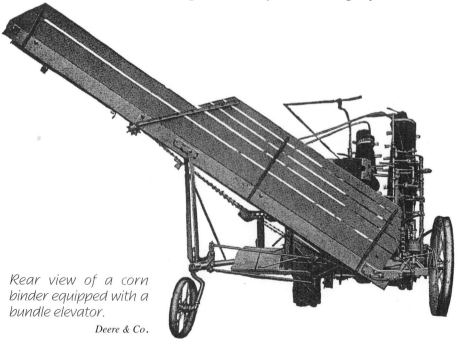

Rear view of a corn binder equipped with a bundle elevator.
Deere & Co.

corn for shocking on the same ground is about the same. Cutting in a wet, muddy field increases draft by as much as 40 percent. A power bundle elevator increases draft by about 100 pounds. A badly worn or poorly adjusted machine increases draft as well. A corn binder usually weighs between 1,500 and 1,700 pounds.

Lubrication and Storage

As with all such complicated machines, a corn binder requires frequent and thorough lubrication. Oil or grease the entire machine twice each day, once in the morning before starting, and again at noon. Lubricate fast moving parts, such as the cutter bar pitman, every two hours. Wipe grease fittings clean before lubricating. Oil the knife, chains, and sprockets unless you are operating the binder in dusty or sandy conditions. Oil the knotter parts, rollers, and the faces of cams and parts that slide against each other.

At the end of each season, clean your corn binder of all dirt and accumulated oil and grease. Check for worn and broken parts, and repair or replace them during the off–season. Thoroughly lubricate the entire machine. Coat the knotter parts with heavy oil or grease to prevent rust. Store your binder under cover.

A corn picker with trailing wagon at work. Photo by Ted Rose

for use with tractors. These machines are all designed to be run by a power take off. For use with horses, the pull–type one–row picker is the most practical, as it may be powered by a motorized forecart or an engine mounted on the machine.

A corn picker snaps corn ears from the stalks, removes the silk and husks, and elevates the cleaned ears into a trailed wagon. The machine consists of three components: a gathering and snapping unit, a husking and cleaning unit, and an elevating unit. The power trains to each of the units are protected by slip clutches.

Gathering and Snapping Unit

The front of the gathering and snapping unit consists of two tapered sheet metal *snouts* or *gathering points* that are run with one on each side of the corn row. The points may be raised or lowered by a lever to allow the points to get under lodged grain. Inside the points is a pair of *gatherer chains* that feed the stalks between the snapping rolls. The stalk is drawn downward between the two spiral *snapping rolls* turning in opposite directions. As a stalk is drawn into the snapping rolls, the space between the rolls passes the stalk, but is too narrow to pass the ear, which is snapped from the stalk and carried to the husking unit. The stalk passes on through the gatherer and is left standing in the field.

International corn binder working in tall corn.

Photo by Ruth Freeman

Corn Pickers

Corn pickers come in a variety of shapes and sizes, including one– and two–row pull–type machines, as well as one–row semi–mounted, and two–row mounted pickers

Corn Harvesting Machines

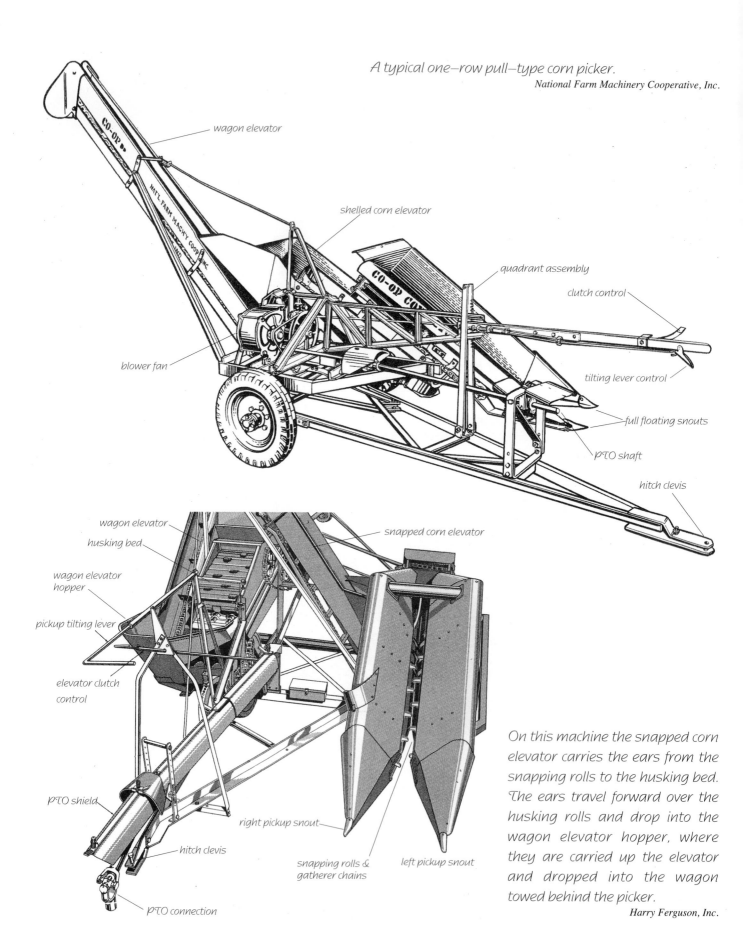

A typical one-row pull-type corn picker.

National Farm Machinery Cooperative, Inc.

wagon elevator

shelled corn elevator

quadrant assembly

clutch control

tilting lever control

full floating snouts

blower fan

PTO shaft

hitch clevis

wagon elevator

husking bed

snapped corn elevator

wagon elevator hopper

pickup tilting lever

elevator clutch control

PTO shield

right pickup snout

hitch clevis

snapping rolls & gatherer chains

left pickup snout

PTO connection

On this machine the snapped corn elevator carries the ears from the snapping rolls to the husking bed. The ears travel forward over the husking rolls and drop into the wagon elevator hopper, where they are carried up the elevator and dropped into the wagon towed behind the picker.

Harry Ferguson, Inc.

Harvesting Machinery

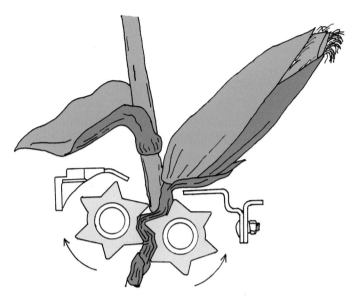

Action of the snapping rolls in removing an ear from the stalk.

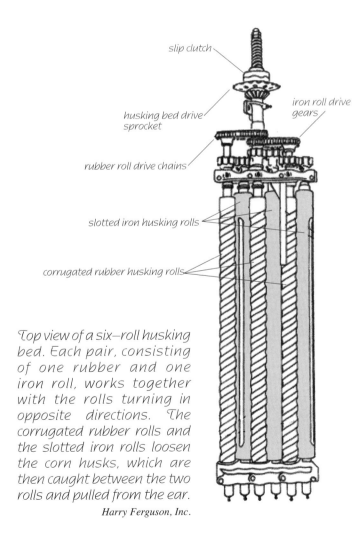

slip clutch

husking bed drive sprocket

iron roll drive gears

rubber roll drive chains

slotted iron husking rolls

corrugated rubber husking rolls

Top view of a six-roll husking bed. Each pair, consisting of one rubber and one iron roll, works together with the rolls turning in opposite directions. The corrugated rubber rolls and the slotted iron rolls loosen the corn husks, which are then caught between the two rolls and pulled from the ear.

Harry Ferguson, Inc.

Husking Unit

The husking unit contains one or more pairs of husking rolls. The paired rolls work against each other and are held in close contact with each other by adjustable spring pressure. One roll of each pair is usually rubber covered or made of rubber, and one or both rolls may contain corrugations or husking pegs for a better grip on the husks. Some kind of device is usually over the husking bed to help evenly distribute snapped ears, keep them moving over the bed, and hold them down against the rolls. This device may take the form of a feed apron, presser wheels, retarder plates, or just a simple conveyor chain. Most corn pickers have a grain saver under the husking bed to catch any shelled grain and move it to the wagon elevator. Most units are also equipped with a fan to blow husks and trash off the husking bed.

Elevating Unit

The husked ears, along with any shelled corn, are delivered into a hopper at the bottom of the wagon elevator. The hopper is normally large enough to hold the surplus ears that accumulate when the elevator is stopped during turns or wagon changes. An endless conveyor chain in the bottom of the wagon elevator carries up the loose grain and clean ears and dumps them into a wagon trailed behind the picker. A hand operated clutch allows the elevator mechanism to be stopped and started from the operator's seat, and prevents corn from being dropped on the ground during turns at the row ends. Many corn pickers have an adjustable chute at the upper end of the elevator that allows the corn to be delivered to the front or rear of the wagon. This chute is controlled by a rope from the operator's seat.

Hitching and Draft

Make sure the engine on your forecart has enough power to properly operate the picker, and the PTO is at the proper speed. Most pickers are designed to operate at a power take off speed of 525 to 550 revolutions per minute. Too low a speed reduces the machine's capacity, while too high a speed causes ears to bounce on the husking bed and results in dirty husking, because the rolls can't grasp the husks to pull them off.

You need enough horses on the forecart to handle the cart and picker, as well as a loaded wagon. The cart drawbar should be about 15 inches above the ground. Make sure that at least 6 inches of the square PTO shaft is inside the telescoping square tube at all times. To avoid excessive wear on the PTO shaft universal joints when you slide the solid, square shaft inside the hollow one, be sure the inner forks of the universal joints are parallel. Make sure *all* safety shields are in position and attached correctly.

When starting a corn picker for the first time, or at the beginning of a new season, start the power source and run the machine at idle speed for a few minutes. While the picker is running, make sure no belts are slipping and all parts are moving properly with no binding or loud noises. If all is okay, gradually bring the machine up to operating speed and again observe for proper operation. After running the machine for a few minutes, stop the engine and carefully check for loose bolts, heated bearings, binding parts, and loose belts. Correct any problems before attempting to use the corn picker in the field.

No draft figures are available for a corn picker, probably because the draft varies widely and depends on many factors. These factors include crop and ground conditions, adjustment of the machine, size of the wagon, and whether the wagon is full or empty. A one–row corn picker weighs about 2,000 to 2,500 pounds.

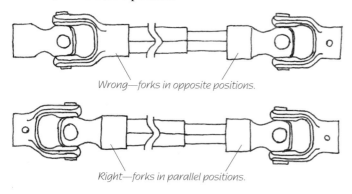

Wrong—forks in opposite positions.

Right—forks in parallel positions.

Right and wrong way to install PTO shaft.
National Farm Machinery Cooperative

Operating a Corn Picker

Each make of corn picker has the same basic features, although construction and adjustments vary widely. Make every effort to obtain the manufacturer's instruction manual for your specific machine. Before taking a corn picker to the field, observe the following steps:
- Check the entire machine for loose or missing nuts and bolts, and badly worn or broken parts, which should be tightened, repaired, or replaced.
- Check the spiral projections on the snapping rolls. If they are badly worn you may need to replace the rolls or built up the old ones by welding. Snapping rolls on which the projections are badly worn will cause shelling. Time the snapping rolls so the spiral ridge on one roll runs halfway between two spiral ridges on the other.

- Check the gathering chains for broken or cracked links or lugs, and for correct tension. The chains are correctly adjusted when the lug links may be bent backward about 1/2 inch.
- Check the husking bed and remove any dirt, corn stalks, roots, stones, or other debris. Check the rubber rolls for excessive wear. Since rubber rolls wear the most at one end, sometimes they may be removed and turned end for end. Reset the roll timing as necessary to keep the projections on one roll fitting into the recesses in the other. Run the rolls close together so they can pull the husks off, but not with so much tension the rubber rolls and roll bearings wear out prematurely.
- Thoroughly lubricate the corn picker. Most models are equipped with high pressure grease fittings. Look for them any place one mechanical component moves against another. The operator's manual, if available, will contain a detailed lube chart showing the locations of the grease fittings. Oil the chains and sprockets, unless you'll be operating the picker in dusty or sandy conditions.

Most corn pickers will do the job even under unfavorable conditions, although picking early means you won't have to contend with bitter cold weather, frozen ground, and lodged, frozen, or rotted stalks. Most pull–type corn pickers are designed to do their best work at a ground speed of 2 1/2 to 3 miles per hour. If the corn is down and the stalks are dry or frozen, you may have to reduce the forward speed. Run the power take off shaft at about 540 RPM under load. Never make sharp turns or back the

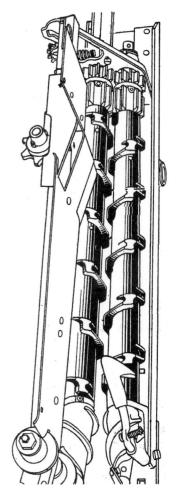

When the snapping rolls are timed correctly, the lugs on one roll are centered between two lugs on the opposite roll, and no part of one roll is in contact with the other roll.

International Harvester

machine with the PTO shaft running. Don't engage or disengage the PTO while the machine is moving.

The rachets operating in any of the slip clutches will make enough noise for you to hear. If you hear a safety clutch, stop immediately, disengage the PTO, and stop the engine. Determine the cause of the slipping clutch and correct the problem. If the ratchet slips for no apparent reason, tighten its spring tension. If the picker chokes or clogs, stop forward movement and allow the picker machinery to run for a few minutes. If that doesn't successfully clear the blockage, *disengage the PTO,* shut off the engine, and clear the problem by hand.

Running the Snapping Unit

To prevent the stalks and ears from being knocked to the ground, drive so the corn row is in the exact center of the snapping rolls. Run the gatherer points just low enough to get all the ears. Pay close attention to the ground in front of the picker, and raise the points over furrows, rocks, or other obstructions that could damage them. Raise the points when turning at the row ends.

Adjust the snapping rolls so the stalks flow through freely. You may need to adjust the rolls several times during the day, as damp corn requires the rolls to be closer together than dry or frozen corn. Under normal conditions, the lower ends of the snapping rolls should be about 1 to 1¹/₈ inches apart. Never set the snapping rolls so close they touch each other. In unusually dry conditions, or if the corn is frozen,

open up the snapping rolls at the bottom, but not so wide the ears get caught between the rolls and crushed or shelled.

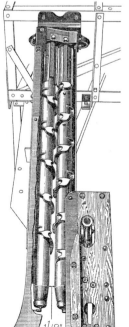

1¹/₈"

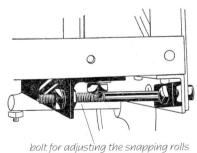

bolt for adjusting the snapping rolls

Safety First!

Corn pickers have likely caused more deaths—not to mention lost fingers, hands, arms, feet, and legs—than any other single piece of farm machinery. Pickers have a strong tendency to clog, and the temptation is great to reach in, while the machine is running, with your hand or kick with your foot to get stuff moving again. These safety rules are recommended by the Farm Equipment Institute and the National Safety Council:

☞ *Always* shut off the power take off before dismounting to clear a clogged picker.

☞ *Never* clean, grease, or adjust the machine while the PTO is engaged.

☞ *Never* use a stick to push stalks through the rolls.

☞ *Always* wear snug fitting clothing—no dangling sleeves, coattails, jewelry, or long hair.

☞ *Always* keep all riders, especially children, off the picker and the wagon.

☞ *Always* keep the operator's platform free of obstructions you could stumble over.

☞ *Always* keep the power take off shaft covered.

☞ *Always* keep the picker on the row.

☞ *Always* keep the snapping rolls and gathering chains in good condition and properly adjusted.

☞ *Always* run the picker at the correct speed for the field conditions.

☞ *Always* make sure the safety clutches are properly adjusted.

☞ *Always* read the instructions.

☞ *Never* hunt and pick corn at the same time.

☞ *Never* allow untrained operators to run the picker.

☞ *Always* be especially careful if you operate your picker when tired.

☞ Although all these safety rules are important, imprint this last one on your mind:

☞ *Never, ever* get off the operator's seat without first disengaging the PTO clutch and shutting down the engine.

On this machine the clearance between the front of the snapping rolls is adjusted by a tie bolt; on other machines it may be adjusted by moving the front bearing bracket on the outer roll. Under normal conditions run the lower ends of the snapping rolls 1 to 1¹/₈ inches apart.

New Idea Farm Equipment Co.

Running the Husking Unit

Make sure the PTO is running at about 540 RPM. If the PTO speed is too fast, ears may jump or bounce on the rolls and poor husking will result. Inspect the husking unit periodically and remove any stones, corn stalks, roots, or other debris. The pairs of husking rolls are held together by spring tension at both ends and should be run with just enough tension to grasp the husks and pull them from the ear with minimal shelling. Less tension is required for damp corn than for corn with dry husks.

Some corn pickers have feed aprons, presser wheels, or retarder plates above the husking rolls. These devices hold the ears against the rolls and keep them moving through the husking bed. Most of these devices are adjustable for varying conditions. They may have to be raised in heavy corn and lowered in a crop with small ears. Damp corn doesn't require the hold–down devices to be as close to the rolls, while the opposite is true for dry corn. Never run them closer to the rolls than necessary, or the result may be bruising and shelling of the corn.

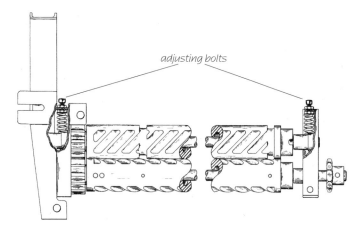

adjusting bolts

A typical pair of husking rolls showing the bolts for adjusting the amount of spring tension between the rolls. Damp husks require less tension than dry husks.

National Farm Machinery Cooperative

Running the Elevating Unit

The elevating unit carries the corn up and drops it into a wagon trailed behind the corn picker. The elevator chain tension may be adjusted at the top of the elevator and should be just tight enough to keep the chain on the sprockets.

If the picker wagon elevator has an adjustable hood or spout, set it initially to drop the corn into the front of the wagon. As the front fills up, a pull on a rope will change the spout to deliver ears to the wagon's rear. When making a turn at the end of a row, operate the hand lever that disengages the elevator clutch, stopping the conveyor and preventing corn from being spilled on the ground during the turn. Remember to re–engage the elevator clutch when the wagon is again straightened out and under the spout.

Don't overload the wagon, which may cause spilled corn and may be too heavy for the team. Change wagons in the row or on the ends. When changing in the row, stop forward travel, but run the PTO until all the corn is out of the picker. Unhitch the wagon, disengage the elevator clutch, and continue to pick corn for 25 feet or so. Pull the empty wagon into position, hook it up to the picker, engage the elevator clutch, and allow the elevator hopper to empty before continuing to pick corn.

Storing a Corn Picker

At the end of each season, clean the corn picker of all dirt and accumulated oil and grease. Check for worn and broken parts, and do any necessary repairs or replacements during the off–season. Thoroughly lubricate the entire machine. Any surfaces that are shiny from use should be repainted or coated with a rust preventive. Remove the chains, wash them in kerosene, and coat them with heavy oil before replacing them. Store your corn picker under cover.

Common Corn Picker Problems

As with most complicated harvesting machines, a careless or inattentive operator can cause many so–called troubles. To avoid such problems:

- Keep the picker engine driving at full throttle, or at the setting that gives 540 RPM on the PTO.
- When stopping the picker in standing corn (unless you've stopped because a clutch is slipping), let the machine clean itself out before cutting the power.
- Carefully monitor the condition of the standing corn and adjust the points so they get all the ears, but not so low they dig into the ground or hit stones or other obstructions.
- Stop forward travel and cut the PTO immediately if you hear the sound of a slipping safety clutch. Determine and clear the cause before proceeding.
- Drive so corn stalks enter the gathering points in the exact center of the snapping rolls.
- Stop the elevator conveyor when turning at the end of rows to prevent spilling corn on the ground.

Gathering and Snapping Unit Problems

Gatherers clog.
>> gatherer chains too loose
>> lugs on gathering chains bent or broken

Stalks break or ears break off before stalks enter the snapping rolls.
>> clogged gatherer
>> driver not following row properly
>> gathering points run low enough to accumulate weeds and mud

Snapping rolls break off dry or frozen stalks.
>> snapping rolls set too close together

Snapping rolls clog.
>> snapping rolls set too far apart

Excessive shelling at snapping rolls.
>> snapping rolls set too far apart

Trash accumulating at lower end of snapping rolls.
>> snapping roll point guards bent out of place
>> snapping roll point guards missing

Husking Unit Problems

Ears not husked clean.
>> too little husking roll tension
>> devices that hold ears against the rolls not set close enough
>> corn stalks or roots, stones, or other debris in husking bed
>> PTO speed too high, causing ears to bounce on rolls

Too many husks and too much trash getting to wagon elevator.
>> insufficient fan blast due to fan belt slipping
>> fan opening clogged

Wagon Elevator Problems

Conveyor chain slipping.
>> conveyor chain clutch slipping
>> drive belt slipping

Elevator spilling corn on turns.
>> conveyor chain clutch not disengaged soon enough when starting a turn
>> conveyor chain clutch re–engaging too soon after completing a turn

A horse-drawn corn picker collecting its harvest in a bang-board wagon.

Courtesy of Mel Klein

18 Potato Diggers

"What I say is that, if a fellow really likes potatoes, he must be a pretty decent sort of fellow."   *A. A. Milne*

Digging potatoes by hand is slow, back breaking work. The unknown farmer who first used his walking plow to turn over the dirt in the row speeded up the operation to some extent, although the method had its drawbacks. The exact depth of potatoes is difficult to judge, and many are cut by the plow share. Then, too, separating the potatoes from the plowed up earth takes much time and labor.

The first diggers were walk behind tools, similar to a plow. The share has a shallow V–shape and, instead of a moldboard, has a series of iron rods extending back from the share. The digger is operated so the share cuts under the potatoes and lifts both the earth and the potatoes onto the rods. As the mixture slides to the rear, the dirt falls through the rods and the spuds are deposited in a row at each side of the digger for pickup by hand. Later models have a star shaped wheel that runs on the ground and imparts an up–and–down agitation to the hinged rods to help knock off the dirt.

During the 1880s a wheeled digger, similar to those used today, became available. The machine has a pointed blade, or shovel, that cuts through the soil beneath the row of potatoes. The soil, potatoes, and vines are carried to the rear over an open bottom conveyor, which agitates the mixture to cause the dirt and small stones to drop through. The potatoes and vines are dropped on the ground in a windrow behind the machine, where the potatoes may be picked up by hand. Later improvements include vine turners to shunt the vines off to one side away from the potatoes.

Walking potato digger in action.   Photo by Walter D. Bernard

By 1871 a potato digger became available that has a seat for the operator and a broad shovel. Behind the shovel are a number of fingers that are agitated by a pitman and gear drive from the main wheel.

Features of a Potato Digger

The horse–drawn elevator–type potato digger is used to dig up and deliver clean potatoes on top of the soil, where they are picked up by hand. A wide, pointed steel shovel at the front of the elevator cuts through the soil beneath the row of potatoes. Digging depth is regulated by the lifting lever and gauged by the front tongue truck. Most

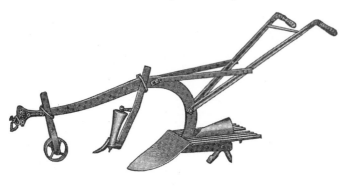

John Deere walking potato digger equipped with gauge wheel, vine fender, and shaker wheel.   Deere & Co.

A potato digger from 1871 with a seat for the operator.
Farm Equipment Institute

machines are equipped with a two–wheel front truck that allows the wheels to run on each side of the row. For hard, crusted soil conditions an optional solid concave roller rides on top of the row and helps break up the soil surface.

Dirt, vines, and potatoes slide across the shovel and onto the elevator, which is a continuous chain of steel rods moving to the rear of the machine. The elevator chain, driven by the rear wheels, is carried on eccentric shaped idler sprockets that impart an up and down shaking motion to the elevator. The shaking causes the earth to separate from the potatoes and fall through the elevator. The potatoes and vines are carried over the rear of the elevator, where they fall onto an agitating rear rack extension and then to the ground. Some diggers are equipped with mechanical raking fingers and curved rods that separate the vines and drop them apart from the row of potatoes.

Potato diggers come in one–row ground or PTO driven, and two–row PTO, versions. Ground drive potato diggers are sometimes fitted with a gasoline engine mounted on the elevator frame to drive the mechanism, thus reducing draft and doing a better job of cleaning in heavy yield conditions, because the elevators run independent of the rate of travel. A PTO driven potato digger with independent PTO has the same advantage. Attachments include stone guards to prevent stones from lodging between the shovel and the elevator, rolling coulters and vine fenders to assist in heavy vine conditions, and a variety of rear rack extensions.

Draft and Hitching

One row riding potato diggers usually weigh from 1,000 to 1,200 pounds without special equipment. The draft ranges from 650 to 940 pounds, with an average of 734 pounds. The use of an auxiliary engine reduces the draft by only about 10 percent because of the weight of the engine.

The weight of the front of the digger is carried by the tongue truck, so the vertical line of draft need not be

A walk–behind potato digger, with the wings and separating rods removed, is handy for lifting onions and garlic.
Photos by Jack Kittredge

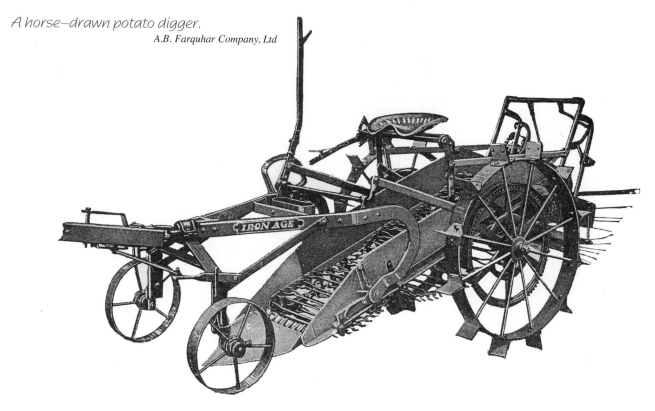

considered. The tongue forms the center of the horizontal line of draft, so hitch the horses accordingly. If you use a forecart and stub tongue, hitch to the center of the cart drawbar. If your digger is a PTO machine and you use a power cart, be sure all PTO shields are in place.

Operating a Potato Digger

Harvest potatoes only when they are thoroughly matured. Drive the potato digger so the front truck wheels straddle the row. Getting off the row causes cut or missed potatoes. Run the shovel just deep enough to get under all the roots.

Features of a potato digger.

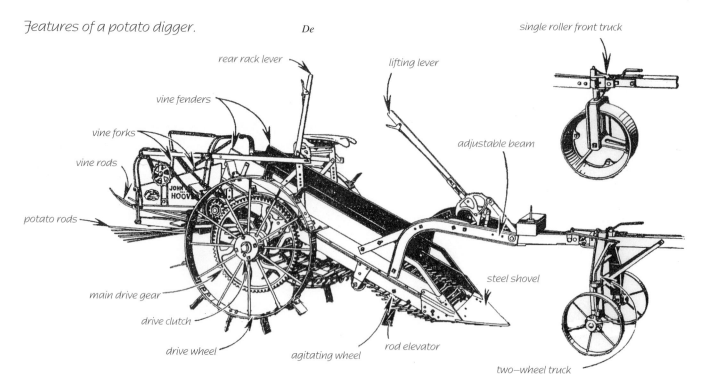

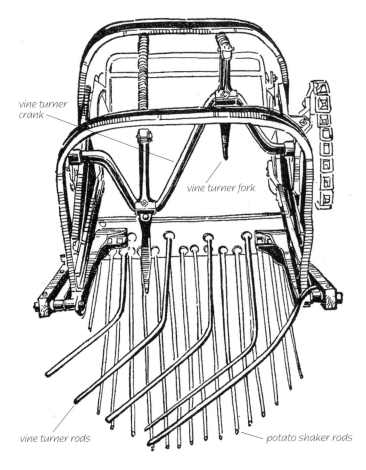

vine turner crank

vine turner fork

vine turner rods

potato shaker rods

The potatoes and vines come off the rear of the elevator and onto the vine turner. The vine turner forks move the vines along the vine turner rods and off to the side of the digger. The potatoes fall through the vine turner rods and are shaken off the back of the potato shaker rods into a row on the ground.

Farm Machinery by Archie Stone.

Running too deep brings up excessive earth, which increases draft, overloads the machine, and makes separation more difficult. Running the shovel too shallow results in missed and damaged potatoes. The shovel should be polished enough to scour freely. If soil sticks to the shovel instead of sliding freely across it, potatoes will be lost to each side of the shovel and operation will be unsatisfactory.

Handle the potatoes gently to prevent bruising. For this reason, delay complete separation of the potatoes from the soil until they are near the top of the elevator, so a layer of dirt remains under the potatoes to act as a cushion. On most machines, the front elevator rollers may be adjusted higher or lower in relation to the rear of the shovel. If the elevator runs higher than the shovel, separation begins as soon as the soil and potatoes leave the shovel. In light, dry soil, lower the elevator rollers to delay separation, thus reducing the possibility of damaging the potatoes due to excessive agitation. Various agitator sprockets are available to make the agitation of the elevator chain more or less aggressive. Depending on harvesting conditions, the rear agitating rack may be given a short or a long shake.

To prevent stones from lodging between the chain and the rollers, operate the elevator chain loosely. A chain that's too loose, however, can drag on the ground under the elevating bed or become disconnected. If the chain needs tightened, remove chain links by gathering slack in the chain and unhooking and removing one or more links.

Lubrication and Care

Lubricate the potato digger twice a day in normal conditions. If the machine is operated in dusty conditions, avoid excessive lubrication. Keep the shovel sharp and shiny, so soil slides easily onto the elevator and doesn't stick.

At season's end, coat the shovel with grease to preserve its shine, and lubricate the entire machine. Check for worn parts and loose bolts and nuts. Make any necessary repairs. Store your digger under cover.

This McCormick-Deering model 5-A potato digger is equipped with the optional extension elevator, designed for use in sticky or hard soil where an extra amount of agitation is needed to clean the potatoes; the extension elevator provides an additional three feet of cleaning capacity and replaces the usual rod type shaker and vine turner.

Photo by Mary Ann Sherman

V: Miscellaneous Indispensables

Three groups of machinery stand alone as being essential for the horse farmer in most farming operations:

1. Forecarts are used to pull plows and discs, planters and drills, mower conditioners and balers, combines and corn pickers, and many other machines utilized in field operations. Forecarts come in a wide array of sizes and shapes, and with many combinations of features and options. In addition to the more common two-wheel versions, forecarts with three or four wheels are also available. Some are equipped with remote hydraulic outlets, or a hydraulically controlled three-point hitch, as well as a gasoline or diesel engine to run PTO driven implements. Although tongue trucks are not forecarts, some of their functions are similar.

2. Spreaders are usually used ahead of tillage and after harvest to help replace soil nutrients used by the previous crop. A spreader may also be used to top dress a growing crop. Manure spreaders shred and scatter animal wastes, while fertilizer distributors and lime spreaders broadcast or drill granulated or powdered substances.

3. Farm vehicles are used for hauling. Wagons haul seed and fertilizer to the field for planting and carry hay and harvested grain from the field to the barn or granary, as well doing almost any hauling job around the farm. Bob sleds perform the same tasks when the snow is deep, while work sleds are handy for carrying heavy loads on light snow, ice, or bare ground. Stone boats are ideal for moving heavy rocks. Work sleds and stone boats make good training vehicles for draft animals.

19

Forecarts

Forecarts may have evolved from the two-wheel foretrucks once used with grain binders, mowers, and other implements. A photograph in a 1928 leaflet published by the Horse Association of America shows a farmer pulling a four-bottom tractor plow with a 12-horse team. Between the plow and the team, the driver rode on a cart (it wasn't called a forecart in those days) that had originally been built for use with an endgate seeder. The cart was made from the wooden rear wheels of a wagon, upon which was mounted a small box arranged with a pole in the center. With this setup the cart traveled on the unplowed ground. The farmer reported averaging 12 acres plowed per day, results consistent with those reported by present-day horse farmers.

A *forecart,* also called a *hitch cart,* allows most implements that are designed for tractor use to easily be used with horses. The basic forecart may be described as a two-wheel cart with horses hitched to the front and an implement attached to a drawbar at the rear. Between the wheels is a platform, often with a safety guardrail across the front, as well as a seat upon which the driver rides and from which he controls both his team and the drawn implement. Many teamsters stand while driving, looking much like modern-day Roman Centurions driving their chariots off to conquer the fields.

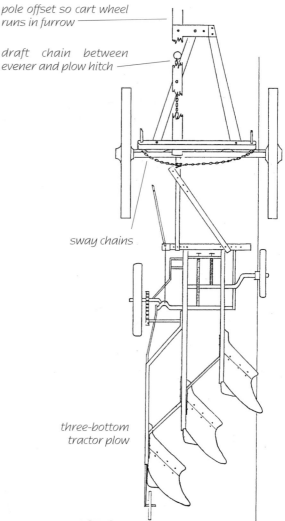

pole offset so cart wheel runs in furrow

draft chain between evener and plow hitch

sway chains

three-bottom tractor plow

A hitch cart for use with an engine plow. The wheel running in the furrow may be a rear wagon wheel, while the other is a front wagon wheel—helping keep the cart level while in the furrow.

Horses & Mules for Power & Profit,
Horse Association of America, 1928

A basic White Horse forecart pulling a drag-type double disc harrow.

Miscellaneous Indispensables

Features of a Forecart

With a basic forecart you can use horses to pull any non-hydraulic or non-power take off (PTO) driven implement. Many specialty forecarts have been developed to further adapt horse power to modern PTO and hydraulic machinery. Forecarts are available with engines, or with ground driven mechanisms, to provide power for machines that are PTO driven.

Most engine carts have hydraulic capabilities as well, with a hydraulic pump driven by the engine. Other ways of furnishing hydraulic power have been developed on forecarts without engines. A small hydraulic pump may be either hand-powered or electrically driven by power from a 12-volt storage battery, although the latter system is often mounted on the implement itself to allow its use with a basic forecart.

White Horse offers a line of ingenious non-motorized carts with different combinations of hydraulic features, all provided by ground driven pumps. These forecarts have remote hydraulic capabilities and are available with a standard three-point hitch, allowing many of the smaller three-point implements to be used with horses. Other three-point hitch forecarts have been built with

A Bartville Welding basic forecart pulling a corn planter; an electric 12-volt hydraulic pump mounted on the tongue, within reach of the operator, provides power for raising and lowering the planting units.

hand-cranked winches and hand-operated hydraulic pumps, as well as ground driven mechanical lifts.

Basic Forecarts

A basic forecart consists of a two-wheel unit featuring an expanded metal floor, roller bearing hubs, a drawbar with several hitch pin holes, and a spring mounted seat that usually swivels and may often be mounted in three different positions. Most manufacturers offer their carts with optional steel wheels or rubber tires, wood or steel tongues, or shafts, and a choice of mechanical, hydraulic, or no brakes.

Some forecarts have provisions for mounting the tongue on either side of the platform, as well as in the center. Single, double, or bench seats are available, and most carts may be ordered with hand-operated steerable wheels, making the cart more easily maneuverable when backing, as well easier to hold in position on a hillside.

A Gateway engine cart with a 20-horsepower gasoline engine, a 540 RPM PTO, and two pairs of remote hydraulic outlets.

Basic forecart made by Pioneer Equipment.

Light-duty forecarts are available for use with small manure spreaders, lawn mowers, and other light implements. In addition to pulling implements, the forecart may be used to train or exercise horses, or as just a cart for joyriding behind a favorite team.

Logging Carts

Standard field forecarts are often adapted for use as logging carts and, of course, many carts have been purpose-built for logging. The chief advantage of using a purpose-built logging cart over a field cart is that a logging cart (the subject of which is beyond the scope of this book) takes advantage of the cart's initial forward movement to lift the front of the log off the ground.

A Forest Manufacturing logging cart with a log in tow.
Photo by Larry DeJohn

Power Forecarts

Most horse lovers decry the noise and stink of an engine, and use horses to get away from all that, but the fact remains that some farm implements cannot work efficiently without the steady source of power offered by an engine. A PTO driven baler, combine, haybine, or even a mowing machine requires a constant speed on the PTO shaft to do good work and not become clogged.

Many formerly PTO driven implements have been converted to ground drive, and ground driven PTO carts have been built. Although they may be satisfactory when crop

and ground conditions are ideal, they're good for use only with light-duty machines such as rotary seeders, or hay rakes and tedders. A ground driven PTO forecart must be large and heavy to provide enough traction to keep the wheels turning and powering the PTO shaft. A huge amount of horse muscle is therefore needed just to pull the thing and keep the shaft turning, especially in heavy crop conditions. Every time the team is slowed—due to heavy or poor crop conditions, poor traction, an uphill pull, or fatigue—the ground driven PTO shaft slows as well, resulting in the the implement not working properly.

Engine powered forecarts are available with engine sizes from 20 to more than 100 horsepower. While most horse farmers would never have a need for the larger sizes, an 18- or 20-horsepower engine cart will furnish enough power to run a small square or round baler, a small pull-type combine, a 9-foot hay conditioner, or a 7-foot mower.

Most engine carts are equipped with foot operated hydraulic brakes and a brake lock for holding the cart in place when stopped. Hydraulic steering allows the cart to be easily maneuvered while on the go. Other features include remote hydraulic and electrical outlets, electric engine start, and a full range of gauges to monitor the condition of the engine and the hydraulic system. The engines, whether gasoline or diesel powered, are well muffled and run quietly.

Many horse farmers have built their own engine carts, often by adding a small gasoline or diesel engine to a basic forecart. Several manufacturers offer engine carts with many features in addition to a power take off shaft. Standard equipment on most power carts includes two to four two-way remote hydraulic outlets with quick-couplers, hydraulic brakes and steering, and

A Pioneer 25-horsepower gasoline engine cart used with a hay conditioner.

a method of hydraulically shifting the axle for front to rear load balance.

Pioneer PTO carts come with an adjustable stabilizer bar that attaches between the cart and the tongue of the drawn implement, converting the implement and cart into a single unit. The cart tongue is then unlatched, allowing

The rear view of a 41-horsepower Pioneer cart showing the operator's station. The seat and brake pedal are on the left side of the platform. To the right of the seat are the PTO clutch lever, the hydraulic control levers, and a console containing the gauges, below which are four remote outlets with a hose connected to one of them. In the center is a PTO shaft (connected, in this case, to a haybine).

Pioneer's stabilizer bar (lower center), with a clamp attaching the bar to the tongue of the pulled implement, effectively locks the implement and forecart together into a single 4-wheel vehicle.

it to steer the cart wheels, which become the front wheels of a four-wheel unit that steers and handles like an auto-steer wagon.

Hydraulic Forecarts

Many modern implements are equipped with remote hydraulic cylinders that lift and lower, or otherwise adjust certain components of the machines. Many other implements are of the three-point hitch type, and require not only a three-point hitch for attaching the machine to the forecart, but a means of raising and lowering the hitch arms as well. Most of the power carts described above have outlets that allow the hoses from remote hydraulic cylinders to be controlled from the cart.

A White Horse hydraulic forecart with hand lever steering and two pairs of double quick connect outlets for operating hydraulic cylinders on a drawn implement. The hydraulic fluid tank and accumulator are at the right of the platform.

White Horse offers several forecarts with ground driven hydraulic pumps. The first is a pretty much standard forecart, except it has a rotary hydraulic pump driven by roller chain from a sprocket on the furrow wheel. A hydraulic fluid tank and a pressure accumulator allow the system to build up and hold reserve pressure. This reserve pressure is monitored by a gauge and is available to lift an attachment when the wheels aren't turning. Two pairs of double quick connect hydraulic outlets operate remote cylinders on towed implements. This cart weighs about 670 pounds and is available with

A heavy duty diesel powered forecart made by Gateway, with a rotary tiller mounted on the cart's three-point hitch.

either a straight axle or hand-operated steering, and either steel wheels or rubber tires.

The second of the carts has the same hydraulic pump and accumulator system, along with the remote cylinder connections, but is also equipped with a category one three-point hitch. The 800-pound cart has a hydraulically powered tongue swing and a powered axle swing for front to rear load balance, and is capable of mounting any category one three-point implement not requiring a PTO.

A couple of four-wheel carts are available with three-point hitches. Cart Horse Machinery offers a small category one three-point hitch cart that may be equipped with either a ground driven or an engine driven PTO, with hydraulic lift that comes from a hand-operated or electrically driven pump.

Gateway makes a heavy-duty four-wheel cart equipped with a category two three-point hitch, available with an approximately 100-horsepower diesel engine. This machine can handle any PTO driven heavy-duty three-point implement.

Light-duty two-, three-, and four-wheel carts with three-point hitches and hand crank, mechanical, or electric hydraulic lifts are available from several manufacturers.

One big problem with three-point carts is the weight of the implement. Many of these implements are quite heavy and can easily unbalance a light-duty two-wheel forecart. The implements were designed for use with tractors that have a heavy engine sticking out in front to counter balance the weight of the raised three-point implement. Exercise extreme care when using such an implement with a forecart.

Operating a Forecart

Hitch a forecart to your team the same as any other wheeled vehicle. The drawbar may bear considerable weight, especially with an implement such as a loaded two-wheel manure spreader. This weight can put a lot of upward pressure on the end of the tongue unless you use some sort of compensation, such as a shiftable cart axle to balance the fore and aft load. A heavy three-point implement in the raised position can also unbalance the cart.

Basic Forecart

Use a basic forecart to draw an implement designed for a non-PTO tractor. Back the forecart into position so the tongue or hitch of the implement can be attached to the forecart's drawbar, usually with a hitch pin. The center of pull of the forecart is at the center hole of the cart's drawbar, which is where most implements should be

A basic forecart with hand lever steering pulling a spring tooth harrow.

Miscellaneous Indispensables

hitched. Drive the forecart into position in the field and adjust the implement for use by manipulating its levers. Since the levers were meant to be operated from a tractor seat, they usually may be operated from the forecart seat as well.

Use the forecart steering, if provided, to keep the implement in place on hillsides and to assist in making turns. Be careful to not turn so short the forecart's wheels hit the implement's tongue, or your cart may be upset. Be extremely careful when turning on a hillside, as a heavy implement can easily push a lighter forecart sideways, causing a wreck.

Power Forecart

When you buy a powered forecart, obtain detailed instructions from the manufacturer or dealer before attempting to use the machine. So many variables are involved in starting, operating, and maintaining the engines and hydraulic systems on these carts that it's impossible to cover them all here.

In general, hitch a power forecart to your team and drive it just like any other wheeled vehicle. When you don't need the PTO, use the cart just like a basic forecart. Since

you'll probably be pulling heavier loads behind your engine cart, give some thought to the number of horses necessary to handle the load.

When using the PTO, make sure your PTO speed matches that required by the implement. Most powered forecarts are equipped with 540 RPM PTO shafts, while some implements require 1,000 RPM to operate.

Align the cart drawbar hitch pin hole vertically with the centerline of the PTO shaft. The center of the drawbar hitch pin hole should be 14 inches to the rear of the end of the PTO shaft. The drawbar height should be between 13 and 20 inches, with 15 inches preferred, from the ground to the top of the drawbar.

The distance from the top of the drawbar to the center of the PTO shaft should be between 6 and 12 inches, with 8 inches preferred. This distance is adjusted by moving the PTO shaft support bracket on the implement.

Make sure the telescoping PTO shaft is firmly locked to the cart and implement PTO shafts to prevent disconnection during use. Make absolutely certain that all PTO shields are in place and that rotating shields are free to turn before operating the machine. Always use a safety hitch pin and make sure the safety pin is in place, to prevent uncoupling of the machine during use.

Avoid making extremely sharp turns with the PTO in gear, which puts undue strain on the driveline components; always disengage the PTO clutch before making sharp turns. When starting a PTO driven machine, engage the PTO clutch slowly and bring the machine up.

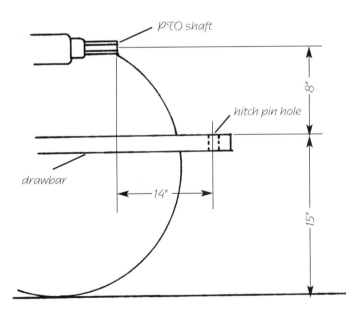

The center of the drawbar hitch pin hole should be 14 inches to the rear of the end of the PTO shaft. Drawbar height should be between 13 and 20 inches, with 15 inches preferred, from the ground to the top of the drawbar. The distance from the top of the drawbar to the center of the PTO shaft should be between 6 and 12 inches, with 8 inches preferred.

A Gateway 24-horsepower engine cart operating a 9-foot mower-conditioner in alfalfa.

☞ *Always* disengage the PTO clutch, turn off the engine, and put the key in your pocket, before dismounting from the forecart.

☞ *Never* attempt to adjust or clean out a PTO machine while it is running.

Hydraulic Forecart

Instructions for operating hydraulic forecarts should come from the manufacturer or dealer. In general, hydraulic forecarts are hitched and driven the same as any wheeled vehicle. Before starting, check the level of the hydraulic fluid in the tank and add oil as necessary.

Dirt is the biggest enemy of any hydraulic system. Before connecting hydraulic hoses from remote cylinders, make sure the cart's hose connections and quick connect outlets are wiped clean. After connecting the hoses to an implement, operate the hydraulic lever several times. If the lever or levers function in reverse, exchange the hose connections in the forecart quick connect couplers. Make sure the accumulator tank has pressure, or the hydraulic pump is running, and move each valve lever to the operating position through one full cycle to purge any air from the hydraulic system.

If you suspect, but can't see, a hydraulic oil leak, be extremely careful. *Do not use your hands to look for hydraulic oil leaks.* The oil is under high pressure and can penetrate your skin, causing serious injury. Use a piece of cardboard or wood to search for hydraulic oil leaks. If you find a leak, release the pressure on the system and repair the leak.

Three-Point Hitch Carts

Regardless of the method used to lift the three-point hitch arms, all implements designed for such a hitch are attached and adjusted in much the same way. To hook up to the implement, center the cart on, and back until the lowered lift arms are approximately in line with, the implement's connecting pins. Secure your team, dismount from the cart, and attach the link on one side by slipping the ball in the end of the lift arm over the implement connecting pin and inserting the lynch pin. Attach the other link in the same way, raising or lowering it by the screw adjustment in the lift link as necessary to line up with the pin.

Attach the center top link. Level the implement from side to side by adjusting the screw type lift links.

In the field, adjust the side to side levelness of the implement as required by means of the screw-type lift links. Make front to rear adjustments by shortening or lengthening the screw-type top center link. These adjustments are especially important if you are using a three-point hitch plow, as the bottoms must run level from side to side, even though the cart is at an angle due to one wheel running in the furrow. The plow must be leveled front to rear as well, to keep the plow from running nose down or nose up.

Three-Point Hitch Trailers

Several manufacturers make a separate tool carrier, or trailer, which may be used as an adjunct to a forecart. The trailer is a wheeled frame with a three-point hitch that allows a three-point implement to be used with a forecart that lacks a three-point hitch.

One version has a hand lift and is intended for use with light-duty three-point implements. Another version

An I&J forecart pulling an I&J three-point tool carrier on which is mounted a 4-foot double disc harrow.

White Horse three-point hitch trailer cart with a spring-tine weeder attached.

features a hydraulic lift and hydraulic drawbar swing, and must be used with a forecart with remote hydraulic capabilities. This machine allows the use of any category one three-point implement that doesn't require a PTO drive.

Hitch a three-point hitch tool carrier to the forecart drawbar and centered on it. Connect remote hydraulic hoses exactly as for a hydraulic forecart. Attach and adjust a three-point implement the same as with a three-point hitch forecart.

Tongue Trucks

A tongue truck operates a little like a forecart, except the wheels are smaller and set closer together, while the operator rides on the regular implement seat. And a tongue truck is usually an integral part of the implement.

Tongue trucks are often used with horse-drawn mowers, grain binders, disc harrows, corn planters, corn binders, potato diggers, and even dump rakes. Most two-wheel horse drawn machines are designed with the seat sticking out behind the axle, thus allowing the operator's weight to help offset the weight of the implement on the horse's shoulders. A tongue truck is used to reduce this weight on the horses, but has other important benefits as well.

To do their best work, many of these implements require a specific and constant position in relation to the ground. Once the machine is adjusted properly, a tongue truck supports the front and maintains this critical operating position without regard to the team's natural movement. The tongue truck eliminates variations in implement operating position caused by different sized

A mower equipped with a tongue truck. The mower's stub tongue is attached to and supported by the truck. The evener clevis is attached to the stub tongue and the long tongue serves only to steer the machine.
1940 John Deere catalog

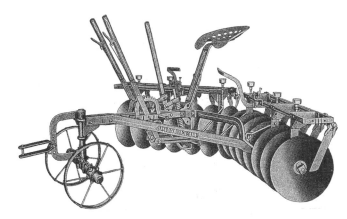

A disc harrow equipped with a tongue truck, but no pole.
1928 John Deere catalog

A dump rake equipped with a tongue truck.

Photo by Pat Hansen

Forecarts

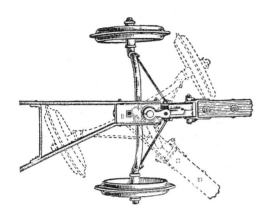

A binder truck, showing how the tongue steers the machine while being free to pivot up and down, thus eliminating the implement's weight on the horses. This method of steering is common to all tongue trucks except the caster type. *1928 John Deere catalog*

teams. The length of the traces, as well as the adjustment of the breast straps, may be made to best suit the load, without worrying about any effect on the implement's optimum operating position.

On some implements with stiff poles, particularly those with considerable side draft, such as corn and grain binders and mowing machines, the use of a tongue truck eliminates the sore shoulders caused by the whipping of the tongue against the horses. The tongue truck is bolted to a stub tongue so it supports the front of the implement. The pole is then attached to the truck in such a manner that it steers the wheels and guides the implement as the team turns. The evener is usually attached directly to the truck itself, or the stub tongue, and the pole is used only to steer the device.

A tongue on a disc harrow makes discing hard on the horses, due to the twisting and bucking of the implement which whips the pole against the team almost constantly. For this reason, a disc harrow may be equipped with a tongue truck, thus relieving the team of neck weight and any side draft, as well as eliminating the necessity for the team to pry the disc

around when turning. On a disc harrow, a front truck is often used without a tongue. In this case, the evener is attached to a clevis that steers the truck wheels. A tongue attached to the truck, however, gives the team much more leverage for turning the disc at the corners.

A tongue truck usually consists of two 15- to 20-inch steel wheels set fairly close together on a flexible frame that allows the wheels and axle to pivot horizontally, as well as to swivel to the right or left. The horizontal pivot feature allows the truck to follow the ground and keeps the wheels steady and the implement tracking properly.

Some implements, such as corn planters, may be furnished with a caster-type tongue truck, which usually has a single wheel mounted at the center

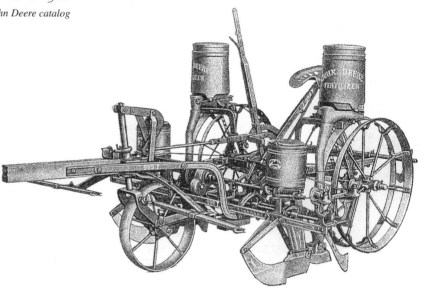

A corn planter with a caster wheel supporting the front. The tongue freely slides up and down on the vertical pipe attached to the caster wheel fork, thus removing weight from the team. *1928 John Deere catalog*

front of the machine beneath the tongue. In this arrangement, the front wheel supports the front of the planter and the tongue, although it is attached to and steers the planter, is free to move up and down, relieving the horses of weight while assuring the planter stays level for uniform planting depth and check pattern. The wheel is mounted as a caster, allowing it to follow the machine as it is steered by the team.

A White Horse forecart with a ground driven hydraulic pump and accumulator tank, valves, and gauges to give it remote hydraulic capabilities, operating a three-point hitch cart and two-bottom mounted plow.

20

Spreaders

"Yet sprinkle sordid ashes all around, and load with fattening dung thy fallow ground." *Virgil, Roman poet who lived from 70 to 19 B.C.*

The idea of using manure to make soil more fertile is an ancient concept, yet early American farmers, reveling in the rich virgin land they found as they moved into the Midwest, were slow to take advantage of it. Starting in the 19th century American agriculturalists began emphasizing the benefits of putting manure on fields to increase yields. Eastern farmers, whose fields were small and had already been run down, heeded the advice and hauled their manure in carts and wagons, spreading it by hand. Hand spreading was slow, hard work and the results weren't satisfactory, since the manure tended to be thrown out in chunks instead of being pulverized and evenly distributed.

Some feeble attempts were made from 1850 to 1875 to perfect a manure spreader, but nothing much came of them until J.S. Kemp of Magog, Quebec, Canada, developed a practical machine patented in the United States on May 1st, 1877. A year later the Kemp and Burpee Manufacturing Company was formed in Syracuse, New York, to build the new spreader, but the machines, being totally new to the American farmer, were slow to be accepted, especially west of the Mississippi River.

In the vast wheat fields of the plains, where early settlers believed the deep, rich soil could never be depleted, manure spreader salesmen grumbled, "Those farmers out there don't know what manure is for." But after years of growing the same crop without putting anything back into the soil, even this fertile land began to return smaller and smaller yields. Spreading manure on such large acreages by hand was impossible, due to time constraints and the huge amount of labor required, and the wheat grower looked for a way to conserve his manure supply and spread it economically.

A modern Pequea ground driven manure spreader with an endgate.

A 1903 ad for Kemp & Burpee's manure spreader claimed it rapidly and evenly spread all kinds of manure, lime, salt, ashes, and compost regardless how hard, lumpy, caked, coarse, strawy, or stalky. The Ohio Farmer, August 27, 1903

Miscellaneous Indispensables

Manure Spreaders

As improvements were made to spreaders and they were sold in larger and larger numbers, farmers everywhere saw advantages in the thorough pulverization and even spreading of manure by machine. Today manure spreaders are available to fit any operation, and range in size from 25-bushel ground driven up to 200-bushel power take off driven models.

Features of a Spreader

A manure spreader consists of a bed or box mounted on a suitable two- or four-wheel chassis to provide transportability. A moving conveyor chain on the bottom carries the load of manure slowly and uniformly to the rear, where it is acted upon by the beaters. On a ground driven spreader, the beaters and conveyor are powered by the rear wheels; the PTO shaft provides power on power take off driven machines.

The conveyor consists of a flat chain at each side of the bed, between which are mounted a series of angle iron cross slats. In operation, these slats move along the floor of the bed and carry the load of manure to the rear. The conveyor drive on most spreaders has several different speeds so the rate of application may be varied. The sides of the bed are wider at the rear than at the front to prevent the load from becoming wedged. At the open rear of the bed is one or two revolving beaters, or toothed cylinders, that tear the manure into small fragments.

Behind the beaters is a revolving distributor, or widespread, with several spiral auger-like blades, or

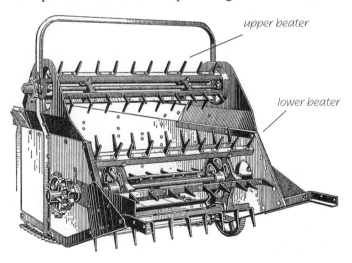

upper beater

lower beater

The rear of a typical manure spreader showing the revolving beaters that tear up manure and throw it back onto the distributor.   *New Idea Farm Equipment Co.*

paddles. Half the blades are inclined toward the right, and half toward the left, and the distributor spins much faster than the beaters. The beaters throw the shredded manure back against the distributor blades, which further reduce the manure, and throw and spread it evenly over a strip about seven- or eight-feet wide.

At the front of the machine are two hand levers. The left one is the drive lever that engages and disengages the main drive chain and the large drive sprocket, which powers the beater and distributor mechanisms. The other, the feed lever, activates the conveyor chain drive and sets the application rate by controlling the conveyor speed.

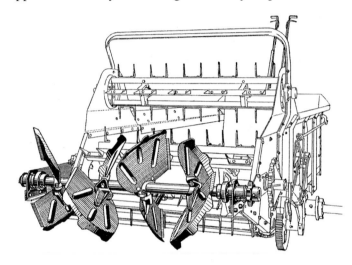

The distributor blades are arranged to throw manure evenly over a wide area.   *New Idea Farm Equipment Co.*

Spreader Draft

The draft of a ground driven manure spreader varies greatly with the type of manure being spread, the condition of the soil surface, and whether the machine has steel wheels or rubber tires. A study made many years ago reported the draft of a 60-bushel steel wheel spreader on corn stubble was 530 pounds when loaded, 428 pounds at the end of the load, and 160 pounds when out of gear. No mention is made of whether the manure was wet or dry. The same source recommended two horses for a 50- or 60-bushel machine, two or three animals for a 70-bushel, and three or four horses for a 100-bushel spreader.

Hitching a Spreader

Hitch a four-wheel manure spreader the same way you would a wagon. A two-wheel spreader must be used behind a forecart. The forecart drawbar should be about 15 inches from the ground, and the spreader should be hitched in the center hole. A loaded two-wheel spreader puts a lot of weight on the drawbar. Be careful on steep slopes, especially if the ground is muddy, as the spreader's weight can push the much lighter forecart sideways, causing a jacknife and possible wreck.

Operation and Care

The manure spreader is one of the most abused implements on the farm. Spreaders are often left out in the weather with little effort made to clean or lubricate them properly. The acids in manure are extremely corrosive; they rust metal and rot wood in a short time if the spreader isn't regularly cleaned and oiled. The boxes, or at least the floors, on many modern spreaders are made of a polyplastic material, which is impervious to manure acids, although the steel parts are not.

Thoroughly lubricate the entire spreader before each use. Grease all pressure fittings and oil the chains and all the other moving parts. Lubricate the spreader twice a day if the machine is used all day. If you use your spreader infrequently, lubricate it before each use. Besides pressure greasing all fittings, oil all minor moving parts. Regular and thorough lubrication of a PTO spreader is more critical than ground drive, due to the faster speeds of moving parts.

Ground Driven Manure Spreaders

Before using your manure spreader, unless it's brand new, carefully check the following items to ensure the machine is ready for use.

Bed—Check all nuts and bolts for tightness, and replace any that are missing. If the bolt heads have been drawn into the wood far enough to cause splintering, remove the bolts and place washers under the heads before replacing the bolts. Replace broken or rotted boards to prevent the conveyor chain from catching.

Conveyor—The upright leg of the angle iron drag bars should lead, or be toward the rear of the machine. Instead of running hook forward, as is required on all drive chains, the conveyor chains should be run with the bar forward (toward the rear of the machine) and the slots out, because the conveyor chain doesn't drive anything, but rather is driven. Check to see that the drag bars are straight and closely follow the floor. Make sure the conveyor chains have the same number of links on each side, and the drag bars don't run askew on the sprocket wheels. Adjust the conveyor tighteners so you can lift a conveyor drag bar about eight inches from the floor at the center of the bed.

To prolong the life of the conveyor, clean it periodically with a solution of lime and water to neutralize the manure

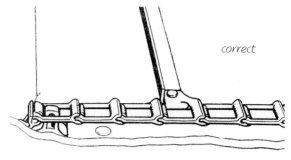

correct

direction of conveyor chain movement toward rear of spreader

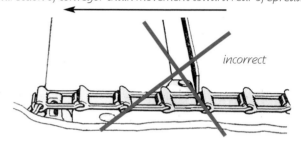

incorrect

The upright leg of the angle iron drag bars should lead, or be toward the rear of the machine, and the conveyor chains should be run bar forward (toward the rear of the machine) and slots out. *New Idea Farm Equipment Co.*

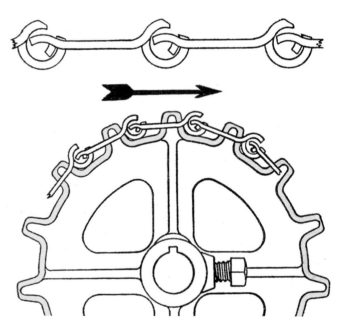

Install drive chains with the hooks forward, or toward the direction of travel, and the slots facing outward away from the sprocket. *New Idea Machinery Co.*

acids. After cleaning, thoroughly coat the chain and bars with oil.

Beaters—Check to see that the cylinder teeth are not bent. Remove any accumulation of binder or baler twine

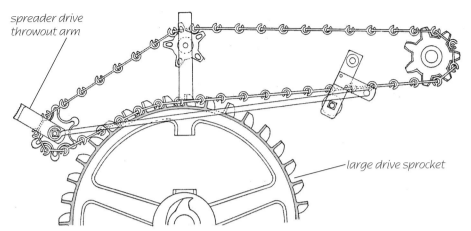

spreader drive throwout arm

large drive sprocket

Install the main drive chain so the open side of the links face upward on the large drive sprocket. Most older spreaders are similar, but some later spreaders use a roller chain in place of the open flat link chain.

New Idea Machinery Co.

that may have wrapped around the beaters or the shafts. Clean out the gear and chain shields at the sides of the beaters. Make sure the beater drive chain is clean and oiled, and is installed with the hooks forward (in the direction of rotation) and the slots facing out. Clean chains by soaking them in kerosene or diesel fuel, and then coating them with oil.

Distributor—Check for a bent distributor shaft and loose or bent blades. Straighten or replace blades as needed. See that the distributor drive chain is clean, lubricated, and installed correctly. Run chains tight enough to stay on the sprockets under load, but not so tight as to cause excessive wear to the chain, sprockets, and bearings.

Drive—Check the ratchet pawls and springs inside each rear wheel hub to see that both wheels transmit full power. Replace broken springs and replace badly worn pawls or

build them up with weld. Check the wheels for excessive end play and make certain the feed cam lines up with the feed arm roller, and the main drive sprocket lines up with the drive chain. Place shim washers where needed. See that the chain is clean, lubricated and installed correctly.

Feed—The conveyor chain is operated by a lobed cam on the right rear spreader wheel. The cam activates a roller equipped feed arm, which in turn moves a ratchet wheel through a ratchet and pawl system. The ratchet wheel turns the conveyor chains at the speed determined by the position of the feed selector lever.

Check the adjustment of the feed mechanism by placing the feed lever in the neutral notch on its quadrant. The tips of the lobes on the feed cam should just clear the feed arm roller. Adjust by moving the collar on the rear of the control rod from the lever.

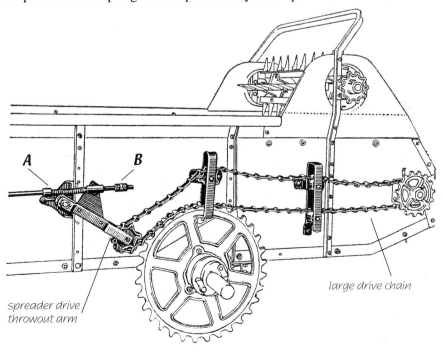

A

B

spreader drive throwout arm

large drive chain

*Adjust the collar **A** to provide enough spring tension on the spreader drive throwout arm to hold the main drive chain tight against the large drive sprocket when the drive is engaged. Adjust the collar **B** so the chain is lifted out of engagement with the sprocket when the drive is disengaged, and is held taut enough to not flop into and catch on the sprocket teeth.*

New Idea Farm Equipment Co.

Adjust the spring tension on the main drive chain so when the drive lever is in the engaged position, the chain will be held firmly against the main drive sprocket. With the lever in the disengaged position, the chain should be taut enough not to flop up and down, allowing it to accidentally engage the sprocket.

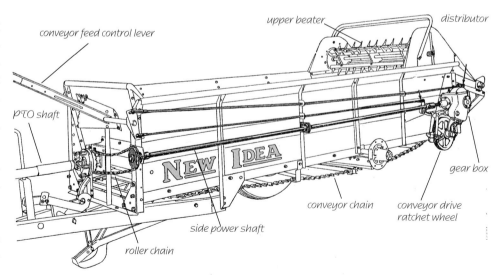

To check the adjustment of the feed mechanism, place the feed lever in the neutral notch on its quadrant. The tips of the lobes on the feed cam should just clear the feed arm roller. To adjust, move the collar on the rear of the control rod.   New Idea Equipment Co.

Field Operation

Before each use, thoroughly lubricate the entire spreader. Grease all pressure fittings. Oil the chains and all other moving parts. If you use your spreader all day, lubricate it again at midday.

Before starting to load your spreader, make sure the feed is disengaged. If the feed is engaged when you start the loaded spreader, something will break. Start loading at the front of the spreader and work to the rear, rounding off the load at a height that will pass under the rear arch. Don't pack any manure into the beaters, which could prevent the

beaters from starting easily and cause damage to the spreader drive mechanism.

When you are in the field and ready to start spreading, *stop* the spreader before engaging the drive lever. Engaging the lever while the machine is in motion can cause the chain or sprocket to break. After engaging the main drive, set the feed lever to the desired application rate and start driving at a steady pace. At the end of the load, when the upper cylinder no longer takes manure, shift the feed lever into the fastest feed position and run the machine until the bed is empty, at which time disengage the drive and then the feed.

Always make certain the feed is disengaged. If the feed is left engaged when you put a new load into the bed, as soon as you start the spreader to the field, the key in the ratchet wheel will shear or some other part will break.

After Use

If you leave your spreader outside, park it so the rear end is lower than the front, allowing any water to drain out. In freezing weather don't leave any manure in the spreader bed. A conveyor frozen to the bottom in manure or ice will damage the drive mechanism when the feed lever is engaged.

Thoroughly clean out the bed and treat the conveyor chains and bars with a lime solution to neutralize acids from the manure.

The power train of a PTO driven spreader (with the safety shields and left wheel removed for clarity).   New Idea Farm Equipment Co.

Miscellaneous Indispensables

Occasionally remove the drive chains, clean them in kerosene or diesel fuel, and coat them with oil. Lubricate the entire machine and store it under cover.

PTO Drive Manure Spreaders

With a PTO spreader the power comes from an engine power take off, and not from the spreader's wheels. The engine driving the PTO may be mounted directly on the spreader tongue or, more often, carried on a forecart to which the spreader is hitched. The PTO shaft from the engine ends in a sprocket at the front of the spreader. A roller chain transmits the power from the front sprocket to another on the end of a drive shaft running back on the left side of the spreader box. This side shaft ends in a gear box from which the beaters and conveyor chain are driven.

A power take-off driven spreader in operation behind a motorized forecart.

Other than the transmittal of power, PTO manure spreaders are identical to two-wheel ground driven versions. All the same instructions apply to PTO driven models, except as noted below.

Hitching a PTO Spreader

Position the center hole of the forecart drawbar ahead of the manure spreader hitch clevis and use the spreader jack to align the clevis with the drawbar. If your spreader has its own mounted engine, keep in mind that the engine will add to the tongue weight of the spreader. The drawbar of a motorized forecart should be 15 inches from the ground. Use a drawbar pin of large enough size to handle the load, and secure it with a lynch pin.

Attach the spreader drive shaft universal joint to the engine PTO shaft, making sure it locks into place. Make sure the PTO shaft guard is in position. PTO spreaders are usually of the two-wheel trailer type and, when loaded, put a lot of weight on the forecart's drawbar. Although a motorized forecart is much heavier than a basic cart, the weight of a heavy load of manure can still push the cart sideways, especially when turning on hilly, wet ground.

Field Operation

Loading a PTO spreader is the same as with a ground driven machine; start at the front and don't pack manure into the beaters. When you reach the spreading location, stop your team. Start the engine, set the throttle to the desired engine speed, and slowly engage the engine PTO clutch. Engage the beater and conveyor drive clutches and set the feed rate. On the popular New Idea spreader, a single feed lever engages both clutches when moved out of its topmost notch. Other machines have separate clutch levers.

Drive forward at a steady pace. To clean out the bed when the load is finished, disengage the beater drive clutch and increase the conveyor speed to its highest feed rate. On a New Idea spreader increasing conveyor speed is accomplished by placing the feed lever in its bottom notch, which disengages the beater and the distributor, while the conveyor continues to run at its highest speed. When you are finished, disengage the feed conveyor, then disengage the engine PTO clutch and shut off the engine.

A PTO spreader is cared for the same as a ground driven machine, although regular and thorough lubrication is more critical, due to the faster speeds of moving parts. The gear box contains heavy oil and should be checked and kept full.

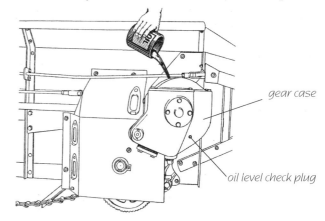

gear case

oil level check plug

Periodically check the oil level in the gear case at the check plug; if the level falls below the plug add #90 transmission oil.   *New Idea Equipment Co.*

Lime and Fertilizer Distributors

Besides air and water, plants need a number of chemical elements for normal, healthy growth. Chief among these elements are nitrogen (nitrates, ammonia), phosphorus (phosphates), and potassium (potash). For maximum utilization, the elements need to be taken into the plant through the roots. While these elements occur naturally in soil, continuous cropping can deplete them to the point that crop yields are drastically reduced. While the application of manure is one way of restoring soil fertility, commercial fertilizers containing nitrates, phosphates and potash became available by the end of the 19th century.

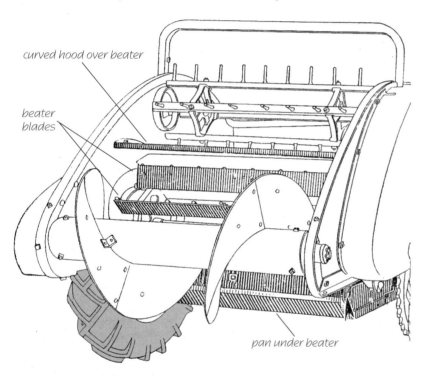

curved hood over beater

beater blades

pan under beater

Basic lime spreading attachment.

Another product that needs to be periodically applied to the soil is lime. While lime is not actually a plant food, it is classed as an indirect fertilizer, and is just as essential to healthy plant life as nitrogen, phosphorus, and potassium. Most crops grow and produce best in soil that is neutral (neither alkaline nor acid) or just slightly acid. Soil that has been depleted of its lime content by poor drainage or constant cropping produces plants that are stunted, yellow, and sickly. Such soil is said to be sour or acid and can be improved by the application of lime.

Most fertilizer is applied at the time the seed is planted, although top-dressing young plants, especially with nitrate

or ammonia, is often beneficial. Today this application usually takes the form of liquid nitrate or ammonia, and requires specialized equipment, while lime is usually spread by large, truck-mounted spreaders.

During the early 20th century, lime and fertilizer distributors were developed to make possible the uniform spreading of the correct amount of material per acre. These distributors, or spreaders, are usually ground driven.

Features of a Distributor

Several methods are available for applying lime and dry fertilizer. Most producers of horse-drawn manure spreaders offered an optional lime spreading attachment. Endgate spreaders were made that attached to the rear of a wagon and were driven by a chain from one rear wagon wheel. Funnel shaped spreaders with electric, PTO, and ground drive are also available. These spreaders are all of the broadcast type and drop the material to be spread onto one or more rapidly rotating horizontal disks that throw the material over a wide strip of ground. Many manufacturers also offered a drill type spreader that resembles a grain drill and drops the material through a series of holes directly onto the ground.

Manure Spreader Attachments

Lime spreading attachments for manure spreaders haven't been sold for a long time, but some are still out there. They are of two different types.

Deere & Co. The simplest attachment consists of horizontal steel blades bolted onto the main beater teeth, a curved sheet metal hood over, and a pan under the main beater. In operation, the feed conveyor on the bottom of the box carries the lime into the main beater. The pan underneath keeps the material from falling to the ground, while the blades on the beater teeth throw the lime, guided by the upper hood, back onto the spiral distributor blades. The distributor throws the material in a wide, even layer behind the machine. The rate of application is controlled by the speed of the feed conveyor.

Spreaders based on New Idea use a more elaborate arrangement. A cross shaft is mounted beneath and a little to the rear of the main beater. To drive the cross shaft, the chain is switched from the upper beater to a sprocket on the left end of the shaft. A pair of short vertical shafts above the cross shaft are driven by two pairs of bevel gears. On the upper end of each short shaft is a dished, horizontal disk with four upright slingers. A tine rake is located just in front of the main beater, and a removable endboard is just in front of that.

In operation, the spreader box is loaded with lime, which is prevented from running out the rear by the endboard. For spreading, the endboard is removed and hung on the side of the box, and the feed conveyor and beater are put into gear. The tine rake assists the main beater in feeding the material onto the tops of the two disks. These disks rotate at high speed and fling the lime in a wide even layer behind the spreader. The rate of application is regulated by the speed of the feed conveyor.

New Idea's more elaborate lime spreading attachment.
New Idea Farm Equipment Co.

Endgate Spreaders

The endgate spreader is mounted on a board that takes the place of a wagon rear endgate. The small end of a galvanized, tapered metal hopper ends above one or two horizontal metal disks that can be flat or dished with several upright slingers attached. The disks are rotated at high speed through a series of bevel gears and a ratchet clutch from a small sprocket on one end of a cross shaft.

The small sprocket is driven by a flat open link chain from a large sprocket attached to one of the rear wagon wheels. The operator keeps the hopper full of material by scooping from the load carried on the wagon. An agitator feeder in the bottom of the hopper feeds the material onto the tops of the spinning disks, which throw it out behind the wagon in an even layer.

An endgate lime or fertilizer spreader.
Agricultural Machinery by J. Brownlee Davidson

Drill Spreaders

A drill-type spreader drops the lime or fertilizer in rows, or drills. A long wooden or steel hopper is supported on a low wheel at each end. The hopper has a tightly fitted cover or lid, under which are full length screens to screen out lumps and debris when the machine is being filled.

A ratchet clutch in each wheel hub drives an agitator shaft that extends lengthwise through the narrow bottom of the tapered hopper. Fingers are spaced at intervals along the agitator shaft to prevent bridging, and to loosen and force the material into the feeds.

The feeds are a series of holes spaced along the bottom of the hopper, which may be closed or regulated by means of a lever or levers. The material falls from the feed holes onto an adjustable scatterer board that is hinged to the bottom of the hopper. The board may be raised or lowered so the material spreads evenly and is

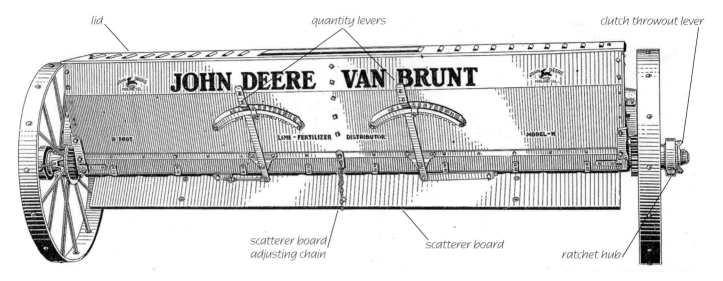

lid quantity levers clutch throwout lever

JOHN DEERE · VAN BRUNT

8 FOOT LIME · FERTILIZER · DISTRIBUTOR MODEL-H

scatterer board adjusting chain scatterer board ratchet hub

A typical lime and fertilizer spreader.

Deere & Co.

Funnel Style Spreaders

Several manufacturers make ground driven spreaders with a steel, funnel shaped hopper mounted on two wheels. At the bottom tip of the funnel is an adjustable gate, below which is a horizontal disk with upright slingers. The wheels drive the disk at high speed through a series of bevel gears.

In operation, the hopper is filled with material and the gate is set for the desired application. As the spreader moves forward, the lime or fertilizer drops onto the rapidly spinning disk which throws it out in an even layer.

A Nordagri funnel spreader in action.

Operating a Distributor

The operation of all lime and fertilizer distributors is similar in that the box or hopper must first be filled with the material being spread. The spreader is then driven to the location where spreading will start, the feeding and/or spreading mechanism is engaged, and the team is driven at a steady pace until the material is spread.

Manure spreaders with lime attachments should not be overloaded. The endboards, or the beater covers, provided with these attachments usually have a line or lines marked on them to designate the maximum height of the load. Regulate the rate of application by using the feed lever, the same as for spreading manure.

Before starting an endgate spreader, put the ratchet clutch into gear, usually by means of a hand lever. Set the rate of application to the desired amount. Fill the hopper with material and start your team. Keep the hopper filled by scooping the lime or fertilizer from the wagon bed.

The hopper of a funnel spreader is filled with material, and the quantity lever is set for the desired application rate. The disk drive is then engaged and the team is driven across the field.

To use a drill type lime and fertilizer spreader, the material should be loaded through the screens that are in place on the top of the hopper. These screens prevent lumps and other objects from becoming wedged in the agitator, which could result in damage to the feeder parts. Set the quantity levers to the desired rate of application. Engage the ratchet clutch in each wheel hub and drive forward. Adjust the scatterer board so the material spreads evenly.

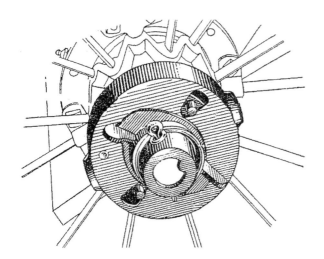 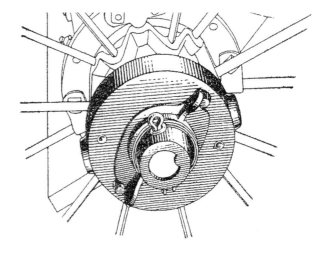

Clutch throwout lever in gear (left) and out of gear (right).   *Deere & Co.*

Lubrication and Care

Lubricate all moving parts at least twice a day. Make sure any enclosed gear boxes are filled with oil. Do not leave fertilizer or lime in the hopper overnight. On a damp night, in just a few hours such material can harden to the point that freeing up the feed mechanism becomes extremely difficult.

At the end of the season thoroughly clean out the spreader. Use kerosene to dissolve any hardened material. Coat all moving parts with oil and store the spreader inside in a dry place.

A 10-foot EZEE Flow fertilizer distributer puts down a thin layer of granulated fertilizer. The log dragged along behind marks the edge of the fertilized ground for the next round.   *Photo by Bud Henderson*

21

Farm Vehicles

Some historians feel the discovery of the wheel and axle is one of the most important developments in the annals of mankind. Certainly the use of wheeled carts and wagons has eased the labor of farmers all over the world from ancient times to the present. Two-wheel carts were probably the first haulers and are still used extensively in many countries, although they are not popular in the United States.

By the middle of the 19th century, American wagon builders had the benefit of generations of experience in building wheels, gears, and boxes, resulting in a vast array of four-wheel wagons that were strong, lightweight, and versatile. Wagons became available for every purpose from delivering milk in New York City to carrying a pioneer family and all their possessions across the Rocky Mountains.

A typical wooden wagon gear with a grain box.　　Electric Wheel Co.

Primitive cart.

A heavily loaded wagon moving over uneven ground puts a huge amount of strain on the supporting parts. Carefully selected, seasoned, and split, not sawn, hickory and white oak were used for axles, while well-seasoned black birch was best for wheel hubs. Felloes and spokes, sand boards, hounds, reaches, and tongues were fashioned of oak. High grade wrought iron was used for the irons and tires that held everything together and protected moving parts from wear.

By the end of the 19th century, all-steel wheels were available for wooden wagon gears. The steel wheels were considerably smaller in diameter, had a much wider tire than their wooden counterparts, and provided lighter draft and less rutting of fields and roads, as well as lowering the wagon bed so it was easier to load. Nevertheless, many farmers didn't believe steel wheels would hold up as well as wooden wheels.

With the growing popularity of tractors and the resulting higher speeds, all-steel wagon gears with auto-steering became available in the 1920s, and by 1950 most farm wagons had all-steel running gear and rubber tires.

As great as wheeled vehicles are, some situations call for a sled or other sliding load carrier. Such conveyances are especially suitable for use over snow-covered ground.

A wooden wagon gear with steel wheels.

Electric Wheel Co.

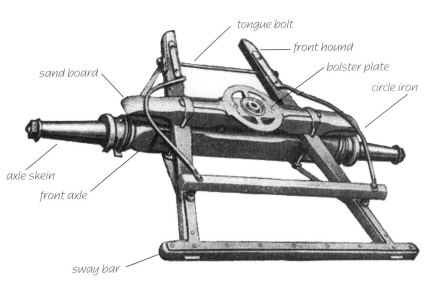

All-steel running gear with auto-steer and rubber tires.   New Idea, Inc.

Wagons

Dozens of different styles and sizes of wagon have been built to cater to every hauling need, from heavy-duty six- and eight-wheel log wagons to light one-horse buckboards—the horse farmer's version of the pickup truck. A basic farm wagon consists of two parts, the *running gear* and the *bed*.

Running Gear

The running gear is made up of the front and rear axles and wheels, along with a *reach* to connect the rear axle to the front, and a *tongue* to which the pulling power is hitched. The front wheels are steerable, and rear wheel brakes are available on some models. Parallel to, and above, each axle is a cross beam called a *bolster,* which provides a support for the bed or for the load itself. A vertical *bolster stake* at each end of the bolster keeps the wagon box or bed from sliding sideways on the bolster.

Diagonal braces, called *hounds,* run from the outer ends of the rear axle forward to the *reach socket.* Older wagons with fifth-wheel steering use a front hound arrangement, usually with a *sway bar* a couple of feet behind the front axle. The front hounds run diagonally forward from the sway bar ends, between the axle and *sand board*, to which they are firmly attached, to a point in front of the axle where the tongue is attached. The front axle, sand board, hounds, and sway bar function as a single unit, and pivot on the *king bolt* as the wagon is steered by side pressure on the tongue.

A wooden wagon gear with steel wheels and no brakes.   Electric Wheel Co.

Rear view of a wagon front gear fifth-wheel assembly. The king bolt goes down through the front bolster (not shown), the hole in the bolster plate, the sand board, the front end of the reach, and the axle. The tongue pivots on the long tongue bolt between the front ends of the hounds.   Deere & Co.

On a modern auto-steer wagon the front hounds run diagonally back from the outer ends of the front axle to the reach. The reach on most wagon gears has a series of holes at the reach socket that allow the overall length of the gear to be extended or shortened as desired to fit beds of different sizes.

Farm Vehicles

Beds

Hundreds of different beds have been built on wagon gears for as many different hauling tasks. The most common ones in use today include grain boxes, flat beds, hay racks, bale throw racks, and hay baskets.

Grain Box

The original wagon grain box was built of wood in a standard 36-inch inside width. Boxes for light wagons were about 20-inches deep and 10-feet long. Medium size was 10-feet 6-inches long, and 24- or 26-inches deep. A heavy box was 28-inches deep and 10-feet 6-inches long.

Flat Beds

Many wagon gears are equipped with an all-purpose flat bed. A flat bed wagon may be used to haul just about anything on the farm, including bags of fertilizer or grain, fencing material, machinery, or bales of hay or straw.

A flat bed is usually built in the farm shop and consists

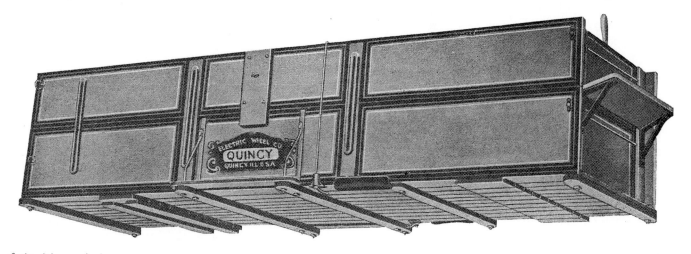

A double grain box.

Electric Wheel Co.

To provide more capacity, a second box of the same size may be added on top of the main box, making a double-box wagon. A third, or tip-top box of 9- or 11-inch depth may be added as well, making a triple-box wagon.

A tongue-and-groove floor and iron edges and grain angles on the side and end boards make the box grain-tight. The tail gate is hinged in the middle and may be easily removed for dumping. An extended shovel or scoop board at the rear makes the load easier to shovel off.

Most grain today is hauled in gravity wagons. The bottom of the all-steel box of a gravity wagon is sloped on three sides to form a chute. A sliding door at the bottom of the chute at one side of the box allows the wagon to be easily unloaded. A large hand wheel operates a rack and pinion arrangement that lifts the door to allow a variable unloading flow of the load into an elevator hopper.

A gravity wagon showing the chute and handwheel for unloading.

250   Miscellaneous Indispensables

A flat bed being loaded with corn stalks to be chopped for feed.   *Photo by Ruth Freeman*

of tongue-and-groove flooring laid lengthwise on cross sills, which are supported on the wagon gear bolsters by two heavy lengthwise stringers. The bed is typically 8-feet wide and 14- or 16-feet long. Steel stake pockets often are attached to the ends of the cross sills and along the front and rear of the bed so side and end boards may be added.

Hay Rack

Where hay is put up loose instead of baled, a hay rack, sometimes called a hay ladder, is a popular item. The grain box is lifted off the wagon gear and the hay rack put on in its place.

Standards at the front and rear increase the capacity for loading loose hay.   *Photo by Michael J. Lacivita*

The hay rack typically is lower than a flatbed to allow easier loading and often has spaces between the boards forming the floor to reduce its weight. A pair of tall ladders, or standards, stand upright at the front and rear of the rack to help hold a larger load of hay. Hay racks usually are home built on the farm and are of many shapes and sizes.

Bale Throw Rack

To save the labor involved in picking up bales behind a pickup baler, a flat bed wagon may be hitched behind the baler. A chute at the rear of the bale chamber pushes the bales up to a person riding on the wagon, who grabs the bales from the chute and stacks them on the wagon.

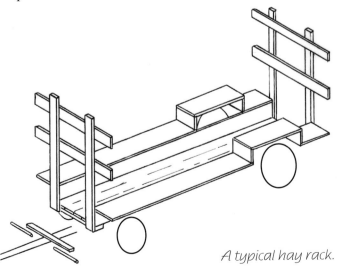

A typical hay rack.

To eliminate the need for a second person on the wagon, balers with bale ejectors have become popular. An ejector hydraulically throws each completed bale to the rear in a high arc. A wagon bed with sides high enough to catch the bales as they are thrown back is known as a bale throw rack.

The bale throw rack is basically a flat bed of wooden planks, 8- or 9-feet wide by 16- or 18-feet long, to which has been added high sides and a rear end gate made of pipe or light box section steel. The sides are 7- or 8-feet high, and catch the bales and drop them into a pile on the wagon floor.

Across the front a low endgate, about 3-feet high, prevents the bales from rolling out the front but is low enough to allow the bales to be thrown over into the rear of the bed. Gates on each side and at the rear allow for unloading the bales.

An E-Z Trail Farm Wagon hay basket.

A typical bale throw rack wagon.

Hay Basket

Although technically not a wagon, a hay basket collects small square bales while being pulled behind a pickup baler without a bale ejector. The hay basket is a large V-shaped basket made of lightweight box-section steel. The basket is carried on two wheels at the point of the V and a dolly wheel at the front.

An angled steel chute at the front receives the bales as they are pushed out the rear end of the baler's chamber. The force of the baler plunger pushes the bales up the chute and drops them into the basket. The rear of the basket is hinged at the top with a catch at the bottom which, when released, allows the bales to tumble out for unloading. The typical hay basket holds nearly 100 full-size bales.

If you use a hay basket, reduce the spring tension of the bale chamber somewhat. Otherwise the extra friction involved in pushing the bales up the ramp will make your bales too tight.

Wagon Draft

The draft of a wagon depends on three main variables. The first variable—especially on an old wooden wagon—is *axle friction*. This friction has been drastically reduced by the use of modern high-speed roller bearings and is rarely considered today.

The second factor is *rolling resistance,* and is dependent on how deep the wheels sink into the surface of the ground. A narrow-tire wheel on soft ground sinks farther into the surface than a wide-tire wheel on dry ground, and forces the team to constantly pull the wagon up an incline. Wide steel wheels offer less rolling resistance than narrow steel tires, while correctly inflated rubber tires provide even more flotation on soft ground and roll much easier.

As you might expect, *grade resistance* is the third factor that greatly influences draft. As a load is pulled up a hill, the weight of the load must be lifted at a rate proportional to the grade's steepness.

The University of California made tests in the 1920s to determine the influence of road surface on the draft of a standard farm wagon. The test wagon and load weighed three tons, had 38-inch front and 46-inch diameter rear wheels, and 4-inch wide steel tires. The total draft on level roads varied from 789 pounds on loose gravel to 83 pounds on concrete. Increasing the tire width to 6 inches resulted in reduced draft on soft surfaces, except where the soil was

Miscellaneous Indispensables

sticky and soft on top and firm underneath. Larger diameter wheels also reduced draft. The tests were made before rubber tired wagons became common.

Operation and Care

Each time you use your wagon, first check the wheels to make sure they are sound and in good order. On a rubber-tire wagon, check the tires for correct air pressure; under-inflated tires increase draft and may cause tire failure under a load. At least once each year, go over the entire wagon running gear and bed.

● Check all welds for cracks, and reweld as needed.

● Be sure gravity boxes are firmly bolted to all four stakes. A loaded gravity box is top heavy and can easily be toppled off the running gear if not securely bolted.

● Remove the wheels and repack the wheel bearings with high temperature grease. Take up endplay in the bearings.

● Check the steering mechanism for free operation. The front wheels of an auto-steer wagon should have a little toe-in when the tongue is centered. This can usually be adjusted by shortening or lengthening the threaded steering tie rods.

● Check any unloading doors for ease of operation and proper latching.

● Replace or repair any badly worn or damaged parts.

Any time you haul fertilizer or any other corrosive material in the steel bed of a gravity wagon, wash out the inside of the box afterward. Store your wagons under shelter if possible. If you have to leave a wagon outside, open the tailgate or the side unloading door so water can drain out.

Non-Wheel Vehicles

Before the invention of the wheel, and for many centuries after, crude sleds, sledges, travois, and similar vehicles were popular. Such load carriers are distinguished by the use of wooden runners to support all or part of the load and are cheap and easily made by the user. Work sleds are being manufactured today, and are handy for many farm hauling jobs. Bobsleds, work sleds, and stone boats are the most common types of sled found on modern horse farms.

Bob Sled

Bob sleds are popular in northern climates that have a significant snow cover for long periods of time. The bob is constructed of two wooden runners, usually shod with iron or steel strips. These runners, with their turned up front ends, may be made of either naturally bent tree limbs, or

An all-wooden bobsled, probably homemade; check out the width of the planks used for sideboards.

sawed or bent lumber. The runners are connected by wood, iron, or steel knees to a framework that holds the bob together and carries the load.

Bobs are usually used in pairs corresponding to the front and rear gears of a wagon, and are connected by a reach. The front bob is pivoted so it may be steered by the tongue. Front and rear bolsters and stakes are usually added to allow winter use of a regular wagon box on the bob sled. Just like on a wagon gear, almost any type of bed may be built on a bob sled gear.

Bob sleds are meant to be used on snow and ice. The depth and consistency of the snow, as well as the width and bend of the runners and the weight of the load, all affect the draft.

A team can handle almost any load you can put on a sled, provided they can start it. Carry a bar for starting the load when the runners get frozen tight. A team that can't start a stuck load may become discouraged and balky. Sometimes starting the load at an angle to the desired direction of travel is enough to get it unstuck.

A bob sled used on hilly terrain should be equipped with some sort of brake to help hold it back when going downhill, and to hold the sled in place when stopping while going uphill. A chain attached to the front of the runners may be let down to drag beneath the runners, where it acts as a brake to slow the sled. Another kind of brake consists of a lever-operated spike rigged on the sled so it can be forced into the snow to act as a brake.

If you use your bob sled on or near a salted road, rinse off the runners and other metal parts before storing it.

Store your bob sled under cover to prevent rotting of the wood and rusting of the steel parts.

Work Sled

A work sled is a low, flat bed conveyance with wood or metal runners and can be used to carry various loads on ice, snow or bare ground. A sled can also be used to train and condition horses, mules or oxen.

Tillers International of Kalamazoo, Michigan, made draft measurements on a sled with two runners 9 feet long and 4 inches wide. The sled and its load totaled 1000 pounds and resulted in a draft of 379

A homemade all-wood work sled.   Photo by Mark Wooddall

Modern work sled built by Pioneer Equipment.

pounds on a gravel road, 419 pounds on firm sod, 576 pounds on firm soybean stubble, and 635 pounds on a freshly seeded oat field. The narrow runners of a sled cut into soft ground and increase the draft.

If a work sled is used on snow or ice, the same concerns about braking are present as with a bob sled. On bare ground, there is usually enough friction that braking is not a problem. In soft ground, short turns are often difficult because the runners cut deeply into the soil. In these cases, wide, gradual turns should be made.

> **Ideal Training Aid**
> A work sled or stone boat is ideal for training young horses, mules, or oxen, especially those with a surplus of energy. Just load on sufficient weight and put them to work.

Stone Boat

A stone boat is made with a heavy timber bed, the underside of which slides on the ground. The bed is only a few inches above the ground, so heavy stones easily may be rolled onto the boat. Manufacturers once sold heavy cast-iron or steel stone boat noses with holes for the hitch and for bolting on the wooden bed. Some stone boats have a turned up nose at each end, so they may be pulled in either direction.

A stone boat usually has less draft than a sled on soft ground, as the broad flat bottom provides more flotation and less friction than the typically narrow runners of a sled. Tests at Tillers International found that a 1,000-pound stone boat, 8-feet long and 35-inches wide, had the following drafts on different surfaces: gravel road, 382 pounds; firm sod, 460 pounds; soybean stubble, 459 pounds; newly seeded oat field, 485 pounds.

A manufactured stone boat with a cast steel nose.   *J.S. Woodhouse Co.*

The operation of a stone boat is pretty straightforward. Hitch your animal or team to the end in which direction you intend to pull, add the load and make sure it's secure and won't fall off, then go. In a situation where the boat tends to stick and not start moving, hitch the team at an angle to the boat. When the team starts, the angle should pivot the boat and break it loose from the soil.

A flat bed being used to haul square bales from the field.   *Photo by Bonnie Nance*

Glossary

acre. A plot of land containing 43,560 square feet, 4840 square yards, or 160 square rods.

acre meter. A mechanical land measuring device that keeps track of the number of acres seeded by a grain drill.

A-harrow. An early form of spike tooth harrow, made of wood with spikes driven through it and shaped like a large letter A so that, when pulled from the pointed end, it slides around the many stumps in newly cleared land without catching.

arbor bolt. The square axle on which harrow discs are mounted; also called a gang bolt.

arch. A frame member on a cultivator that straddles a row and to which a pair of gangs attach.

auger. A screw-shaped device inside a sheet metal tube used to move grain.

axle. A rod upon which a wheel turns.

back furrow. In plowing, the slightly raised ridge that occurs when two furrows are thrown toward each other while opening up or completing a land.

baler. A machine that compresses hay or straw into a dense, compact, round or rectangular shape and then holds it while it's tied with wire or twine.

baling chamber. The enclosure in a hay baler in which the hay or straw is compressed before being tied.

baling wire. Lengths of iron wire, usually with a preformed loop at one end, used to tie bales of hay, straw, or other material after being compressed in a baler or press.

bale bumper. A device on a large round baler that rolls an ejected bale away from the baler, allowing the rear door to be closed without interference from the bale.

bale throw rack. A high, open framework built around the sides and ends of a flat wagon and designed to be towed behind a small square pickup baler equipped with a bale thrower, so the rack catches and contains the thrown bales.

bale unroller. A device that allows a large round bale to be pulled along the ground so it may be unrolled.

bale wrap. Plastic film used to wrap large round or square bales.

bale wrapper. A machine for wrapping large round or square bales with plastic film.

baler twine. Heavy plastic or sisal twine used to tie bales of hay or straw after being compressed by a baler.

band cutters. Reciprocating knives on a thresher that cut the twine bands around sheaves of grain before they enter the cylinder.

band seeding. A method of placing seed and fertilizer in the ground so there is a narrow band of fertilizer adjacent to, but not touching, the seed.

bang board. A board placed along one side of a wagon to make it high enough to intercept thrown ears of corn.

base. A plow bottom.

beam. The part of a plow to which the bottom is attached at one end and the pulling power at the other.

bill hook. The heart of the knotting mechanism on a corn or grain binder, or a twine tie baler, the function of which is to grasp and turn the ends of the twine to form the knot.

binder trip. A lever on a grain or corn binder that, when moved by the weight of the accumulating stalks of the bundle, starts the tying operation.

binding deck. The angled sheet metal or wooden deck on a grain binder that supports the incoming stalks until enough have accumulated to make a sheaf, or bundle.

bob sled. A vehicle for use in snow that consists of two short sleds, or bobs, connected by a reach and steered by a tongue on the front bob.

bolster. A cross piece above each axle on a wagon that supports the wagon box or other load.

bolster stake. The vertical stake at each end of a wagon bolster that holds the wagon box or other load in position.

bottom. The collective parts of a moldboard plow consisting of the share, moldboard, landside, and frog; also called the base.

bottom suction. The action of a plow being drawn into the ground due to the end of the plow share's point dipping slightly downward.

breast plate. The curved plate on a binder's tying mechanism that protects the knotter from being damaged by the completed bundle being ejected.

broadcast seeder. A device used to drop or scatter seeds onto the soil's surface.

buckrake. A sweeprake.

bullrake. A sweeprake.

bull wheel. A large, cleated wheel used to furnish the power to drive the mechanism of an implement, such as a grain binder.

bundle carrier. On a corn or grain binder, a cradle, usually consisting of a series of long steel fingers, that catch and carry the tied bundles as they come from the tying mechanism.

bundle elevator. On a corn binder, the apparatus that collects the tied bundles as they come from the tying mechanism and elevates the bundles to a wagon pulled alongside the binder.

bundle stripper. Two or three steel rods attached to the outer end of the breast plate on a binder, the function of which is to strip the ejected bundle from the discharge arms.

butt board. On a grain binder, a vertical board at the front of the binding deck against which the cut ends of the grain stalks ride to assure the bottom of the bundle is flat and even.

butter. A butt board.

cart. A load-carrying vehicle with two wheels.

center of draft. The center of the load to be pulled, for example the center of draft of a 14-inch two-horse

walking plow is about 2 inches in from the landside and directly under the middle of the plow beam; also called the center of load, or center of resistance.

center of load. The center of draft.

center of power. A point midway between the inside hame hooks of a two horse team, or at the center of the middle horse's collar on a three horse team.

center of resistance. The center of draft.

chaffer. A thresher's conveyor sieve that assists in cleaning grain.

chain harrow. A harrow consisting of steel rods joined together by chain links to form a square flexible mat.

check board. On a thresher or combine, a hanging device, usually made of wood or canvas, that deflects grain thrown back by the beater.

check-row planting. A method of planting corn in hills at regular intervals from each other, resulting in a checkerboard effect that allows cross cultivation.

chisel plow. A primary tillage tool with a series of rigid curved or straight shanks equipped with relatively narrow shovel points, the function of which is to stir, pulverize, and loosen the soil without inverting it, as would a moldboard plow.

choking down. The condition that occurs in a grain or corn binder that accumulates a bundle too large to tie and eject from the tying mechanism.

closed-end harrow. A spike tooth harrow with guard rails at the ends of the sections.

combination harrow. A spring tooth harrow with a raker bar, or a harrow with a gang or gangs of discs, followed by a gang or gangs of spring or spike teeth.

combine. A grain harvesting machine that cuts, threshes, and cleans the crop in a single pass.

coulter. A sharpened device that slices vertically through the soil just ahead of a plow bottom.

cover board. A curved attachment bolted to a plow beam or standard, just above the moldboard, that throws the top layer of the furrow slice into the bottom of the furrow; also called a trash board.

covering wire. A piece of heavy wire fastened to a plow ahead of the bottom and dragged in the furrow to fold high vegetation down into the furrow where it will be easily covered.

crown. The top of a plowed furrow.

crown wheel. A large sprocket attached to the inside of the bull wheel of a grain binder, the function of which is to drive a heavy chain that powers the binder.

cultipacker. A roller-pulverizer made of a number of heavy V-shaped steel wheels mounted next to each other on a common axle, the function of which is to roll, pulverize and mulch the soil in a single pass.

cultivator. Any implement used to loosen and pulverize soil without turning it over as in plowing, usually with the object of destroying growing weeds.

cutter bar. The tapered flat steel bar on a mower to which all the parts of the cutting mechanism are connected; or the knife, guards, and other parts that make up the cutting mechanism of a grain binder, combine, or hay mower-conditioner.

cylindrical reel rake. A side-delivery rake with four or six bars equipped with spring teeth, arranged so the hay being raked moves along the front of the reel and comes off the trailing end in a loose roll.

dead furrow. In plowing, an open furrow occurring when two furrows are thrown away from each other while completing a land.

dial hitch. A rod hitch.

disc cultivator. A secondary tillage implement that uses rotating discs, rather than shovels or sweeps.

discharge arms. Arms on the tying mechanism of a grain or corn binder that rotate and kick the tied bundle away from the knotter.

disc mower. A mower that cuts with knives on fast-moving whirling discs and is unsafe for horse farming.

disc plow. A primary tillage implement that uses one or more rotating discs in place of moldboards to turn the furrow.

double disc harrow. A harrow with a second set of gangs behind the first, with the discs set to throw the soil toward the center; also called a tandem disc harrow.

double run feed. A grain drill force-feed mechanism consisting of a two-sided feed wheel, one side for large seeds and the other for small seeds, with a flap-type valve to direct seeds to the appropriate side.

draft. The power required to accomplish work, formally measured in units of horsepower; also, a horse or other animal used to provide pulling power.

draft iron. The part of a rod or dial hitch attached about 18 inches back on a plow beam and extending to the front of the beam.

draft link. A drag link.

drag. Two or three overlapped planks held together by cross members and used to level soil and crush clods.

drag bar. On a mower, the heavy, angled brace that goes from the cutter bar yoke back to and underneath the left rear of the frame.

drag link. A short rod with a hook at each end that connects a spring tooth harrow section to the evener.

drag harrow. A spike tooth harrow.

draper. One of the canvas-and-wood slat conveyor belts on a grain binder or combine that carry the cut grain from the cutter bar to the binding deck or the threshing cylinder.

drawbar. A steel bar, usually with a series of holes, at the rear of a forecart for coupling to an implement.

drill. A row of planted grain; also, to plant grain in a row.

drills. Evenly spaced rows of seeds planted by a grain drill.

dump rake. A series of curved spring steel teeth on a straight frame between two large, light wheels, the function of which is to gather hay as the rake moves forward and dump the accumulated hay in a windrow when the teeth are raised; also called a sulky rake.

endgate seeder. A broadcast seeder mounted on the rear of a wagon or cart.

evener. A combination of levers, such as doubletrees and tripletrees, or a system of ropes and pulleys that connect a team to a load so each animal bears a proportionate amount of the load.

fan blinds. On a thresher or combine, adjustable devices used to regulate the amount of air the cleaning fan blows across the cleaning shoe.

fertilizer distributor. A device for broadcasting agricultural lime or granular fertilizer.

field cultivator. A wheeled implement with teeth or shovels for preparing a seedbed, incorporating fertilizer, or destroying weeds.

finger guards. Pointed iron or steel fingers projecting ahead of the knife of a cutter bar, the function of which is to gather and hold the standing crop while it's being cut by the knife, and to protect the moving knife sections from damage.

finger wheel rake. A side-delivery rake with a series of large wheels set at an angle to the direction of travel, with spring steel fingers around the circumference of each wheel that gather and move the hay into a windrow.

fishbacks. On a thresher, the sawtooth projections above the oscillating straw rack that aid in moving straw to the rear over the rack.

fixed chamber baler. A big round baler with a series of rollers surrounding the bale chamber; also called roll baler.

fluted feed. A grain drill force-feed mechanism consisting of a fluted feed roll, feed cutoff, feed cup, and adjustable gate for each row.

forecart. A wheeled cart to the front of which the horses are hitched, and to the rear of which is a drawbar for attaching an implement, with a platform and seat between the wheels on which the driver rides, and from which both the team and the drawn implement are controlled.

fore truck. A tongue truck.

frog. The foundation of a moldboard plow on which the share, moldboard, and landside are mounted, and which attaches the bottom to the plow's beam or standard.

furrow horse. The horse in a plowing team that walks in the previously made furrow.

furrow opener. A hoe, shoe, or single or double disc on a planting device that makes a trench in the soil to receive seeds.

gang. A set of couplings, beams, shanks and cultivator shovels, plow bottoms, or discs operating as a unit.

gang bolt. The square axle on which harrow discs are mounted; also called an arbor bolt.

gang plow. Any plow with two or more bottoms.

gathering boards. On a corn binder, the two wooden boards that angle downward and taper to iron points at the front, one of which travels on each side of the row of corn stalks.

gathering chains. On a corn binder, the chains with projecting fingers that gather the corn stalks and guide them into the knife.

gauge wheel. An auxiliary wheel that runs along the ground near the working parts of an implement to keep those working parts in correct relationship to the ground.

gavel. A bundle of cut grain stalks that has not yet been tied into a sheaf.

grade resistance. The resistance offered to a wheeled vehicle by a hill or other upward grade in the surface of the ground.

grain drill. A machine that opens a series of evenly spaced small furrows or trenches, places grain seeds in those trenches, then covers the seeds with soil, resulting in evenly spaced rows known as drills.

grain wheel. A small wheel on a grain or corn binder that supports the end of the machine opposite the bull wheel and runs next to the unharvested grain.

grass board. A board fastened at an angle to the outer shoe at the end of a mower's cutter bar that helps move the cut hay away from the uncut grass, leaving a cleared strip so the mower won't clog on the next round.

grass stick. A stick bolted at an angle to the inside of a mower's grass board to help the grass board lay the cut grass into a neat, flat swath.

ground drive. A method of powering the mechanism of an implement by using the turning force of one or more of the wheels that support the machine.

groundhog thresher. A crude early thresher consisting mainly of a spiked cylinder and a concave, so named because its profile resembled a groundhog.

gumbo. Fine, silty soil that becomes sticky when wet.

harrow. An implement used to stir and level the soil, crush clods, and destroy weeds.

harrow cart. A light two-wheel cart that attaches to a spike or spring tooth harrow, allowing the operator to ride in the dust rather than walk (in the same dust).

hay baler. A device for compressing hay into round or square bales for easy transport and storage.

hay fork. A device, usually used in conjunction with a rope and pulley and track and carrier system, to lift a large amount of loose hay and move it to a place of storage.

hay ladder. A light framework, often with ladder-like vertical standards at front and rear, mounted on a wagon gear and used for carrying a large amount of loose hay; also called a hay rack.

hay loader. An implement with a revolving cylinder that picks up loose hay from the swath or windrow and elevates it up a sloping deck to where it may be loaded on the wagon behind which the loader is towed.

hay mow. The part (or parts) of a barn where loose hay is stored.

hay press. An early name for a hay baler.

hay rack. A hay ladder.

hay rake. A machine for raking hay or straw into windrows.

hay sling. A system of ropes or cables arranged on the bottom of a hay wagon, on top of which hay is loaded and then unloaded by drawing together the ends of the sling around the hay and lifting the whole thing by a rope and pulley system.

hay tedder. A machine that lifts and fluffs hay to facilitate drying prior to baling.

headlands. The two ends of a field that are plowed or planted last and perpendicular to the primary furrows or rows, allowing room to turn the implement at the ends of the furrows or rows.

heel. The rear end of a plow's landside; also, a plow share's outside corner; also called the wing.

high-lift plow. A sulky plow with a frame and three wheels.

hill-drop planting. A method of planting corn in groups of seeds spaced at regular intervals along the row.

hillside plow. A moldboard plow with its moldboard and share shaped like an arrowhead that swivels underneath the frame so the plow can be set to throw the furrow to either the right or the left.

hitch. The part of an implement to which the draft animals are attached; also, the draft animals providing the pulling power.

hitch cart. A forecart.

hitch pin. A heavy steel pin that connects the tongue of a pulled implement to the drawbar of a forecart.

hook and link chain. A drive chain consisting of flat square or rectangular, open links made of malleable iron or steel, in which a hook that is part of one end of each link engages the opposite end of the next link.

hound. An angled brace that reinforces some part of a wagon running gear.

jointer. A miniature plow that cuts a small furrow of soil just above and a little ahead of the main plow bottom, throwing this furrow into the main furrow to aid in covering all vegetation.

king bolt/pin. On a wagon, the heavy vertical pin that connects the front axle, front of the reach, and sand board to the front bolster.

knife clip. On a cutter bar, the part that holds the knife section close to the ledger plate to maintain a shearing action; also called a knife holder.

knife guard. On a cutter bar, the portion that protects the knife, divides the grass being cut, and holds the ledger plates in position.

knife harrow. A harrow similar to a single disc harrow, but with curved stationary knives or cutters instead of discs, the two gangs of which may be angled to provide more aggressive action of the knives.

knife holder. A knife clip.

knife register. On a mower, the position of each knife section in relation to the guards.

knife section. On a cutter bar, the sharpened triangular blades fastened to the knife to form the upper half of the shear cut.

knotter. On a corn or grain binder, or a twine tie pickup baler, the device that ties the knot

ledger plate. On a cutter bar, the sharpened plate, attached to the knife guard, that forms the bottom stationary half of the shear cut.

left-hand plow. A plow that throws the furrow slice to the left.

lag. On a mower, the distance of the outer end of an idle cutter bar behind the inner end (the opposite of lead).

lands. Sections of a field that are plowed out sequentially.

landed beam. A plow beam that is bent toward the furrow's land side.

land roller. A weighted cylinder rolled over the ground to crush clods and firm the soil.

landside. The vertical part of a moldboard plow bottom that runs against the furrow wall to offset side pressure from the turning of the furrow slice by the moldboard.

land suction. The action of a plow being drawn into the ground due the share point being slightly angled toward unplowed ground.

lead. On a mower, the distance of the outer end of an idle cutter bar ahead of the inner end (the opposite of lag).

line of draft. An imaginary line running from the center of load through the point of hitch to the center of power; also called line of hitch.

line of hitch. The line of draft.

low-lift plow. A frameless sulky plow with its wheels and axles attached directly to the beam.

low-till farming. A planting practice in which disturbance of the soil prior to planting is kept to a minimum.

manure spreader. A machine with a box for holding manure, a conveyor chain for moving the manure to the rear of the box, and various combinations of shredders and paddles to spread the manure in a thin layer on the ground.

moldboard. The curved extension of a plow bottom that turns and pulverizes soil cut by the share.

no-till farming. A practice in which no seedbed preparation precedes planting.

offset disc harrow. A disc harrow operated to one side of the pulling power, used primarily in orchards.

open-end harrow. A spike tooth harrow with no guard rails at the ends of the sections.

overshot stacker. A machine for stacking hay, onto the forks of which hay is unloaded and then raised by a horse-powered system of pulleys and cables, dumping the load on top of the stack.

packers. On a grain or corn binder, the curved reciprocating arms that pack incoming grain stalks into a bundle for tying.

packer shaft. The crank-shaped shaft that operates the packers on a binder.

parallel bar rake. Similar to a cylindrical reel side-delivery rake, except the raking bars are mounted differently on the spiders, resulting in the teeth moving the hay with less agitation than with the cylindrical reel model.

pawl. A mechanism that allows rotation in only one direction.

peg tooth harrow. A spike tooth harrow.

pickup baler. A hay baler equipped with a pickup mechanism to gather a windrow of hay or straw from the ground and feed it into the baling chamber.

pintle chain. A heavy-duty drive chain with open links joined by separate pins.

pitch. Action of a moldboard plow that throws surface trash far enough to remain uncovered on the surface instead of being buried in the furrow.

pitman. A wooden or metal bar that connects a crank or pitman wheel to a cutter bar knife, or any similar bar that converts the rotary motion of a wheel into a reciprocal, or back and forth, motion.

planker. A wooden drag made of two or more planks lapped over each other lengthwise, and used to level soil and crush clods.

plow pan. A layer of soil just beneath the usual plowing depth that can't be penetrated by moisture or plant roots; also called plow sole.

plow sole. Plow pan.

point. The forward portion of a plow share that penetrates the ground.

pole. A tongue.

power take-off. A revolving shaft, usually equipped with two universal joints to provide flexibility, that uses power from an engine or ground driven device to drive the mechanism of field and other machines.

primary tillage. The initial operation to turn or loosen the soil to prepare it for planting.

PTO. Power take-off.

PTO shield. A metal, or more commonly plastic, shield to prevent anyone from becoming entangled in a power take-off shaft and being injured.

pulverizer. A cultipacker.

raddle. The conveyor chain on a thresher that moves grain into the cylinder or straw to the rear.

raker bar. A straight steel bar with a row of straight steel tines.

raspbar. The corrugated crossbars used on the cylinders of most combines in place of teeth.

Raydex. Oliver's trademark name for a plow bottom with a replaceable share.

reach. A wooden or steel beam connecting a wagon's rear axle to the front axle.

reciprocating knife/blade. A knife or blade that moves back and forth in a linear motion.

reel tedder. A machine that uses a revolving toothed reel to kick cut hay, loosening it for quicker drying.

register. On a mower, the position of each knife section in relation to the guards.

rig. A gang, as on a cultivator.

right-hand plow. A plow that throws the furrow slice to the right.

rod hitch. A hitch with a draft iron or rod attached to the beam about 18 inches back from the front, with the front end of the rod adjustable horizontally by rotating a support attached to the front of the beam; also called a dial hitch.

rod weeder. A cultivator with a horizontal rotating square bar run a couple of inches below the surface of fallow ground to uproot weeds.

roll baler. A fixed chamber round baler.

rolling coulter. A round sharpened blade mounted just ahead of a plow bottom to both slice through surface trash and make a vertical cut in the soil, reducing draft by starting the separation of the furrow slice from the unplowed land.

rolling landside. A smooth-surface wheel that runs in the furrow behind some plow bottoms to take up the side thrust against the furrow wall.

rolling resistance. The increased draft of a wheeled vehicle from the weight of the vehicle, the terrain over which it move, and the friction of the wheels on the axles.

roll timing. Timing the rolls on a corn picker so the projections on one fit into the recesses in the other.

rotary hoe. A secondary tillage tool consisting of two gangs of rimless wheels (hoes) with curved teeth.

rotary rake. A side-delivery rake with a series of horizontal arms revolving around a central hub, with steel spring teeth hanging down from each arm that rake hay into a windrow.

rotary tedder. A machine with one or more sets of revolving arms equipped with spring teeth that, as the arms revolve, kick and toss cut hay to promote drying.

round baler. A machine that rolls and compresses hay or straw until it reaches a given size, then wraps the bale with twine, netting, or plastic wrap.

row marker. On a planting implement, a device that marks the soil's surface to ensure that succeeding rows are parallel and an equal distance apart.

running gear. A wagon's assembly of wheels, axles, bolsters, reach, and tongue.

RPM. Revolutions per minute.

runner teeth. The curved teeth at the corners of a spike tooth harrow on which the harrow rides during transport.

running in. The tendency of a plow to be forced toward the furrow wall because of side draft.

running out. The tendency of a plow to be forced toward the open furrow because of side draft.

sack seeder. A style of hand-carried broadcast seeder that holds the seed in a canvas bag.

sand board. On a wagon, the cross timber that sits atop the front axle, forming the top of the reach pocket and holding the bottom half of the fifth wheel.

scoop board. On a grain wagon, a flat gate that may be let down level with the rear of the wagon bed while shoveling off a load.

scour. Action of a plow whereby the soil slides over the share and moldboard without sticking.
scratch furrow. A shallow furrow used as a marker.

screen. On a thresher or combine, a flat screen over which grain, chaff, and bits of straw pass while a blast of air through the screen blows away the chaff and straw, or without a blast of air, through which weed seeds and other particles smaller than grain fall while the grain passes over.

secondary tillage. Any operation undertaken to smooth and level plowed soil, pulverize clods, firm the soil, or to destroy weeds.

separator. A thresher.

shafts. The light parallel poles on a one-horse vehicle or implement that are attached to the harness on each side of the horse; also called thills.

share. The cutting edge of a plow bottom, usually easily removed and replaced.

sheaf. A bundle of cut grain stalks tied with twine, wire, or straw.

shear. Action of a cutter bar on which the parts are adjusted so every knife section rests smoothly on the ledger plate of a guard and is held by knife clips and wearing plates, ensuring a clean, smooth cut; also called shear cut.

sheave. A grooved pulley wheel for use with rope, chain, or cable.

sheaves. More than one tied grain bundle (sheaf), or more than one grooved pulley (sheave).

shield. An attachment used between a cultivator shovel or sweep and emerging plants to prevent thrown soil from covering the plants; also a safety cover over a PTO attachment.

shin. The vertical front edge of a plow's moldboard.

shoe. On a mower, a runner supporting each end of the cutter bar.

shock. A group of grain sheaves or bundles stood together on their butt ends and, often, covered with one or two sheaves laid flat to deflect rain.

shocker. A person who arranges grain bundles into shocks.

shovel. A wide, flat point at the business end of a cultivator.

shovel board. A scoop board.

sickle bar. The combination of knife, guards, and knife clips on a mower, mower-conditioner, or grain binder.

side-delivery rake. A rake that leaves a long, continuous windrow to one side of the machine.

side draft. An increase in a plow's resistance because the team is hitched to one side of the line of draft.

sieve. On a combine or thresher, a flat section containing a series of holes of a certain size that, as the threshed grain and straw passes over, the grain drops through while the straw moves on.

single disc harrow. A harrow with two gangs of discs placed end to end and set to throw the soil away from the center.

singletree. A bar of wood or steel with a hook at the front of each end to which the traces of a draft animal's harness are hooked, and a ring or hook at the center rear to which a load is attached.

slip clutch. A spring loaded device designed to protect moving parts on a machine by slipping in case of a blockage.

slitter. A subsoil plow.

slugging. The clogging that occurs if too much grain is fed into the cylinder of a thresher or combine.

smoothing harrow. A spike tooth harrow.

snout. On a corn picker, one of a pair of corn ear gathering points.

soil surgeon. A style of knife harrow.

sole. On a mower, the replaceable and adjustable bottom part of the inner or outer shoe that helps regulate the height of cut.

spiders. The discs mounted on a threshing cylinder's shaft that hold the raspbars, or the crossbars, that in turn hold the teeth; also the discs at each end of a cylindrical or parallel bar side-delivery rake that hold the toothed crossbars.

spike tooth harrow. A harrow with a series of stationary spiked teeth to stir the soil; also called a peg tooth harrow, drag harrow, or smoothing harrow.

spring tooth harrow. An implement with several staggered rows of spring teeth that are dragged over the ground to loosen the soil and uproots weeds.

spring tine. A curved cultivator or harrow shank made of spring steel.

square baler. A pickup baler that makes rectangular shaped bales.

standard. On a plow with a straight beam, the vertical member that attaches the frog to the beam; on a hay wagon, a pair of tall ladders, standing upright at the front and rear of the rack to help hold a larger load of hay.

stationary baler. A hay baler in a fixed position, into which the material to be baled is fed by hand and compressed by power provided by a horse or a belt driven by an engine.

stone boat. A heavy sled made of timber with a turned up front and the bed only a few inches above ground level so heavy stones may be easily rolled on.

straddle-row cultivator. A wheeled carriage mounted with gangs of shovels that cultivate up to four rows at a time.

straw rack. One of several moving devices that carry straw to the rear of a thresher or combine.

straight-through design. In a baler or combine, a design that gathers the crop at the front and carries it straight to the rear into the baling chamber or the threshing cylinder.

stripper rods. On a dump rake, the horizontal rods running to the rear between the curved raking teeth that, when the teeth are raised to dump, force the hay from the teeth.

stubble. The short, lower stalks of a harvested crop left standing in the field.

subsoiler. A subsoil plow.

subsoil plow. A heavy-duty plow with a narrow point designed to penetrate deeply and break up hard pan.

suction. The action of a plow being drawn into the ground by the design of its bottom.

sulky. A two-wheel vehicle with a seat.

sulky plow. A single bottom, wheeled riding plow.

sulky rake. A dump rake.

sway bar. On the front gear of a wagon, the cross piece that connects the rear ends of the two front hounds.

sweep. A wing-shaped point at the business end of a cultivator.

sweeprake. An apparatus with a series of long, slender wooden teeth, sometimes pointed with iron and spaced about a foot apart on a frame, that when pushed ahead of a team or between two horses, gathers and carries loose hay.

tandem disc harrow. A double disc harrow.

tailings. In a threshing machine or combine, any trash and unthreshed heads that drop through the chaffer extension and are transported via the tailings elevator to the cylinder for rethreshing.

tedder. A hay tedder.

tier wheel. The toothed wheel on the knotter of a grain or corn binder or a pick up baler that operates the bill hook, twine knife, and twine holder.

thills. Shafts.

throat spring. On a corn binder, a long flat spring that holds the incoming corn stalks into contact with the gathering chains.

three-point hitch. A system for connecting an implement to a forecart or trailer that uses a lower link arm on each side, and a single link arm on top.

thresh. To beat kernels of grain to separate them from the husks in which they grew.

thresher. A machine for threshing and cleaning grain; also called a separator.

tillage. The process of stirring, pulverizing, and smoothing soil prior to planting.

tilting lever. The lever on a mower or grain binder that regulates the angle between the front of the cutter bar and the ground.

tongue. A long wooden or steel pole extending forward from an implement or vehicle.

tongue truck. A wheeled device that supports the front of an implement to reduce tongue weight on the horses' necks and to help keep the implement steady and level.

transport disc. A disc with wheels that make it readily transportable.

trash board. A cover board

tribulum. A heavy, flat board with sharp teeth imbedded in its underside that in Roman times was dragged over cut ripe grain to separate the kernels from the husks.

trip dog. The catch that holds a knotter from tying until it is tripped by a grain bundle or hay bale reaching the proper size for tying.

two-way plow. A riding plow with two opposing bottoms, only one of which is in the ground at any given time, allowing the plow to throw the furrow to either the right or the left.

type D grain binder. A designation used by International Harvester on their McCormick-Deering grain binders to indicate that the knotter is of the type used on the old Deering binders.

type M grain binder. A designation used by International Harvester on their McCormick-Deering grain binders to indicate that the knotter is of the type used on the old McCormick binders.

unlanded beam. A plow beam bent away from the furrow's land side.

variable chamber baler. A machine for making large round bales using a series of flat belts that spin and compress the incoming hay, and that expand as the bale grows larger.

vertical lift mower. A mower with a lever that moves the cutter bar into a vertical position, at the same time throwing the cutting mechanism out of gear.

weed hook. A curved rod attached to a plow beam to help bury weeds and other trash.

wearing plate. On a mower cutter bar, the parts that support the rear side of the knife and hold the knife sections into position so the crop is sheared off cleanly.

widespread. On a manure spreader, the revolving distributor at the rear of the bed that scatters the manure.

windrow. Hay, straw, or other material that has been raked into a long, narrow row.

windboard. On a combine, an adjustable barrier that helps control the direction of the air blast through the cleaning shoe.

windstacker. A device on a thresher that blows the separated straw into a stack.

wing. A plow share's outside corner; also called the heel.

wing bearing. The flattened edge of a plow share's outside corner.

wing down. Action of a plow with so little wing bearing it runs wide.

wing up. Action of a plow with so much wing bearing it won't suck in properly on the wing side.

winnow. To separate grain from the chaff and other debris.

work sled. A vehicle fitted with runners instead of wheels and equipped with a platform or box to carry a load.

Photo by J. C. Norbeck

Index

(Charts and tables are indicated by page numbers in **bold.**)

About the Author

Sam Moore was born in 1933 and grew up on the family farm in Beaver County, in western Pennsylvania. The farm had been established by his great-great grandfather Robert Moore in the early part of the 19th century. His father and uncle raised chickens, milked cows, and raised crops during the 1930s, '40s, and into the '50s. Although he left the farm after high school, he has always been interested in farming and farm machinery, has restored a number of farm implements, and at one time or another has used virtually every implement featured in this book.

His main interest these days is in the history and products of the many farm equipment manufacturers that flourished during the 19th and 20th centuries. To further his research he has accumulated an extensive library of old farm and implement magazines, old and new books about agriculture, equipment sales literature, and hundreds of owner's and parts manuals. His work has been published in *Belt Pulley, Antique Power,* and *Green Magazine.* His farm machinery column "Let's Talk Rusty Iron" regularly appears in *Farm and Dairy, Farm Collector* and *Rural Heritage.*

Rural Heritage

a bimonthly journal published since 1976 in support of farming and logging with horses, mules, and other draft animals. Each issue is packed with how–to articles and up–to–date information related to training and working horses, mules, and oxen along with profiles of the teamsters who farm and ranch with them.

In *Rural Heritage* you will find out what's going on in today's draft animal world and discover gems of rural wisdom you won't find anywhere else. We are so sure you'll love this family magazine, we offer a money–back guarantee—if you are not completely satisfied after receiving your first issue, cancel and get a full refund. Join teamsters across North America by making *Rural Heritage* part of your life.

Call now: 931–268–0655
or visit online: www.ruralheritage.com

Just a sample of great articles from past issues:

Hitching a Combine
Round Bale Mover
Economics of Growing Spelt
McCormick Reaper
Palouse Plowing
Wooden Spoke Wheels
Check-Row Planting
Hillside versus Two-Way Plows
Hercules Stump Puller
Cutting Chaff
Winter Logging Arch
Wheeled Walking Plows
Lighting Vehicles in Winter
Sleigh & Harness Bells
Work Wagons
Rehabilitation Harrow
Ohio Hay Press
Forecarts Galore
Dirt Scrapers
Work Carts
Levers Are Everywhere
MN-Moline Dump Rakes
Bits for Draft Work
Bummers & High Wheels
Wheat Harvest in the Palouse
Too Wet to Hay
Right-Hand vs. Left-Hand Plows
Log Skidding and Forwarding
Mini Round Baler

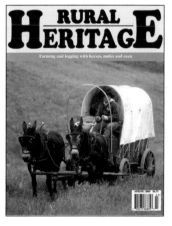

For a complete list of related books, videos and DVDs
visit our bookstore at
www.ruralheritage.com